LYLE PRICE GUIDE
ART NOUVEAU
& DECO

The publishers wish to express their sincere thanks to the following for their involvement and assistance in the production of this volume:

Editor	TONY CURTIS
Text By	EELIN McIVOR
Editorial	ANNETTE CURTIS
	DONNA RUTHERFORD
	JACQUELINE LEDDY
Art Production	CATRIONA DAY
	NICKY FAIRBURN
	DONNA CRUICKSHANK
Graphics	FRANK BURRELL
	JAMES BROWN
	EILEEN BURRELL

A CIP catalogue record for this book is available from the British Library.

ISBN   86248-139-2

Copyright © Lyle Publications MCMXCII
Glenmayne, Galashiels, Scotland.

Typeset by Word Power, Auchencrow, Berwickshire
Printed and bound in Great Britain by
Butler & Tanner Ltd, Frome and London

LYLE PRICE GUIDE
ART NOUVEAU
& DECO

TONY CURTIS

Moorcroft Pottery

Clarice Cliff

British Decorative Arts

Doulton Wares

Decorative Arts

Christie's South Kensington now hold ten specialist sales of
Decorative Arts a year. For free verbal valuations and advice on
all aspects of buying and selling at auction please contact
Mark Wilkinson or Jane Hay on (071) 321 3236/3015.

85 Old Brompton Road, London SW7 3LD
Tel: (071) 581 7611 Fax: (071) 584 0431

CHRISTIE'S

CONTENTS

Acknowledgements

AB Stockholms Auktionsverk, Box 16256, 103 25 Stockholm, Sweden
Abbots Auction Rooms, The Auction Rooms, Campsea Ash, Woodbridge, Suffolk
Abridge Auction Rooms, Market Place, Abridge, Essex RM4 1UA
Allen & Harris, St Johns Place, Whiteladies Road, Clifton, Bristol BS8 2ST
Jean Claude Anaf, Lyon Brotteaux, 13 bis place Jules Ferry, 69456 Lyon, France
Anderson & Garland, Marlborough House, Marlborough Crescent, Newcastle upon Tyne NE1 4EE
Antique Collectors Club & Co. Ltd, 5 Church Street, Woodbridge, Suffolk IP 12 1DS
Auction Team Köln, Postfach 50 11 68, D-5000 Köln 50 Germany
Auktionshause Arnold, Bleichstr. 42, 6000 Frankfurt a/M, Germany
Barber's Auctions, Woking, Surrey
Bearnes, Rainbow, Avenue Road, Torquay TQ2 5TG
Biddle & Webb, Ladywood Middleway, Birmingham B16 0PP
Bigwood, The Old School, Tiddington, Stratford upon Avon
Black Horse Agencies, Locke & England, 18 Guy Street, Leamington Spa
Boardman Fine Art Auctioneers, Station Road Corner, Haverhill, Suffolk CB9 0EY
Bonhams, Montpelier Street, Knightsbridge, London SW7 1HH
Bonhams Chelsea, 65–69 Lots Road, London SW10 0RN
Bonhams West Country, Dowell Street, Honiton, Devon
British Antique Exporters, School Close, Queen Elizabeth Avenue, Burgess Hill, Sussex
William H Brown, The Warner Auction Rooms, 16–18, Halford Street, Leicester LE1 1JB
Butterfield & Butterfield, 220 San Bruno Avenue, San Francisco CA 94103, USA
Butterfield & Butterfield, 7601 Sunset Boulevard, Los Angeles CA 90046, USA
Central Motor Auctions, Barfield House, Britannia Road, Morley, Leeds, LS27 0HN
H.C. Chapman & Son, The Auction Mart, North Street, Scarborough.
Christie's (International) SA, 8 place de la Taconnerie, 1204 Genève, Switzerland
Christie's Monaco, S.A.M, Park Palace 98000 Monte Carlo, Monaco
Christie's Scotland, 164–166 Bath Street Glasgow G2 4TG
Christie's South Kensington Ltd., 85 Old Brompton Road, London SW7 3LD
Christie's, 8 King Street, London SW1Y 6QT
Christie's East, 219 East 67th Street, New York, NY 10021, USA
Christie's, 502 Park Avenue, New York, NY 10022, USA
Christie's, Cornelis Schuytstraat 57, 1071 JG Amsterdam, Netherlands
Christie's SA Roma, 114 Piazza Navona, 00186 Rome, Italy
Christie's Swire, 1202 Alexandra House, 16–20 Chater Road, Hong Kong
Christie's Australia Pty Ltd., 1 Darling Street, South Yarra, Melbourne, Victoria 3141, Australia
A J Cobern, The Grosvenor Sales Rooms, 93b Eastbank Street, Southport PR8 1DG
Cooper Hirst Auctions, The Granary Saleroom, Victoria Road, Chelmsford, Essex CM2 6LH
Nic Costa/Brian Bates, 10 Madely Street, Tunstall
The Crested China Co., Station House, Driffield, E. Yorks YO25 7PY
Clifford Dann, 20/21 High Street, Lewes, Sussex
Julian Dawson, Lewes Auction Rooms, 56 High Street, Lewes BN7 1XE
Dee & Atkinson, The Exchange Saleroom, Driffield, Nth Humberside YO25 7LJ
Diamond Mills & Co., 117 Hamilton Road, Felixstowe, Suffolk
Dowell Lloyd & Co. Ltd, 118 Putney Bridge Road, London SW15 2NQ
Downer Ross, Charter House, 42 Avebury Boulevard, Central Milton Keynes MK9 2HS
Hy. Duke & Son, 40 South Street, Dorchester, Dorset
Du Mouchelles Art Galleries Co., 409 E. Jefferson Avenue, Detroit, Michigan 48226, USA
Duncan Vincent, 105 London Street, Reading RG1 4LF
Sala de Artes y Subastas Durán, Serrano 12, 28001 Madrid, Spain
Eldred's, Box 796, E. Dennis, MA 02641, USA
Ewbanks, Welbeck House, High Street, Guildford, Surrey, GU1 3JF
Fellows & Son, Augusta House, 19 Augusta Street, Hockley, Birmingham
Finarte, 20121 Milano, Piazzetta Bossi 4, Italy
John D Fleming & Co., 8 Fore Street, Dulverton, Somerset
G A Property Services, Canterbury Auction Galleries, Canterbury, Kent
Galerie Koller, Rämistr. 8, CH 8024 Zürich, Switzerland
Galerie Moderne, 3 rue du Parnasse, 1040 Bruxelles, Belgium
Geering & Colyer (Black Horse Agencies) Highgate, Hawkhurst, Kent
Glerum Auctioneers, Westeinde 12, 2512 HD's Gravenhage, Netherlands
The Goss and Crested China Co., 62 Murray Road, Horndean, Hants PO8 9JL
Graves Son & Pilcher, 71 Church Road, Hove, East Sussex, BN3 2GL
W R J Greenslade & Co., 13 Hammet Street, Taunton, Somerset, TA1 1RN
Peter Günnemann, Ehrenberg Str. 57, 2000 Hamburg 50, Germany
Halifax Property Services, 53 High Street, Tenterden, Kent
Halifax Property Services, 15 Cattle Market, Sandwich, Kent CT13 9AW
Hampton's Fine Art, 93 High Street, Godalming, Surrey
Hanseatisches Auktionshaus für Historica, Neuer Wall 57, 2000 Hamburg 36, Germany
Andrew Hartley Fine Arts, Victoria Hall, Little Lane, Ilkely

ART NOUVEAU & DECO

Hauswedell & Nolte, D-2000 Hamburg 13, Pöseldorfer Weg 1, Germany
Giles Haywood, The Auction House, St John's Road, Stourbridge, West Midlands, DY8 1EW
Heatheringtons Nationwide Anglia, The Amersham Auction Rooms, 125 Station Road, Amersham, Bucks
Muir Hewitt, Halifax Antiques Centre, Queens Road/Gibbet Street, Halifax HX1 4LR
Hobbs & Chambers, 'At the Sign of the Bell', Market Place, Cirencester, Glos
Hobbs Parker, Romney House, Ashford, Ashford, Kent
Hotel de Ventes Horta, 390 Chaussée de Waterloo (Ma Campagne), 1060 Bruxelles, Belgium
Jacobs & Hunt, Lavant Street, Petersfield, Hants. GU33 3EF
James of Norwich, 33 Timberhill, Norwich NR1 3LA
P Herholdt Jensens Auktioner, Rundforbivej 188, 2850 Nerum, Denmark
G A Key, Aylsham Saleroom, Palmers Lane, Aylsham, Norfolk, NR11 6EH
Kunsthaus am Museum, Drususgasse 1–5, 5000 Köln 1, Germany
Kunsthaus Lempertz, Neumarkt 3, 5000 Köln 1, Germany
Lambert & Foster (County Group), The Auction Sales Room, 102 High Street, Tenterden, Kent
W.H. Lane & Son, 64 Morrab Road, Penzance, Cornwall, TR18 2QT
Langlois Ltd., Westway Rooms, Don Street, St Helier, Channel Islands
Lawrence Butler Fine Art Salerooms, Marine Walk, Hythe, Kent, CT21 5AJ
Lawrence Fine Art, South Street, Crewkerne, Somerset TA18 8AB
Lawrence's Fine Art Auctioneers, Norfolk House, 80 High Street, Bletchingley, Surrey
David Lay, The Penzance Auction House, Alverton, Penzance, Cornwall TA18 4KE
Brian Loomes, Calf Haugh Farm, Pateley Bridge, North Yorks
Lots Road Chelsea Auction Galleries, 71 Lots Road, Chelsea, London SW10 0RN
R K Lucas & Son, Tithe Exchange, 9 Victoria Place, Haverfordwest, SA61 2JX
Duncan McAlpine, Stateside Comics plc, 125 East Barnet Road, London EN4 8RF
John Maxwell, 75 Hawthorn Street, Wilmslow, Cheshire
May & Son, 18 Bridge Street, Andover, Hants
Morphets, 4–6 Albert Street, Harrogate, North Yorks HG1 1JL
D M Nesbit & Co, 7 Clarendon Road, Southsea, Hants PO5 2ED
Onslow's, Metrostore, Townmead Road, London SW6 2RZ
Outhwaite & Litherland, Kingsley Galleries, Fontenoy Street, Liverpool, Merseyside L3 2BE
J R Parkinson Son & Hamer Auctions, The Auction Rooms, Rochdale, Bury, Lancs
Phillips Manchester, Trinity House, 114 Northenden Road, Sale, Manchester M33 3HD
Phillips Son & Neale SA, 10 rue des Chaudronniers, 1204 Genève, Switzerland
Phillips West Two, 10 Salem Road, London W2 4BL
Phillips, 11 Bayle Parade, Folkestone, Kent CT20 1SQ
Phillips, 49 London Road, Sevenoaks, Kent TN13 1UU
Phillips, 65 George Street, Edinburgh EH2 2JL
Phillips, Blenstock House, 7 Blenheim Street, New Bond Street, London W1Y 0AS
Phillips Marylebone, Hayes Place, Lisson Grove, London NW1 6UA
Phillips, New House, 150 Christleton Road, Chester CH3 5TD
Pinney's, 5627 Ferrier, Montreal, Quebec, Canada H4P 2M4
Pooley & Rogers, Regent Auction Rooms, Abbey Street, Penzance
Rennie's, 1 Agincourt Street, Monmouth
Riddetts, Richmond Hill, Bournemouth
Ritchie's, 429 Richmond Street East, Toronto, Canada M5A 1R1
Derek Roberts Antiques, 24–25 Shipbourne Road, Tonbridge, Kent TN10 3DN
Rogers de Rin, 79 Royal Hospital Road, London SW3 4HN
Russell, Baldwin & Bright, The Fine Art Saleroom, Ryelands Road, Leominster HR6 8JG
Sandoes Nationwide Anglia, Tabernacle Road, Wotton under Edge, Glos GL12 7EB
Schrager Auction Galleries, 2915 North Sherman Boulevard, Milwaukee, WI 53210, USA.
Selkirk's, 4166 Olive Street, St Louis, Missouri 63108, USA
Skinner Inc., Bolton Gallery, Route 117, Bolton MA, USA
Southgate Auction Rooms, Munro House, Cline Road, New Southgate, London N11.
Henry Spencer, 40 The Square, Retford, Notts. DN22 6DJ
G E Sworder & Son, Northgate End Salerooms, 15 Northgate End, Bishop Stortford, Herts
Taviner's of Bristol, Prewett Street, Redcliffe, Bristol BS1 6PB
Tennants, 27 Market Place, Leyburn, Yorkshire
Thomson Roddick & Laurie, 24 Lowther Street, Carlisle
Thomson Roddick & Laurie, 60 Whitesands, Dumfries
Venator & Hanstein, Cäcilienstr. 48, 5000 Köln 1, Germany
T Vennett Smith, 11 Nottingham Road, Gotham, Nottingham NG11 0HE
Duncan Vincent, 105 London Road, Reading RG1 4LF
Wallis & Wallis, West Street Auction Galleries, West Street, Lewes, E. Sussex BN7 2NJ
Ward & Morris, Stuart House, 18 Gloucester Road, Ross on Wye HR9 5BN
Warren & Wignall Ltd, The Mill, Earnshaw Bridge, Leyland Lane, Leyland PR5 3PH
Dominique Watine-Arnault, 11 rue François 1er, 75008 Paris, France
Wells Cundall Nationwide Anglia, Staffordshire House, 27 Flowergate, Whitby YO21 3AX
Woltons, 6 Whiting Street, Bury St Edmunds, Suffolk IP33 1PB
Woolley & Wallis, The Castle Auction Mart, Salisbury, Wilts SP1 3SU
Austin Wyatt Nationwide Anglia, Emsworth Road, Lymington, Hants SO41 9BL
Yesterday Child, 118 Islington High Street, London N11 8EG

ART NOUVEAU & DECO

Even the most cursory glance at the history of style down the ages reveals how often one particular fashion seems to develop as a direct reaction against the one immediately preceding it. So indeed it was with Art Nouveau. During the Victorian period, the style of everything from furniture to dress had become progressively heavier, darker, more constrained, and often laden with fussy, ponderous decoration in the same way that the Victorians cluttered their parlours with ornaments and geegaws. Basic forms too were a mere cold academic repetition of famous styles of the past.

Into this stuffy atmosphere, in the last decade of the 19th century, the principles of Art Nouveau burst like a breath of fresh air. The artists and practitioners of Art Nouveau claimed to base their art not on the past, but on present reality or a vision of a future to come. Youth and vitality were the keynote, and, where they did borrow from past styles, it was from so far back, notably the medieval period, that the results still seemed fresh and modern.

Art Nouveau, however, was not a naturalistic style. While it borrowed heavily from nature for forms and decoration (for example basic plant forms were a favourite

motif), these were not naturalistically presented but stylised in flowing lines, extended and convoluted and integrated with the design of the object as a whole. The aim was not to portray the outward form of nature but to capture the essential vitality of the endless process of natural creativity.

Art Nouveau style permeated almost all branches of arts and crafts. In the case of furniture design, its influence was typified by long, undulating curves following sculptural patterns. Wood was often treated almost as a malleable material, and again there was much use of plant-inspired decoration. In glassware, the movement coincided with the emergence of such great names as Daum, Tiffany and Gallé, all of whom designed, and, more importantly perhaps, decorated, in Art Nouveau style. There was much use of iridescent surface effects, and cameo glass.

All the great ceramics producers were also affected by Art Nouveau principles, again chiefly in terms of decoration, though Art Nouveau-inspired elongated and contorted shapes were also popular. Silver showed a rather more restrained expression of the style, mainly through the influence of the Arts & Crafts movement. The Liberty designer Archibald Knox was a key figure in this field.

In Germany, however, WMF produced some of the most outrageous curvilinear metalwork which came to be known as the spaghetti or whiplash style, while Charles Rennie Mackintosh was rather less complimentary in describing it as "resembling melted margarine".

Jewellery too was a prime medium for expressing Art Nouveau principles, and artists such as Mucha and Lalique used a wide range of semi-precious stones and enamels to make pieces in the form of flowers, leaves, insects and female heads.

Finally, Art Nouveau was not a mass movement, though it flourished right across Europe, for while many Art Nouveau artists had a high degree of social awareness, they believed their duty was not to reflect what was an often wretched reality, but to create an image of a world of universal happiness and beauty. It was indeed their ideal to create that beauty for as wide a public as possible, but their concern with complexity of design and their use of varied materials inevitably meant that it appealed to a somewhat restricted and essentially upper middle class public.

The Art Nouveau movement reached its apogee around 1900, when the Universal Exhibition was held in Paris. It was to a degree doomed by its rejection of the machine, and when attempts were made to adapt its forms for industry the results were catastrophic. Its more austere and abstract variations were, however, adopted by the succeeding movement, which might be said to owe much to the rapturous reception given in Paris in

A Clarice Cliff 'Age of Jazz', two sided plaque, 17.5cm. high.
(Phillips) £4,000

1909 to Diaghilev's Ballets Russes. The costumes and sets for these were reduced to a few stark lines and employed unusually brilliant colours, and enthusiasm for them carried on right up to the outbreak of war in 1914.

By 1918, in the wake of the holocaust, perceptions of life had changed drastically. Advances in communications and transport meant that life appeared to be lived now at a much higher speed, and a style attempting to reflect the dynamism of the new environment was emerging. This comprised simple, bold forms, in the cult of the 'machine' aesthetic, and lines often typifying speed. The opening of Tutenkhamun's tomb in the 1920s led to an increased interest in things Egyptian, and there was much use of Egyptian motifs such as scarab and palmetto forms. Many designs too reflected the geometric forms of Cubism.

The movement, like Art Nouveau before it, was a pan-European one. In the German speaking countries, the Bauhaus, Deutsche Werkbund and the Wiener Werkstatte were primary sources of inspiration, while in France Lalique, Puiforçat and Daum were amongst those influenced by Cubism.

With its simple angular lines and bright, uncompromising colours, the Art Deco style was fully in tune with the somewhat frantic and frivolous spirit of the time, when those who counted themselves lucky to be alive at all tended to live for the day. Unlike Art Nouveau it was a style with mass appeal, and designers furthermore took full advantage of the many new technological developments on offer. The first synthetic resin, Bakelite, had been introduced in 1909, and was followed by others such as perspex. All were remarkably cheap and cheerful, in comparison with many traditional materials, and also very adaptable, and leading craftsmen of the time were perfectly happy to incorporate them in their repertoire. For example, some really stunning 1920s plastic jewellery by leading designers can be found today.

The Depression of the 1930s struck the first blow at the Art Deco style, and its bright defiance was finally killed off by the austerity and shortages which the Second World War imposed. Nevertheless, there can be few households today where some Art Deco object, however humble, is not still lurking. They are worth seeking out, given the enormous upsurge of interest in the period today.

ADVERTISING

Street Jewellery is the thoroughly apt term now coined for the wonderful enamel advertising signs of the past. So sought after have they become that old railway stations and other places that they once adorned have to lock them up now for fear of theft. They breathe instant nostalgia and speak of an age of comparative innocence, a far cry from the high powered media advertising to which we are all subjected today.

The most valuable signs are enamel on metal from the Art Nouveau or Art Deco periods, though cardboard ones in good condition are also popular. Famous artists like McKnight Kauffer, Nerman and Harry Rountree designed signs for brand name firms like Oxo, Fry's, Nestle's, Rowntree's, petrol and oil companies. Car manufacturers' signs are very collectable – especially those for Lagonda, Bentley, Rolls Royce and Bugatti.

Hall's Distemper. (Street Jewellery)   £120

A photographic electric advertising lamp with decorated shade *Travel with a Kodak* and *Remember with a Kodak*, 13½in. high, mid 1920s. (Christie's S. Ken) £275

Tin advertising sign for 'Murphy Da-Cote Enamel', lithograph by H. D. Beach, Co., Ohio, circa 1925, 27 x 19in. (Robt. W. Skinner Inc.) £503

'Flea Circus' stained glass window, circa 1900, 5ft. long. (Robt. W. Skinner Inc.) £500

A leaded glass pharmacy sign, America, 64½in. wide. (Robt. W. Skinner Inc.) £600

Walter Wilson's 'Smiling Service', circa 1920, 27 x 20in. (Street Jewellery) £100

ADVERTISING

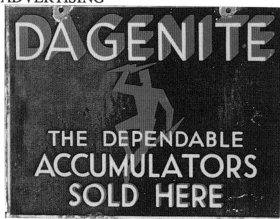

'Dagenite, The Dependable Accumulators, Sold
Here', enamel advertising sign.
(Street Jewellery)   £50

Jones Sewing Machines, enamel
sign, circa 1900, 32½ x 34½in.
(Street Jewellery)   £100

Belga Vander Elst (Street
Jewellery)   £65

Enamel advertising sign 'Karpol,
Buy It Here'.
(Street Jewellery)   £100

'Cunard Line Europe-America'
advertising poster by Kenneth
D. Shoesmith.
(Onslows)   £2,800

London and North Eastern Railway poster,
'You always dine well on the L.N.E.R.
(Onslows)   £1,100

'Cleveland Petrols' enamel advertising sign.
(Street Jewellery)   £75

ADVERTISING

'Robbialac Paints' enamel sign, circa 1925, 25 x 16in. (Street Jewellery) £100

'Puritan Soap, Pure as the Breeze', enamel advertising sign, 24½ x 37in., circa 1920. (Street Jewellery) £125

'Selo Film' enamel sign in yellow, red and black, 14in. wide. £200

Carlton ware Guinness lamp complete with shade, 1950s. (Muir Hewitt) £275

An enamel sign, 'Hush!! He's Busy', a political cartoon of Lloyd George, 51 x 71cm. (Osmond Tricks) £170

W H Smith enamel sign, circa 1930. (Street Jewellery) £100

There's no tea like Phillips's, 40 x 30in. (Street Jewellery) £300

'Burma Sauce, The Only Sauce I Dare Give Father'. (Street Jewellery) £100

ADVERTISING

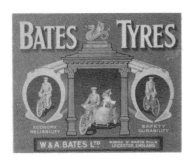

Bates Tyres Leicester, showcard, 48 x 61cm., framed.
(Onslow's) £300

Enamelled metal advertising sign for Morris Service.
(Street Jewellery) £125

A Foley rectangular pottery advertising plaque, the central reserve depicting a potter and a classical maiden carrying a pitcher of water, 10in. wide.
(Christie's S. Ken) £750

Olympic Ale, showcard, published Brussels 1937, 46 x 31cm.
(Onslow's) £20

A fine painted plaster advertising figure of a young girl wearing a petticoat, with a plastic sign for Sparwick Underwear, 21½in. high.
(Christie's S. Ken) £100

'La Raphaelle, Liqueur Bonal' advertising sign by Rossetti, circa 1908, 62½ x 46½in. £100

Camp Romain, Vin Rouge, Rose, Blanc, by L. Gadoud, lithograph in colours, on wove paper, 1600 x 1200mm. £200

A metal Kodak store sign, triangular with heavy metal bracket, 'Developing Printing Enlarging'. £125

Lithographed advertisement for Egyptienne 'Straights' cigarettes, 31in. high. £125

ADVERTISING

Advertising signs, Cooperative Society of Chauffeurs of Bourgeoise Houses Diploma of Honorary Membership, 28 x 41cm. (Onslow's)　　　　£200

'Cafe' leaded glass window, in metal frame, circa 1900, 4ft.4in. high. (Robt. W. Skinner Inc.)　　　　£368

Aero Shell Lubricating Oil The Aristocrat of Lubricants, by E McKnight Kauffer, printed tin advertisement, 1932, 48 x 74cm. (Onslow's)　　　　£700

Advertising counter sign for 'Thompson's Bread' by E. H. Thompson & Son Ltd, circa 1930, 39 x 30in.　　£75

A painted resin figure of a young girl holding a large ice cream cone, with black lettering 'Ice Cream With a Facchino Cone It's Lovely', 21in. high.　　　　£100

London Mail enamel sign, circa 1930, 36 x 24in. (Street Jewellery)　　£100

'Wills' Gold Flake', mirror, 48 x 38cm., framed. (Onslow's)　　　　£45

R. Geri, 'Exide The Long Life Battery', showcard, 30 x 22in. (Onslow's)　　　　£50

A metal 'El Roi-Tan' chromolithograph advertising sign, 24¼ x 20in.　　£80

ADVERTISING

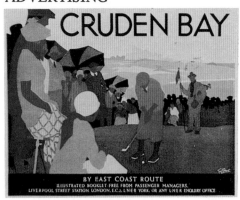

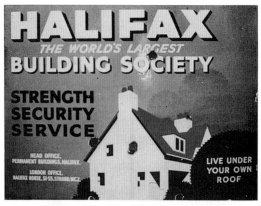

London & North Eastern Railway travel poster
for 'Cruden Bay' by Tom Purvis.
(Onslows)   £1,800

'Halifax The World's Largest Building
Society', enamel advertising sign.
(Street Jewellery)   £100

Wincarnis, 'The World's
Greatest Wine Tonic and Nerve
Restorative', 72 x 40in. (Street
Jewellery)   £500

'How to buy oil-cheaper-cleaner-quicker'
by Tom Purvis, published by Shell No.
117, 75 x 114cm., 1925.
(Onslows)   £1,400

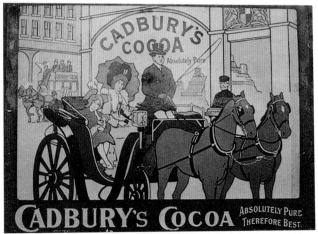

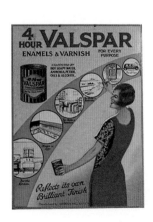

'Cadbury's Cocoa, Absolutely Pure, Therefore
Best', enamel advertising sign.
(Street Jewellery)   £400

1930's Valspar enamels and varnish
hanging display card, 14 x 19in.
(Bermondsey)   £20

ADVERTISING

'Players Navy Cut Cigarettes', enamel advertising sign, 9 x 6in., circa 1885.
(Street Jewellery)   £250

1930's Liquid Lino counter display card with folding stand, 15in. x 25in.
(Bermondsey)   £20

'Bovril, Oh Mamma Don't Forget to order Bovril'.
(Street Jewellery)   £400

Ruberoid Roofing enamel sign made by Willings & Co., 1930's, 36 x 27in.
(Street Jewellery)   £75

Cardboard counter display sign for 'Vesta, Paints for Every Home'.   £25

Crow Bar Tobacco enamel sign, circa 1920, 37 x 24½in.
(Street Jewellery)   £100

'Persil' advertising sign made by Ferro Email, 23 x 15in., circa 1930.
(Street Jewellery)   £80

'P. & R. Hay, Dyers and French Cleaners', enamel advertising sign, 22 x 12in., circa 1899.
(Street Jewellery)   £175

Singer Sewing Machines, enamel sign, circa 1910, 11 x 7½in.
(Street Jewellery)   £85

ADVERTISING

My Goodness – A 200th Birthday Label! by John Gilroy. (Onslow's) **£90**

"Two-Steps, fits better, wears longer", plaster and wood advertising figure depicting a little boy in a blue check shirt, 14in. high. **£100**

Elastic Sportszalag, published by Athenaeum, double royal. (Onslow's) **£45**

Nick, Terrot Cycles Motorcycles, pub by Pertuy, Paris, on linen, 158cm. x 119cm. (Onslow's) **£280**

A set of four Robertson's Golly coloured plaster musicians, 3in. high. **£25**

A metal Rose & Co. lithograph sign, and advertisement for 'Merchant Tailors', circa 1900, 26½in. high. **£300**

Enamel sign for Raleigh, The Gold Medal Motor-Cycle. (Onslow's) **£750**

A golfer mascot, circa 1960, 39cm. high. **£280**

Will's Star Cigarettes, laminated showcard of Raymond Mays at Brooklands, 48 x 37cm. (Onslow's) **£800**

ADVERTISING

'White Rock' advertising tip tray, copy reads 'White Rock, The World's Best Table Water.' £60

A composition painted caricature figure of an early golfer advertising the Penfold golf ball, 21½in. high. (Christie's) £324

Lovely Day For A Guinness by John Gilroy. (Onslow's) £85

Carlton advertising piece for Pear's soap, 110mm. high. (Goss & Crested China Ltd.) £80

Staffordshire Pottery teapot, inscribed 'Nectar Tea', complete with milk jug. (Border Bygones) £75

Display sign for 'Army Club Cigarettes' depicting the bust of a soldier. £125

'Cadbury's Cocoa' advertising sign. (Street Jewellery) £300

Diamond Dye advertising display box, with compartmented shelves. (Robt. W. Skinner Inc.) £435

Marfia Kalap Minden Minosegben poster, published by Athenaeum, double royal. (Onslow's) £90

AMUSEMENT MACHINES

Amusement machines are the logical development of the Victorian fairground peepshow and other similar attractions. With advancing technology, they became more sophisticated as the 20th century progressed, and enjoyed a great surge of popularity in America and Europe in the 1930s, when many fascinating and ingenious examples were produced.

Some of these, unlike the garish, flashing-light one-arm-bandits of today, even achieve a kind of intrinsic elegance, with fine wooded casings and intricately fretted wheels.

'Pussy Shooter' made by the British American Novelty Co., U.K., circa 1930's.
(Costa/Bates)   £1,500

All the prices quoted in these pages are for machines in perfect working order and pristine condition. Condition is vital when determing value. Beware too of reproductions of the Rol-a-top and War Eagle machines which have no escalator and a different mechanism respectively.

'Egyptian Bell', made in the U.K., circa 1932. (Costa/Bates)   £2,000

'Rol-a-top' produced by Watling with twin jackpot, made in the U.S.A., circa 1936. (Costa/Bates)   £2,000

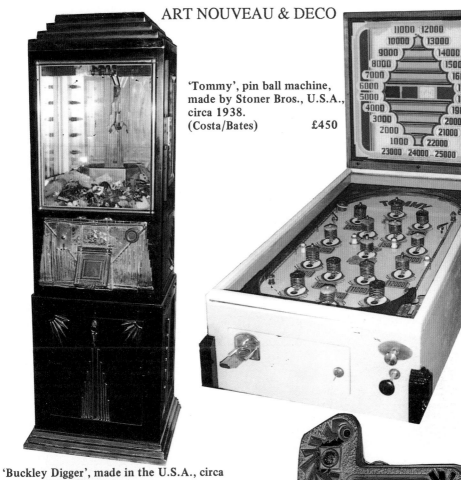

'Tommy', pin ball machine,
made by Stoner Bros., U.S.A.,
circa 1938.
(Costa/Bates)   £450

'Buckley Digger', made in the U.S.A., circa
1934. (Costa/Bates)   £2,000

1930's wooden cased amusement machine, in
the Art Deco style. (Costa/Bates)   £450

'War Eagle' produced by Mills in the U.S.A.,
circa 1932. (Costa/Bates)   £1,200

AMUSEMENT MACHINES

A Pen-nee Golf pin-ball game, 17½in. high. (Christie's) £605

Columbus, Ball Chewing Gum Vendor, circa 1932, U.S.A. £100

Matrimonial Bureau, U.K., circa 1930. (Costa/Bates) £400

Beromat, circa 1959, Germany. £225

A wood body electrically-operated wall-mounted stereo viewer proclaiming *40 different pictures. You see ten for 3d and 3-D Beauty Parade* featuring stereoscopic pairs of posed nude and semi-nude women. (Christie's S. Ken) £1.320

Clown machine, circa 1925. £325

Bursting Cherry, U.S.A., circa 1938. (Costa/Bates) £475

An oak cased old penny operated skill machine, circa 1920, giving as a prize a single cigarette and a returned coin, 46cm. high. (Spencer's) £110

'Beat the Goalie', British, 1933. (Brierley/Bates) £500

ASHTRAYS

The Art Deco period, following the First World War, coincided with the universal acceptance of smoking, and the ashtray became a versatile medium for embellishment. Many were designed as advertising giveaways and are cheap and cheerful, if interesting as a reflection of the times. Others were whimsical in tone, such as those produced by Goss and other Crested china manufacturers. Occasionally, however, craftsmen such as Tiffany and Lalique would turn out something special, and the prices which such examples fetch reflect their status as an objet d'art, rather than a humble receptacle for cigarette litter.

Empire Nut Brown Tobacco ashtray featuring Bruce Bairnsfather's character 'Ol' Bill', circa 1915.   £20

Lalique amber glass shell duck ashtray, 2¾in. high. (Reeds Rains)   £120

Podmore dog sitting next to a red pillar box on ashtray inscribed, *Sorry I've missed the post.*
(The Crested China Co.)   £95

A Daum acid etched and enamelled verrerie parlante ashtray, the clear and amber tinted glass with ribbon motto amid mistletoe on an acid textured ground, 14cm. diam. (Christie's)   £462

Pip Squeak and Wilfred ashtray made for the Daily Mirror, circa 1930.   £250

'Archers', a Lalique frosted glass ashtray, the rim moulded with vignettes of naked Greek archers, heightened with grey staining, 4¹/₂in. diameter. (Christie's S. Ken)   £308

Royal Doulton Lambeth stoneware combined ashtray and match holder made in the Art Nouveau style for Queen Anne's Mansions, circa 1912.   £30

'Medicis' or 'Quatre Figurines', a Lalique emerald green ashtray, with moulded decoration of four sirens and a running border of flowerheads, 15cm. long. (Christie's)   £1,540

ASHTRAYS

Sylvac golfing ashtray, 1950s.
(Muir Hewitt)   £20

Metal ashtray mounted with an
Alfa Romeo 158, made by Alfa to
celebrate their victory in the
World Championship in 1950.
(Finarte)   £670

Noritake ash tray, 1930s.
(Muir Hewitt)   £20

1950s Guinness ashtray with
Dickens decoration, 3$\frac{1}{2}$in.
diameter.
(Muir Hewitt)   £35

Ashtray with Map of the
Isle of Wight by W. H. Goss.
                    £50

Stylized negro butler
figure with ashtray,
1930's.(Muir Hewitt) £75

Armchair pipe rest with stylized
dogs, Continental, 1930s.
(Muir Hewitt)   £35

Stylized dog ashtray and
matching corkscrew, 1930s.
(Muir Hewitt)   £30

Guinness match holder and
ashtray.
(Muir Hewitt)   £40

1938 Glasgow Exhibition
souvenir in chrome and butterfly
wing. (Muir Hewitt)   £25

Ashtray in shape of negro's
head, 1930s.
(Muir Hewitt)
                    £20

MABEL LUCIE ATTWELL

The English artist and author Mabel Lucie Attwell (1879–1964) was born in London and studied at Heatherley's and other art schools. She married the cartoonist Harold Earnshaw. She was noted for her child studies, both humorous and serious, with which she illustrated her own and other authors' children's stories. Her 'cherubic' style had immediate and lasting appeal, and was perpetuated in annuals and children's books by her daughter, who worked under her mother's name.

'Wright's Biscuits' tin tray with Mabel Lucie Attwell design. (Muir Hewitt) £25

Celluloid Mabel Lucie Attwell "Curate" egg-timer. (Muir Hewitt) £25

Mabel Lucie Attwell postcard by Valentine & Sons. £2

Shelley, Mabel Lucie Attwell baby-plate. (Muir Hewitt) £40

Mabel Lucie Attwell household wants reminder board, 1950s. (Muir Hewitt) £20

Water colour copy of Mabel Lucie Attwell picture. (Muir Hewitt) £85

Shelley, Mabel Lucie Attwell child's bowl. (Muir Hewitt) £30

Mabel Lucie Attwell print "And that's the tale you told my muvver". (Muir Hewitt) £35

BAKELITE

It was in 1909 that an American research chemist, Leo Baekeland, mixed phenol with a derivative of methyl alcohol to produce an astonishing synthetic resin, which, it was found, could be moulded and used for a huge variety of purposes. Not only that, it was inexpensive to produce. Bakelite, the forerunner of modern plastic, had arrived.

Its original colour was amber, but later the most usual colours were cream or black. Bakelite's only real drawback was that it was brittle and could be easily cracked.

A Lalique red bakelite box and cover, of square section, the cover moulded and carved, with carved signature R. Lalique, 7.5cm. x 7.5cm. (Christie's) £825

Bakelite wall clock, 1930s. (Muir Hewitt) £35

Silver plated and bakelite dish, 7in. diameter, 1930s. (Muir Hewitt) £40

A German Schott bakelite hair-drier, circa 1935. (Auction Team Koeln) £13

Bakelite lemon squeezer with shaped base, circa 1930. (Muir Hewitt) £12

1930s green Bakelite thermos flask. (Muir Hewitt) £25

An Art Deco bakelite comb, brush and mirror set, by R. Amerith, France, 1920's. (Robt. W. Skinner Inc.) £300

A white bakelite tea box, 1940's. £5

BOXES & TINS

Art Nouveau/Deco influence filtered down to even the humblest artefacts of the period. Whilst one would expect handsome jewel and cigarette boxes to be fashioned and decorated in the current vogue, even gramophone needles and coffee tins often bear characteristic embellishment. This makes them particularly attractive and collectable today, and while some will fetch only a few pounds, rarer examples can attract bids into three figures.

A Galle marquetry casket inlaid in various woods, circa 1900, 35cm. wide. £5,720

'Bohin' a French gramophone needle tin in yellow and green. £8

A Guild of Handicraft Ltd. copper and enamelled box, the hinged cover set with an enamelled landscape panel painted in naturalistic colours, 21cm. long. (Phillips)   £900

Arts & Crafts miniature smoker's cabinet, circa 1900, 18in. high. £265

A Guild of Handicraft hammered silver box, the lid with repoussé decoration of tulips, with gilded interior, with London hallmarks for 1905, 19cm. wide, 1040 grams. (Christie's)   £1,045

'Herald Tango', a German gramophone needle tin depicting a couple in evening dress. £8

A German lithographed tinplate money box, with lever action eyes and extending tongue, 1920's, 7½in. high. (Christie's S. Ken.)   £330

Taddy – a Myrtle Grove cigarette tin, depicting a pretty girl, 8 x 7.5cm. (Phillips) £130

BOXES & TINS

Chrome cigarette box with
wooden lining, 1930s.
(Muir Hewitt)   £25

1930's, tin money bank in
the form of a post box. £8

Thornes toffee tin, 1930s.
(Muir Hewitt)   £10

Poker work magazine rack
1930s, depicting an American
Indian.
(Muir Hewitt)   £35

Bridge set, 1930s, in simulated
snake skin case.
(Muir Hewitt)   £15

A silver cigarette box with
enamelled panels depicting
a ballerina dancing at the
edge of a stream.
(David Lay)   £620

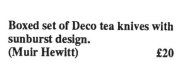

An olive and ash jewellery
casket by Robert Ingham
enclosing ripple sycamore
partitioned trays.
(Christie's)   £1,500

Hand painted wooden box with
poker work decoration, 1930s.
(Muir Hewitt)   £20

Boxed set of Deco tea knives with
sunburst design.
(Muir Hewitt)   £20

BOXES & TINS

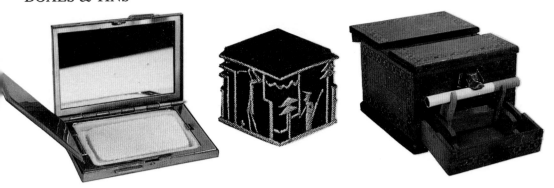

Gilt metal powder compact
complete with mirror, 1950s.
(Muir Hewitt)   £10

A Hagenauer chromed metal
and glass square box, the
openwork frame cast with
stylised golfing scenes, 2¼in.
high.
(Christie's)   £308

Novelty wooden cigarette
dispenser, 1940s, with parquetry
decoration.
(Muir Hewitt)   £20

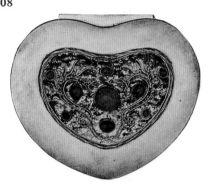

1930s biscuit tin decorated with
a country scene.
(Muir Hewitt)   £12

Advertising tin with Deco design,
Sto-Mike coffee.
(Muir Hewitt)   £5

A Continental heart shaped
gilt lined white metal trinket box, the lid mounted
with an enamel cartouche
of serpents.
(Christie's)   £1,320

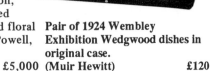

Poole Pottery 1970s Art Nouveau
revival lidded trinket container.
(Muir Hewitt)   £20

An ivory panelled wooden
casket by Ernest Gimson,
the interior with painted
polychrome scenic and floral
decoration by Alfred Powell,
35.6cm. wide.
(Christie's)   £5,000

Pair of 1924 Wembley
Exhibition Wedgwood dishes in
original case.
(Muir Hewitt)   £120

BRASS & COPPER

The rich warm tones of brass and copper have made these popular metals throughout the ages for a wide variety of household items. As media, too they appealed to the craftsmen of the Art Nouveau period, and in particular to the Arts & Crafts Movement, as they lent themselves so well to hand hammering and working. Many fine pieces date from this time, and those by Gustav Stickley are perhaps particularly sought after.

A hammered brass umbrella stand, possibly Belgium circa 1900-20, 24in. high.
£500

An Arthur Stone decorated copper bowl, Mass., circa 1910, stamped with Stone logo, 5¼in. diam. (Robt. W. Skinner Inc.) £3,000

A Newlyn copper umbrella stand, the body with a relief pattern of fish and crabs swimming amid embossed banding, 58cm. high. (Phillips London) £520

A fine pair of 20th century brass candlesticks, 8½in. high. (Robt. W. Skinner Inc.) £202

An unusual Arts and Crafts kettle, by Fred Courthorpe, with domed cover having abalone shell finial and overhead handle with wooden grips, 75cm. total height. (Phillips) £1,150

A large enamelled copper wall plaque, the roundel bearing a repoussé galleon and fish on enamelled blue and eau-de-nil ground, in square frame, circa 1895, 90cm. diameter. (Christie's) £715

Victorian firescreen of polished copper, 1880. £100

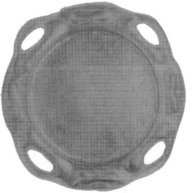

A hammered copper and repousse serving tray, attributed to Gustav Stickley, circa 1905, with simple leaf decoration, unsigned, 20in. diam. £500

BRASS & COPPER

Chase coffee urn, sugar, creamer and undertray, Chase Brass and Copper Co., Waterbury, Connecticut, circa 1930, 12¼in. wide. (Skinner Inc.) **£171**

A Karl Kipp copper vase, model no. 218, East Aurora, N.Y., circa 1919, 6½in. high. (Robt. W. Skinner Inc.) **£148**

Early 20th century Arts & Crafts hammered copper wood box with loop handles, 23½in. wide. (Robt. W. Skinner Inc.) **£524**

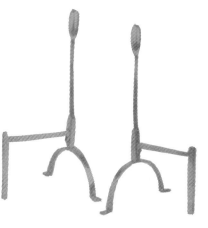

An Art Nouveau brass and copper jug, embossed in relief with cartouches between linear and foliate borders, 15½in. high. (Christie's S. Ken) **£83**

A pair of brass fire dogs, the design attributed to C. F. Voysey, on splayed trestle feet. 39.4cm. high. (Christie's) **£605**

A triangular hammered copper umbrella stand, with single panel of stylised poppies, circa 1900, 23in. high. (Robt. W. Skinner Inc.) **£229**

One of a pair of brass electric headlamps, stamped 'Carl Zeiss Jena', 10½in. diam. (Christie's) **£100**

A Roycroft copper and brass wash handled basket, East Aurora, N.Y., circa 1920, 9in. diam. **£100**

A hammered copper jar with enamelled cover, Boston or Worcester, Mass., circa 1915, 4½in. diam. (Robt. W. Skinner Inc.) **£216**

BRASS & COPPER

A hammered copper wall plaque, by Gustav Stickley, circa 1905, 20in. diam.
£3,500

A hammered copper chamber-stick, by Gustav Stickley, circa 1913, 9¼in. high. (Robt. W. Skinner Inc.) £378

A nickel plated brass stylised tyre with seated speed god inside, inscribed Coffin, 6in. high. (Christie's) £400

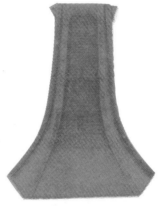

Late 19th century Art Nouveau style brass coal box. £100

An Arts & Crafts hammered copper fireplace hood, circa 1910, 43in. high, 12½in. wide at top, 36in. wide at bottom. £600

Art Deco style brass tea box, circa 1930. £15

Kayser patinated copper covered punch bowl, probably Austria or Germany, circa 1905, stamped with hallmark, 12in. diam. (Skinner Inc.) £262

An Arts and Crafts hammered copper and iron log bin, with relief decoration of stylised foliage, with lacquered iron mounts and on bracket feet, 43.4cm. high. (Christie's London) £495

A Benham & Froud brass kettle designed by Dr. C. Dresser, on three spiked feet, 24.5cm. high. £500

BRASS & COPPER

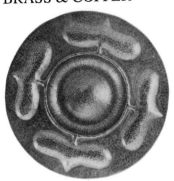

A hammered copper wall plaque, by Gustav Stickley, circa 1905, 15in. diam.
£3,830

Roycroft copper American Beauty vase, East Aurora, New York, circa 1910, flared rim, original patina, signed with logo, 19¼in. high. (Skinner Inc.) £1,235

An Onondaga Metal Shop hammered copper and repousse wall plaque, circa 1905, 20in. diam. (Robt. W. Skinner Inc.)
£2,972

Hammered copper umbrella stand, attributed to Benedict Studios, East Syracuse, New York, circa 1910, unsigned, 25in. high. (Skinner Inc.)
£370

A large copper wall mirror by John Pearson, embossed in high relief with stylised mythical creatures reserved against a textured ground, 63cm. diam. (Phillips London)
£1,495

An early 20th century Arts & Crafts hammered copper umbrella stand, 25in. high.
£400

A Perry, Son & Co. brass chamber stick, designed by Dr. Christopher Dresser, with curving wooden handle, stamped *C. Dresser's Design,* and with registration lozenge for 1883, 14.5cm. high. (Christie's) £396

Silver wash hammered copper kettle on stand, Europe, circa 1905, riveted loop handle, 11½in. high. (Skinner Inc.)
£370

A WMF brass standing table mirror, circa 1900, 40cm. high.
£345

BRASS & COPPER

A Jean Dunand lacquered metal bowl, signed in red lacquer, circa 1925, 10cm. high.   £1,000

A brass buckle depicting a copulating couple, incorporating a chassis, 4in. long. (Christie's)   £150

Jarvie brass candlestick, Chicago, Illinois, circa 1910, with angled handle, signed on base, 6in. high. (Skinner Inc.)   £525

 (lower center)

Metcalf Co. hammered copper vase with silver strapwork, circa 1910, silver tacked border on conical form, 12in. high. (Robt. W. Skinner Inc.)   £55

Pair of relief decorated copper plaques, signed by Raymond Averill Porter, 1912 and 1913, 10½ x 9½in. (Robt. W. Skinner Inc.)   £324

A hammered copper wine pitcher, no. 80, by the Stickley Bros., circa 1905, 15in. high.   £200

Patinated hammered copper jardiniere, attributed to Gustav Stickley, circa 1910, 12in. diam.   £500

Pair of brass candlesticks, possibly Jarvie, Chicago, circa 1910, unsigned, 6in. high, 5in. diam. (Robt. W. Skinner Inc.)   £245

A late Victorian brass coal box with domed lid and pierced finial, 17in. wide. (Christie's)   £330

BRASS & COPPER

An Edwardian satin brass coal receiver on claw feet. **£100**

An Art Union brass and copper pen tray, designed by Katie Harris, cast with a central seated female figure flanked by two male busts, stamped *Art Union of London 1902,* 33cm. wide. (Christie's London) **£374**

An electric kettle, designed by Peter Behrens for AEG, circa 1910, 21cm. **£400**

Early 20th century hammered copper lamp base with mother-of-pearl mountings, 13in. high. **£350**

Pair of Perry & Co. brass candlesticks, designed by Dr. C. Dresser, with wood handles, 5½in. (Christie's) **£1,100**

Hammered copper plant stand, design attributed to Joseph Maria Olbrich, Germany, late 19th century, unsigned, 29in. high. (Robt. W. Skinner Inc.) **£982**

An Art Deco patinated copper globular vase by Claudius Linossier, decorated around the upper body with a band of silver and black patinated lozenges, 17cm. high.
(Phillips) **£4,370**

An early 20th century English copper electrotype bust of Eliza Macloghlin, cast by A. Toft from a model by Sir A. Gilbert, dated 1906, 40.5cm. high. (Christie's) **£11,000**

A hammered copper vase by John Pearson, with repoussé decoration of fantastical creatures, base engraved *J.P. 1899,* 20cm. high.
(Christie's) **£352**

BRONZE FIGURES

France had been one of the leading countries in bronze figure production throughout the nineteenth century, and was to adopt a major role also during the Art Nouveau/ Deco periods. The medium lent itself particularly well to the flowing lines and themes of Art Nouveau, while the Art Deco period saw the increasing use of bronze in combination with ivory, or chryselephantine as it came to be known. The figures conceived in this medium have a character which is all their own.

'Valkyrie', a bronze group cast from a model by Stephan Sinding, a spear maiden astride a stallion, on the naturalistic bronze base, 56cm. high. (Christie's) £2,860

A bronze bust of an Art Nouveau maiden cast after a model by van der Straeton, circa 1900, 31cm. high. (Christie's) £432

'Anagke', (Compulsion), a bronze figure cast after a model by Gilbert Bayes, signed and dated 1918, 59cm. high. (Christie's) £10,800

Huntress, a silvered bronze figure cast from a model by G. None, Paris, 34cm. high. (Christie's) £1,320

A French bronze figure of an Aborigine maiden, cast from a model by Cordier, shown dressed only in a grass skirt decorated with shells, late 19th or 20th century, 20¼ in. high. (Christie's) £4,400

A Raoul Larche gilt-bronze figure of Loie Fuller, the veils swept up concealing two light fittings, circa 1900, 45.75cm. high. £15,000

Dancers, a dark and silver patinated bronze group, both dancers wearing pointed caps, elaborate bodices and pantaloons, 10in. high. (Christie's S. Ken) £660

'Dancer', a bronze and ivory figure by H. Fournier of a girl standing on tiptoe, holding out her skirt, 35cm. high. (Christie's) £2,640

BRONZE FIGURES

An early 20th century Italian bronze bust of a maiden in folk costume, cast from a model by E. Rubino, 44cm. high. (Christie's)   £462

'Penthesilia, Queen of the Amazons', a bronze figure cast from a model by A. Bouraine, 48.2cm. long. (Christie's)   £880

Bronze figure of a woman, signed Oscar Glandebeck, circa 1900, 12in. high. (Lots Road Chelsea Auction Galleries)   £190

'Dance of the Harlequinade', a gilt bronze and ivory figure, cast and carved after a model by Th. Ullmann, 30cm. high. (Christie's)   £1,080

A bronze figure of a nude dancer by Alexander Kelety, 40.2cm. high.   £8,000

A bronze and ivory figure cast and carved from a model by Kovats, 39cm. high. (Christie's)   £7,700

A bronze figure, 'Egyptian Priestess', 80cm. high. (Christie's)   £880

A bronze figure of a skier in a twisting posture on a naturalistic base above a variegated marble plinth, 12½in. long. (Christie's S. Ken)   £495

Bear Hug, a bronze figure cast after a model by F. Rieder, 30.8cm. high. (Christie's)   £1,430

BRONZE FIGURES

An Austrian bronze of a foot-baller with his leg raised to kick a football, signed Fuchs, 13½in. high. (Christie's S. Ken)
£495

'Thoughts', a bronze figure cast after a model by M. Giraud Riviere, circa 1930, 17.8cm. high. (Christie's)
£486

A late 19th or early 20th century English bronze bust of a handsome youth, in the style of Brock, on turned red marble socle, 14.5cm. high. (Christie's)
£99

A bronze figure of a naked young lady dancing, by Karl Perl, 24½in. high. (Christie's)   £1,200

An early 20th century gilt bronze and ivory group of a little girl and a baby snuggled-up in an armchair signed A. Croisy, 6¾in. high.
(Woolley & Wallis)   £1,550

The Rejected Suitor, a gilt bronze and ivory figure, cast and carved from a model by Roland Paris, as a small bald headed man, 24.8cm. high. (Phillips London)   £780

An Anglo-Australian early 20th century bronze figure of Diana wounded, cast from a model by Sir Bertram Mackennal, 42cm. high overall. (Christie's)   £8,800

A bronze cigarette box in the form of a girl in Middle Eastern dress, 4in. high. (Capes, Dunn & Co.) £350

Sabre Dancer, a Viennese bronze figure of a scantily clad Oriental dancing girl in jewelled headdress, 55.5cm. high. (Christie's London)
£4,840

BRONZE FIGURES

Dancer with Tambourine,
a gilt bronze figure cast
from a model by Agathon
Leonard, 55.5cm. high.
(Christie's)   £3,960

A 20th century French
bronze group of three running athletes, entitled Au But,
cast from a model by Alfred
Boucher, 32cm. high.
(Christie's London)   £1,540

A bronze and ivory figure
cast and carved from a
model by Marquetz and
modelled as a girl with a
long robe tied at the waist,
28.5cm. high. (Phillips)
        £380

A 20th century English green
patinated bronze figure of a
naked young girl, signed and
dated *Pibworth, 1923,* 25in.
high. (Christie's S. Ken) £462

A late 19th century Viennese
bronze portrait bust of a
young girl, cast from a model
by Arthur Strasser, dated 1894,
42cm. high. (Christie's) £550

Eastern Dancer, a bronze and
ivory figure, cast and carved
from a model by G. Schmidt-
Cassel, on a black marble base,
37.6cm. high. (Christie's
London)   £7,700

A bronze figure, cast from a
model by H. Molins, as a
female dancer, 58.5cm. high.
(Christie's)   £880

Morning Walk, a parcel gilt
bronze and ivory group cast
and carved after a model by
A. Becquerel, 26.8cm. high.
(Christie's)   £1,320

An Art Deco bronze figure,
by Fesler Felix, modelled as
a naked girl with an elaborate
headdress and belt, 37cm.
high. (Phillips)   £220

BRONZE FIGURES

An Art Deco bronze group of a male and female nude, 65cm. high. (Christie's) £2,160

1920s bronze figurine of a lady from the demi-monde. (Muir Hewitt) £350

A gilt bronze tray cast from a model by Maurice Bouval, formed as a leaf with the figure of a nymph holding flowers, signed M. Bouval, 17.5cm. high. (Christie's) £715

'Bubble Dance', a bronze and ivory figure by A. Goddard, of Georgia Graves at the Folies Bergere, 1930, the female figure in short silver-patinated dress, 52.5cm. high. (Christie's) £6,050

An Art Deco cold painted and silvered bronze figure, the young woman wearing a brief skirt, with arms outstretched, lampholders suspended from her hands, overall height 48.5cm. (Bonhams) £2,600

'Elegant', a gold patinated bronze and ivory group, cast and carved from a model by S. Bertrand, of a finely dressed woman standing with a greyhound at her side, 31.2cm. high. (Christie's) £2,200

Early 20th century bronze bust of Woman, signed Wigglesworth, stamped Gorham Co. Founders, 13¾in. high. (Robt. W. Skinner Inc.) £555

A green patinated bronze group cast from a model by Amy Bitter as three naked children, 'See no evil, speak no evil, hear no evil', 25cm. high. (Phillips) £2,000

A late 19th century French 'Chryselephantine' bronze and ivory figure of 'La Liseuse', base signed A. Carrier-Belleuse, 62cm. high. (Christie's) £1,760

BRONZE FIGURES

A bronze model of a fox, modelled in stylised fashion, 35cm. high, stamped on reverse Seiden-Stucker. (Phillips) £300

A bronze bust of a woman cast from a model by Dora Gordine, Paris, 1925, 36.8cm. high. (Christie's) £935

'Source d'Or', a bronze sculpture by Ernest Wante of a gold patinated maiden standing in a rocky enclave, 25.4cm. high. (Christie's) £880

Tambourine Dancer, cast from a model by D. Simon, of a nude maiden dancing with a tambourine, 44cm. high. (Christie's London) £660

An Art Deco bronze and ivory figurine of a young bather reclining on a large rock. (Biddle & Webb) £4,600

A stylish Art Deco bronze figure, cast from a model by Gilbert, as a naked girl with silvered body poised above a fluted bullet shaped base, 46cm. high. (Phillips London) £1,200

A bronze and alabaster figure cast and carved from a model by Lothar of a maiden tying beads in her hair, 50.5cm. high. (Christie's) £1,100

An early 20th century Belgian bronze bust of a stevedore, cast from a model by Constantin Meunier, inscribed Anvers, 58cm. high. (Christie's) £3,520

A bronze Spirit of Ecstasy showroom display, signed *Charles Sykes,* mounted on a circular marble base, 20½in. high. (Christie's London) £7,920

BRONZE FIGURES

Bronze, 'Young Girl Looking Down at Frog', circa 1900, 18in. high. (J. M. Welch & Son) £410

'A Savage Drinking from a Stream', a bronze figure cast from a model by J. De Roncourt, 81.2cm. wide. (Christie's) £880

An Austrian erotic gilt bronze figure of a dancing girl, her skirt hinged to the front, 6in. high. £320

A gilt bronze and ivory figure, modelled as an Egyptianesque girl, inscribed Bohm fec, 33cm. high. (Phillips) £3,700

An early 20th century French bronze statuette of a naked woman, known as 'La Verite Meconnue', after Aime Jules Dalou, 22.5cm. high.(Christie's) £1,026

'Flower maiden', a gold-patinated bronze and ivory figure by Lipszyc, of a partly naked girl, 43cm. high. (Christie's) £3,850

An Art Deco bronze two dimensional sculpture, of a long haired woman dressed in sarong, supporting a hoop on the left hip, engraved initials *ER*, 25in. high. (Christie's S. Ken) £418

'Valkyrie Rider', a parcel gilt bronze and ivory equestrian figure statue, signed L. Chalon, 54.5cm. high. (Christie's) £4,950

A bronze figure cast after a model by Hugo Lederer, modelled as a naked maiden wearing a turban, signed, circa 1925, 43cm. high. (Christie's) £756

BRONZE FIGURES

An Art Deco bronze and ivory Grecian figure on marble plinth, 11¾in. high. (Capes, Dunn & Co.) £580

A 19th century French bronze group of the Voyage of the Nations, cast from a model by Edouard Drouot, 49cm. high. (Christie's) £1,650

'Salammbô', a gilt bronze bust cast from a design by Louis Moreau, of a young female with long flowing hair, wearing an elaborate head-dress, on rock form base, 74.5cm. high. (Christie's) £4,400

An Art Nouveau bronze of a young woman wearing a long aubergine dress, signed L. Alliot, on a green marble base, 25in. high. (Hy. Duke & Son) £800

'Speedskater', a bronze figure cast from a model by Carl Fagerberg of a racing skater, dated April 1932, 51.4cm. high. (Christie's) £2,200

Art Deco bronze and ivory figurine of a young woman on a jetty holding a canoe paddle. (Biddle & Webb) £2,200

'Dancer', a bronze luminaire cast and carved from a model by Alex Kelety, of a naked female running, her head thrown back and with one leg kicking backwards, 49.5cm. high. (Christie's) £6,600

An early 20th century German bronze group of Europa and the Bull, cast from a model by A. Grath, 60 x 51cm. (Christie's) £1,980

The Sleep of Reason, cast from a model by Maurice Bouval, the dark patinated female figure, with eyes closed, her hair bedecked with flowers, 43.5cm. high. (Christie's London) £1,980

CHIPARUS

Of the many figurine artists who emerged during the years following the First World War one of the most important was Dimitri (Demetre is the Gallicised form) Chiparus. Chiparus was a Rumanian who came to Paris to study under A Mercié and J Boucher. He started exhibiting at the Salon des Artistes Français in 1914, when he received an Honourable Mention, and continued to do so until 1928.

His figures include realistic reproductions of nudes and women in everyday clothes, as well as columbines and pierrots, and dancers, some in amazing postures and obviously influenced by the Ballets Russes.

Much of his work was executed in chryselephantine, a medium encouraged at the time by the Belgian government who were anxious to create a European market for Congolese ivory.

'Sheltering from the Rain', a bronze and ivory group cast and carved from a model by D. Chiparus, 26cm. high. (Christie's) £1,760

'Golfer', a bronze and ivory figure, by D. H. Chiparus, of a girl swinging a golf club and wearing a green-patinated skirt, 36.8cm. high. (Christie's) £9,900

Lioness, a bronze figure cast after a model by Demetre Chiparus, 57.8cm. long. (Christie's) £1,045

'Nubian Dancer', a bronze and ivory dancing girl, cast and carved after a model by D. H. Chiparus, 15½in. high. (Christie's) £12,000

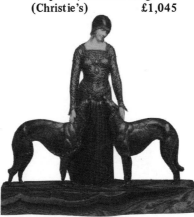

'Dourga', a bronze and ivory figure by D. H. Chiparus, of a girl standing on tiptoe with her arms raised above her head, 62.5cm. high. (Christie's) £7,700

'Les Amis de Toujours', a bronze and ivory figure by Demetre Chiparus, of a standing lady, flanked by two borzois, on a rectangular amber-coloured onyx base, 63cm. high. (Christie's) £13,200

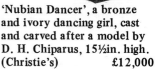

'Dancer with Ring', a bronze and ivory figure by D. H. Chiparus, of an oriental dancing girl wearing a jewelled headdress, 46.5cm. high. (Christie's) £13,200

CHIPARUS

A painted bronze and ivory figure, 'Hush', 42cm. high, inscribed D. H. Chiparus. (Phillips)   £2,700

'The Fan Dancer', a bronze and ivory figure by Chiparus, on marble and onyx base, 15in. high. (Christie's) £4,500

A painted bronze and ivory figure, 'Oriental Dancer', 40.20cm. high, inscribed on the marble Chiparus. (Phillips)   £4,600

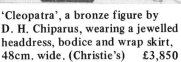

A bronze and ivory figure cast and carved after a model by D. H. Chiparus, 16in. high. (Christie's)   £4,500

'Cleopatra', a bronze figure by D. H. Chiparus, wearing a jewelled headdress, bodice and wrap skirt, 48cm. wide. (Christie's)   £3,850

An Art Deco period figure in bronze and ivory of a lady holding a muff, signed D. H. Chiparus, 12½in. high. (R. H. Ellis & Sons) £2,160

'Leaving the Opera', a bronze and ivory figure by D. Chiparus of a woman wrapped in a silver-patinated cloak, walking down a stepped brown onyx base, 23.4cm. high. (Christie's)   £1,870

A gilt bronze and ivory group of three young girls, signed Chiparus, 6in. high.   £1,800

'Fancy Dress', a cold-painted bronze and ivory group, cast and carved from a model by Demetre Chiparus, as a Pierrot wearing a green-silver costume dancing with his female companion, 48.5cm. high. (Phillips)   £12,000

COLINET

Claire Jeanne Roberte Colinet was born in Brussels and studied sculpture there under Jef Lambeaux. After moving to Paris she was elected a member of the Société des Artistes Français. She exhibited at their Salon from 1914, and at the Salon des Indépendants between 1937 and 1944.

It is noteworthy that Colinet was the only woman among the figurine artists who emerged in the years after the First World War. She worked in the hieratic style which was quite close to that of the artists of the 1890s, featuring mysterious dancers dressed in flowing garments of costly fabrics, laden with jewels at wrist and ankle. Colinet's best works show athletic dancers, beautifully proportioned, arranged in strange balletic poses and obviously much influenced by the Ballets Russes.

A Colinet bronze group of two dancing bacchantes, 56.5cm., 1930's. £2,500

'Snake Dancer', cast from a model by C J R Colinet of cold-painted bronze and ivory, on a marble base, 24in. high. £5,000

A Colinet bronze dancing girl in eastern costume, circa 1930, 39.5cm. high. £1,500

'Danseuse de Thebes', a bronze and ivory figure cast and carved from a model by C. J. Roberte Colinet, 25.8cm. high. (Christie's) £8,100

A bronze figure, the design attributed to C. J. R. Colinet, the female dancer dancing standing on tiptoes, 15½in. high. (Bonhams) £1,200

A bronze lamp cast and carved from a model by C. J. R. Colinet modelled as a dancing girl, her arms outstretched supporting a lamp in each hand. (Christie's) £4,500

A bronze figure by Cl. J. R. Colinet, modelled as a nude female standing on one foot, the other leg and both arms outstretched before her, supporting a ball on each, 26.7cm. high. £1,500

COLINET

Colinet cold-painted bronze and ivory figure of an 'Erotic Dancer', on an onyx base, 14in. high. **£1,500**

Gilt bronze and ivory figure of a girl in pantaloons, possibly by Colinet, 45cm. high. **£2,000**

Egyptian Dancer, a gilt bronze and ivory figure cast and carved from a model by C. J. Roberte Colinet, 42.5cm. high. (Christie's) **£19,800**

A cold painted bronze figure, attributed as a model by Colinet, of a naked girl with brown hair, poised above a stepped marble base, 49.5cm. high. (Phillips) **£1,200**

Towards the Unknown (Valkyrie), a cold painted bronze and ivory group, cast and carved from a model by Claire Jeanne Roberte Colinet, 31.5cm. high. (Phillips London) **£2,700**

'Oriental Dancer', a bronze figure cast from a model by C. J. Roberte Colinet, 19½in. high. (Christie's) **£1,800**

'Egyptian Dancer', a bronze figure, cast from a model by Cl. J.R. Colinet, of a dancing girl, with flowing skirt and Egyptian headdress, 43cm. high. (Christie's) **£2,860**

A gilt bronze figure of a girl, 'Modern Venus', cast from a model by C. J. R. Colinet, 47cm. high. (Phillips) **£3,000**

A cold-painted bronze and ivory figure of a dancing girl by Colinet on a bronze and onyx base, 18in. high overall. **£4,000**

FAGUAYS

Pierre le Faguays was a native of Nantes in France. A member of the Société des Artistes Français, he exhibited at their salons, where he gained an Honourable Mention in 1926. He was also a member of the La Stèle and Evolution groups, where artist craftsmen exhibited bronzes, ceramics, lamps and other decorative objects.

Le Faguays worked in the 'stylised' mode, which combined elements from many contemporary influences.

Le Faguays bronze male figure of an Olympian hero holding a palm leaf, 66cm. high, 1930's.   £1,400

A bronze nude female figure of a dancer by Le Faguays, signed, 21¾in. high overall.   £1,000

'Dancer with Thyrsus', a parcel gilt bronze figure cast after a model by Pierre Le Faguays, 27.6cm. high. (Christie's)   £1,512

'Bacchante', a bronze green and brown patinated figure, cast from a model by Pierre Le Faguays, of a nude female kneeling on one leg, the other bent forward, 66.5cm. high. (Christie's)   £6,600

A silvered bronze figure of a dancer, cast from a model by Pierre Le Faguays, the young woman wearing a pleated dress with panelled skirt, 1920s, 65cm., overall height. (Bonhams)   £1,400

'Diana'. A bronze figure, cast from a model by Pierre Le Faguays, modelled as a lithe young woman wearing a short classical tunic, 66.5cm. high. (Phillips)   £1,100

'Fawn and Nymph', a bronze sculpture cast from a model by Pierre Le Faguays mounted on a rectangular wooden base, 46.5cm. high.(Christie's)£7,260

'Pitcher', a bronze figure cast from a model by Pierre Le Faguays, of a young girl in a short dress, 25cm. high.   £850

GERDAGO

Gerdago (this may or may not even be a name) is one of those producers of Art Deco bronzes about whom absolutely nothing is known. His pieces, while set firmly within the mainstream tradition of the period, i.e. having as subjects exotic dancers in wildly balletic poses, are nevertheless highly distinctive. The figures are always dressed in extravagant, angular costumes, often with tall, pointed hats, and are cold painted in the most brilliant and magnificent colours.

A bronze and ivory figure of a dancer in a floral dress by Gerdago, 12in. high. £6,000

A bronze and ivory figure of a dancer cast and carved from a model by Gerdago, 10½in. high. (Christie's) £4,000

'Dancer', a bronze and ivory figure, cast and carved from a model by Gerdago, of a female dancer poised with arms outstretched, 32.8cm. high. (Christie's) £3,916

A cold-painted bronze and ivory figure of a dancer from a model by Gerdago, on a green onyx base, 11in. high. £7,000

'Exotic Dancer', a gold-patinated bronze and ivory figure by Gerdago of a female dancer making a theatrical curtsey, 30.5cm. high. (Christie's) £13,200

GORY

'Exotic Dancer', a gilt bronze and ivory figure cast and carved from a model by A. Gory, 37.5cm. high. (Christie's) £2,160

The Cape, a gilt bronze and ivory figure cast and carved from a model by A. Gory, of a small child, 20.1cm. high. (Christie's London) £440

'Flower Seller' a gilt bronze and ivory figure cast and carved from a model by A. Gory,38.5cm. high. (Christie's) £2,808

NAM GREB

Who is, or was, Nam Greb, the impudent sculptor of these erotic bronze figurines? You won't find the answer in any of the reference books, for the simple reason that no one by that name existed. Nam Greb is, in fact, Bergman spelt backwards!

Little enough, indeed, is known about the Franz Bergman foundry, save that it flourished in Austria during the first two decades of this century. Bergman, spelt the right way round, is known for fairly conventional cold painted bronze groups, notably of Arabs on carpets or Arabs with camels.

It is always the erotic pieces that are signed Nam Greb. These were, in fact, designed by a man called Thuss, about whom absolutely nothing more is known. It has been suggested, perhaps a little tongue in cheek, that he signed them thus because he didn't want his mother to know what he was up to!

'Sword Dancer', a large cold painted bronze figure cast from a model by Nam Greb, 21¼in. high. £1,320

A bronze rectangular casket and cover by Nam Greb, on four cockleshell feet, 4¾in. wide. £500

A cold painted bronze figure of Cleopatra cast from a model by Nam Greb, 10in. across. (Christie's) £770

The secret of the mummy: an encased bronze nude figure by Nam Greb, 23cm. high. £1,250

A Bergman cold painted bronze musical box, inscribed 'Nam Greb', modelled as an amorous young beau kneeling beside his willing consort, 13½in. (Lawrence Fine Arts) £2,090

A Bergman painted bronze figure, modelled as a bathing belle in one piece swimsuit and hair tied in a mobcap, 12.5cm. high. £810

An amusing Bergman painted bronze group, modelled as an owl, with a seal which when pressed, parts the owl's body to reveal a naked female figure, 19.5cm. high, signed *Nam Greb*. (Phillips London) £1,650

GUERANDE, JAEGER

It seems amazing today that so little should be known about so many of the sculptors whose bronzes are quite commonly sold at auction. After all, we are not talking about the dark ages, but only about sixty or seventy years back into the past. Sketchy biographical details are available on a few of the most illustrious figures, such as Chiparus and Colinet, for example, but for others, such as Guerande and Jaeger, not even as much as their dates or nationalities are freely available. Even the auction houses who regularly feature their works have little information to give.

Why should this be? One possible explanation is that many were just foundry workers, turning out pieces in a current fashion, or sometimes in imitation of more notable artists.

Also, many worked in Germany or Austria, which the Second World War would shortly leave largely in ruins, and where many records must have been destroyed. It seems a shame that the history of these bronze designers should be lost for ever, and it is certainly a subject which would amply repay some intense investigation.

KAUBA

Carl Kauba worked in Vienna in the interwar period, producing bronzes which stand a little apart from the mainstream subjects of dancers, sportsmen etc. Fairly conventional Art Nouveau type maidens do figure among his output, but he also tackled more offbeat themes such as amusing groups of children. Commonest of all, however, are his Red Indian figures, which show little Art Deco influence.

An Art Deco gilt bronze figure of a dancer kneeling with arms outstretched, signed J. D. Guerande, 21in. high overall.   £800

A bronze group cast from a model by Guerande of a dancing lady, 62.9cm. high. (Christie's)   £1,512

A bronze table lamp cast from a model by G. Jaeger of a naked sea nymph poised holding a conch shell to her ear, 70cm. high. (Christie's)   £1,500

'The Swing', a bronze and ivory figure cast and carved from a model by Jaeger, 10½in. high. (Christie's)   £1,300

A bronze group cast from a model by C. Kauba, on a variegated square marble base, signed, 14.3cm. high. (Christie's)   £385

A mechanical bronze figure cast after a model by C. Kauba, on a square bronze base, circa 1920, 21cm. high. (Christie's)   £756

LORENZL

K Lorenzl was a German Art Deco figurine modeller, who also designed ceramics for the Austrian firm of Goldscheider. He often copied well known Preiss figures, though his carving was not as skilled.

He did succeed however in capturing in bronze the 'new woman', slender and boyish, with bobbed hair, dressed either in floppy pyjamas or as an Amazon. Some of his figures are signed *K Lor* and *Ronr*.

A bronze group of a girl with a borzoi by Lorenzl.
£1,800

An Art Deco bronze figure cast from a model by Lorenzl, modelled as a dancing girl, 43.9cm. high. (Phillips) £650

A golden-patinated bronze figure cast from a model by Lorenzl, as a dancing girl wearing a long-sleeved dress, 49cm. high. (Phillips) £750

'Diane', a silvered bronze group of a naked goddess flanked by two running borzois, modelled by Lorenzl, 46cm. high. £2,500

A Lorenzl silvered bronze figure, the naked maiden in dancing pose, tip-toed upon one leg, 49.5cm. high, signed. (Lawrence Fine Arts) £682

A Lorenzl gilt and painted bronze figure of a lady holding the hem of her skirt, on onyx base, 10in. high. (Christie's) £500

A Lorenzl gilt bronze dancing girl, poised on one leg, 15in. high. (Christie's) £820

A bronze figure of a nude girl, cast from a model by Lorenzl, she has bobbed hair and stands demurely with her hands clasped, 64cm. high. (Phillips) £1,800

LORENZL

A Lorenzl bronze figure of a naked dancing girl, standing on one leg, kicking the other, 28cm. high. (Phillips) £280

'Dancing Girl', a silvered bronze and ivory figure cast from a model by Lorenzl, decorated by Crejo, 22.3cm. high. (Christie's) £648

A bronze and ivory figure of a dancer by Lorenzl. £1,500

'Nude Girl with Shawl', a silvered bronze figure cast from a model by Lorenzl, decorated by Crejo, 37.5cm. high. £2,000

A patinated silvered bronze group of a pair of Russian dancers, cast from a model by Lorenzl, on a rectangular green onyx base, 11½in. high. £2,000

The Dancer, an enamelled bronze and ivory figure, cast and carved from a model by Lorenzl, on green onyx pedestal, 27.4cm. high. (Christie's London) £1,540

A large Lorenzl silvered bronze figure of a dancing girl, 28½in. high. (Christie's) £1,800

A Lorenzl cold-painted bronze figure of a nude in dancing pose, 1930's, 23.5cm. high. £1,500

A gilt bronze and ivory figure cast and carved from a model by Lorenzl, 11in. high. (Christie's) £520

PHILIPPE

Philippe was an Austrian by birth, who created stylish models and dancers characterised by their theatrical and extravagant gestures. His treatment of the clothes is particularly striking, and often is a pure product of the new Machine Age.

A painted bronze and ivory figure, 'Le Grand Ecart Respectueux', 21.50cm. high, inscribed P. Philippe. (Phillips) £2,300

Bronze figure of a dancing woman, P. Phillipe, 20th century, costumed figure, marble plinth, signed and titled, 15^1/$_2$ in. high. (Skinner Inc.) £767

'The Swirling Dress' a cold painted bronze and ivory figure by Philippe, 40cm. high. £3,000

'Dancer', a bronze and ivory figure cast and carved from a model by P. Philippe of a girl standing on tiptoe, her hands outstretched, wearing a short flared dress and jewelled turban, 64.5cm. high. (Christie's) £9,000

'Pierrette', a cold-painted bronze and ivory figure, cast and carved from a model by P. Philippe, 37.8cm. high. (Phillips) £4,000

'Andalusian Dancer', a cold-painted bronze and ivory figure cast and carved from a model by P. Philippe, 35.3cm. high. (Phillips) £4,000

Philippe coloured bronze and ivory figure of a young woman, signed, 24cm. high, 1930's. £5,000

'Rahda', a bronze and ivory figure by P. Philippe, of a dancer standing on tiptoe, arms outstretched, 43.4cm. high. (Christie's) £6,050

PROF OTTO POERZL

As with many of the sculptors of the Art Deco period, very little is known about Professor Otto Poerzl. Where did his title come from, for example? Such sketchy details as are available tell us that he was born in Scheiben, and worked out of Coburg, both in Germany. He produced figures which in many cases are so similar to those produced by Preiss that speculation has abounded that they are one and the same person. However, their respective interpretations of some examples, Bat Dancers, for instance, do show significant differences in treatment. The confusion has not been helped by the fact that both appeared to use the same foundry, and a founder's mark with the initial PK are found on both Poerzl and Preiss figures.

A Poertzel bronze and ivory group of a pierrot and partner, 1930's, 37cm. high.   £7,500

'Snake Dancer', a bronze and ivory figure by Prof. O. Poertzel, on black marble base, 52cm. high. (Christie's)   £8,800

Poertzel bronze and ivory group of a woman and two hounds, 49.5cm. high, 1920's.   £8,000

Bronze and ivory dancer by Prof. O. Poertzel, 1930's, 32cm. high.   £1,500

'Butterfly dancers', a bronze and ivory group cast and carved from a model by Prof. Otto Poertzel, of two ballerinas dancing in formation, 41.5cm. high.
(Christie's)   £9,350

'Page Girl' a cold-painted gilt bronze and ivory figure of a young girl by Poertzel, on a green marble base, 11½in. high. (Christie's)   £1,210

'Bat Dancer' by Prof. O. Poertzel in bronze and ivory, on a marble base, 8in. high.   £2,000

PREISS

Art Deco found one of its most vivid expressions in the bronze and ivory, or chryselephantine, figures of F Preiss. Virtually nothing is known about Preiss, save that he was probably born in Vienna. Even his forename is in doubt, though an Ideal Home Exhibition Catalogue of the time refers to him as Frederick, which is probably simply an anglicisation of Friedrich. His work, which appeared in the 20s and 30s, was closely copied by one Professor Otto Poerzl of Coburg, so closely in fact that there has been speculation that they may be one and the same. His figures were distributed in Britain by the Phillips and MacConnal Gallery of Arts, which published an illustrated catalogue with model numbers. They chiefly featured classical and modern nudes, children, some nude and some clothed, and a few dancers. The ivory is always beautifully carved, and the subjects have sweet, pretty faces, and graceful arms and hands. The bronze is usually cold-painted in cool colours such as silver, blue and grey, and while the classical nudes can be somewhat stilted, the modern counterparts are lithe and vibrant.

Most lively of all are, however, the Olympic figures, a series including golfers, tennis players, skaters and javelin throwers. They glorify physical prowess and the body beautiful, enthusiasms which came to be hijacked by the Nazis in their preoccupation with the physical superiority of the Aryan master race. Preiss captured this so well that, rightly or wrongly, suspicion has always abounded that he was an adherent of the movement.

'Bat Dancer', a bronze and ivory figure cast and carved after a model by F. Preiss, 23.6cm. high. (Christie's) £3,672

'Mandolin Player', a bronze and ivory figure by Ferdinand Preiss, the gold and silver patinated girl wearing a top-hat and loose fitting skirt, 58.4cm. high. (Christie's) £12,650

'The Archer', a bronze and ivory figure cast and carved from a model by Ferdinand Preiss of a girl with drawn bow, in a gold-patinated tunic with train, with polychrome enamelled sword and headdress, 22.3cm. high. (Christie's) £6,000

Charleston Dancer, a cold painted bronze and ivory figure, cast and carved from a model by Ferdinand Preiss, as a slender female dancer wearing silvered tights, 43.5cm. high. (Phillips London) £5,500

A painted bronze and ivory figure, 'Hoop Girl', 20.50cm. high, inscribed F. Preiss. (Phillips) £1,300

'Skater', a silver-patinated bronze and ivory figure cast by Ferdinand Preiss, of a girl skating with one leg behind her, 33.4cm. high. (Christie's) £4,620

PREISS

'Cabaret girl', a bronze and ivory figure, cast and carved from a model by Ferdinand Preiss, 38cm. high. (Christie's) £9,350

The Torch Dancer, a painted bronze and ivory figure, cast and carved from a model by Ferdinand Preiss, as a bare-breasted girl wearing floral bloomers, 39cm. high. (Phillips London) £6,000

A painted bronze and ivory figure, 'Sonny Boy', 20.50cm. high, inscribed F. Preiss. (Phillips) £1,500

'Gamin', a bronze and ivory figure by F. Preiss, of a girl dressed in a silver patinated short skirt suit, standing with her hands in her pockets, 34.3cm. high. (Christie's) £6,600

A painted bronze and ivory figure, cast and carved from a model by Ferdinand Preiss, as a female skater wearing golden, short-skirted costume 23.5cm. high. (Phillips London) £2,700

'Moth Girl', a bronze and ivory figure by Ferdinand Preiss, of a girl standing on tiptoe and examining a glass over her shoulder, 41.6cm. high. (Christie's) £4,950

Art Deco bronze and ivory figure of a young woman, after a model by Johann Philipp Ferdinand "Fritz" Preiss, circa 1930, 8¾in. high. (Skinner Inc.) £2,329

'Con Brio', a bronze and ivory figure cast and carved from a model by F. Preiss, 29cm. high. (Christie's) £5,500

Flute Player, a bronze and ivory figure cast and carved from a model by F. Preiss, 48.5cm. high. (Christie's) £18,360

VILLANIS

No biographical details are available for Emmanuele Villanis. His work, however, is set firmly in the Art Nouveau period and also has strong links with traditional 19th French century bronze casting. His subject matter is drawn very often from Classical mythology, and simply given an Art Nouveau treatment. Busts, another very traditional form, figure largely among his output.

An early 20th century patinated bronze figure of 'Les Nenuphars' by Emmanuel Villanis. £2,500

Bronze bust of 'Dalila', by E. Villanis, circa 1890, seal of Societe des Bronzes de Paris. £1,500

'Sapho', a cold-painted bronze bust cast from a model by E. Villanis, of a young maiden, her hair tied in a bun, green and amber patination, 58cm. high. (Christie's) £3,300

Pair of late 19th or early 20th century French bronze busts of Mignon and Diana, signed on the shoulders E. Villanis, 36.5cm. high. £2,000

An early 20th century French patinated bronze bust of Omphale, cast from a model by E. Villanis, 53cm. high. (Christie's) £1,320

La Sibylie, a bronze bust cast from a model by E. Villanis, with Societe des Bronzes de Paris foundry mark, 72cm. high. (Christie's) £2,420

An early 20th century bronze and cold-painted figure of a slave girl, by Emmanuele Villanis, 16in. high. £2,000

Silvia, cast from a model by Emmanuele Villanis, the green patinated Art Nouveau maiden mounted on a pedestal, 28cm. high. (Christie's London) £1,430

BRUNO ZACH

Bruno Zach was the post World War One artist in bronze who is generally associated with an overtly erotic style. His insolent, leather or scantily clad women, girls in slips or stockings holding a whip or naked beneath fur coats reflect the decadence of interwar Berlin with its sado-masochistic, often downright bizarre tendencies. Zach worked mostly in bronze, but he made the occasional figure in chryselephantine, and these are now particularly sought after.

A large decorative figural bronze and cameo glass table lamp, the bronze base cast from a model by Bruno Zach. (Phillips London)   £1,500

'Spanish Maiden' cast from a model by Bruno Zach of a standing maiden with her hands on her hips, 30cm. high.   £1,500

A bronze figure, cast from a model by Bruno Zach, 15½in. high. (Christie's)   £950

'Dancing Satyr and Nymph' cast from a model by Bruno Zach, 36cm. high.   £2,800

'Girl with a riding crop', a bronze figure cast from a model by Bruno Zach, Made in Austria, 46cm. high. (Christie's)   £2,420

'The Riding Crop', an erotic bronze figure cast from a model by Bruno Zach. £2,500

'Warrior Maiden', a bronze group cast from a model by Bruno Zach of a scantily clad girl astride a galloping stallion, 45cm. high. (Christie's)   £4,000

Athlete, a dark patinated bronze figure cast from a model by Bruno Zach, with impressed mark, 73.8cm. high. (Christie's London)   £2,860

BRONZE PLAQUES

A Leon Jallot bronze platter, circa 1900, 31cm. diameter. £300

Bronze medallion, 1935 Radio Stars Award for Distinguished Service, signed by the artist Helen Liedlof, 2in. diameter. (Skinner) £80

A Richard Garbe circular bronze plaque, 32.3cm., 1917. £450

A bronze medallion, the obverse embossed with a pilot's head, embossed 'Lindbergh Medal of the Congress United States of America', signed 'Lavra Gardin Fraser Sculptor' and further embossed 'Act May 4 1928', 2³/₄ in. diameter. (Christie's) £165

A late 19th/early 20th century bronze memorial relief, attributed to Sir Alfred Gilbert, 25cm. high. (Christie's) £330

A bronze medallion, the obverse with Statue of Liberty, Eiffel Tower, Maiden in flowing robes, embossed 'Commemorating the First New York-Paris Flight by Capt. Charles A. Lindbergh "Spirit of St Louis" New York May 20th Paris May 21st 1927', 3¹/₄ in. diameter. (Christie's) £176

An Edgar Brandt bronze panel 'Scorpio', 1928, 47 x 35.5cm. £1,500

A bronze panel by Doris Flynn, rectangular, cast decoration of people queuing, mounted in wooden frame, signed in the bronze Flynn, 88cm. wide. (Christie's) £550

An Edgar Brandt bronze panel 'Cancer', 1928, 47 x 35.5cm. £1,500

BRONZE VASES

An Art Nouveau bronze ewer by Auguste Ledru, a naked maiden forming the handle, 12½in. high. £800

A pair of baluster-shaped bronze vases, signed Aug. Moreau, 10in. high. £250

A Donenech polychrome patinated bronze vase, circa 1900, 36.5cm. high. £1,210

An Art Nouveau bronze vase, cast from a model by Louis Chalon, the top with icicle-like rim, 45.5cm. high. (Phillips London) £5,600

A bronze and marble tazza cast after a model by G. Gurschner, signed, circa 1915, 17.7cm. high. (Christie's) £648

'Fisherman', a bronze vase cast from a model by J. Ofner, inscribed, 17.9cm. high. (Christie's) £540

An Art Nouveau gilt bronze mounted ceramic vase by Charles Korschann, with a central gilded panel moulded with an Art Nouveau maiden, 65.3cm. high. (Christie's London) £12,100

A pair of Art Nouveau metal vases, each cast with the heads of three maidens with long hair, 42.5cm. high, indistinctly signed *Maurele?* (Phillips London) £260

An Art Nouveau bronze vase embellished at the top with two girls, faces in relief with flowers and foliage, 43.5cm. high. (Phillips) £300

CANE HANDLES

Canes, walking sticks and parasols have been an important fashion accessory for both men and women for several hundred years, and one which has only comparatively recently gone out of vogue. Certainly their popularity lasted well into the periods covered by this book, and leading designers such as Cartier and Tiffany were responsible for cane handles which could be either opulent, stylish or whimsical. Some came with extra embellishments or gadgets such as concealed snuff boxes or coin holders, or even, in the case of the toper's stick, a secret compartment for spirits!

A walking stick with silver collar, the ivory handle carved with the heads of two reined horses. (Christie's S. Ken.) **£198**

A French translucent blue guilloche enamel parasol handle, the body mounted with a band of foliage and flowers, by Cartier, Paris, 2¼in. long. (Christie's London) **£1,650**

A malacca cane, the silver snuff box handle in the form of a golf club. (Christie's S. Ken) **£550**

An Edward VII jewelled gold mounted tortoiseshell parasol handle, with a collar of matted gold set with diamonds and demantoid garnets, by Charles Cooke, 1906, 10¾in. long. (Christie's London) **£715**

A cane handle by Tiffany & Co., New York, circa 1900, formed as a bird's head above a barrel-shaped collar, 4in. wide, 2oz. 10dwt. (Christie's) **£281**

A gold mounted silver and rock crystal parasol handle, by Tiffany & Co., late 19th century, 4¼in. in fitted case. (Christie's London) **£1,540**

A malacca walking stick, the white metal handle modelled with a figure of a young woman kneeling amidst reeds. (Christie's S. Ken.) **£528**

A simulated bamboo walking cane, the ivory grip carved in the form of a cat's head. **£500**

CAR MASCOTS

The best known car mascots must surely be Charles Sykes' Spirit of Ecstasy for Rolls Royce, and the wonderful glass offerings by Lalique, quintessentially Art Nouveau in spirit, with their fluid, streamlined forms.

Later, mascots became less concerned with glorifying the speed of the new transport medium, perhaps as it in turn became more commonplace, and reflected the mood of Art Deco by becoming often more whimsical, even impudent in theme.

A chromium plated car mascot figure of 'Puss in Boots', 6in. high. (Christie's) £300

A chromium plated Goddess of Sport, inscribed A.E.L., 5in. high. £200

A silver plated brass golfer, with head modelled as a golf ball, 6in. high. (Christie's) £1,760

'Spirit of the Wind', a red-ashay car mascot on chromium plated metal mount, 11.5cm. high. (Christie's) £825

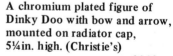

A chromium plated figure of Dinky Doo with bow and arrow, mounted on radiator cap, 5¼in. high. (Christie's) £110

A riveted aluminium Voisin Cocotte, circa 1924, 9in. high. (Christie's) £308

'Pharaoh', a Red-Ashay, car mascot in clear and satin finished glass, 11.5cm. high. (Christie's) £864

Hirondelle, a Lalique glass car mascot, moulded as a swallow perched on a circular base, 14.8cm. high. (Phillips London) £1,400

CAR MASCOTS

A brass dragonfly, the base
stamped M. Bertin, circa 1920,
6½in. high. (Christie's)   £242

'Cinq Chevaux', a Lalique glass
Car Mascot, the model
commissioned by Citroën in
1925, 11.5cm. high.
(Phillips)   £2,800

A nickel-plated Mickey Mouse
car mascot, shaped as Mickey
Mouse with his hands on his
hips, 5¾in. high, circa 1930's.
(Christie's S. Ken)   £198

A silver plated grinning cat
mascot, the base marked *Rd
No. 676202*, 4½in. high.
(Christie's London)   £572

'Saint-Christophe', a Lalique
glass Car Mascot of disc shape,
intaglio-moulded on the reverse,
11.5cm. high.
(Phillips)   £880

A nickel plated policeman
with right hand raised, the
base stamped *Asprey*, 12cm.
high. (Christie's S. Ken)
                              £165

Bright Young Things, a nickel-
plated car mascot of a young
couple dancing cheek to cheek,
the base signed Ruffony, 5in.
high. (Christie's New York) £629

'Grande Libellule', a Lalique
glass Car Mascot, modelled as a
large dragonfly resting on a
circular base, 21cm. high.
(Phillips)   £4,000

A brass Felix the Cat, 1930's,
4in. high. (Christie's)   £198

CAR MASCOTS

'Coq Nain', a coloured car mascot, the topaz and satin finished glass moulded as a cockerel, 20.2cm. high. (Christie's) £2,750

'Comete', a rare Lalique moulded glass car mascot, moulded as a star with an angular vapour trail streaming behind it, 18.5cm. long. (Phillips) £5,000

A brass stylised car mascot bust of Minerva, inscribed P. de Soete, 5½in. high. (Christie's) £380

Touch Wud, a leather headed and brass good luck charm, 4½in. high. (Christie's) £165

A silvered bronze wind spirit, the crouching female figure with flowing hair and cloak, signed *Guiraud Riviere*, 7½in. high. (Christie's London) £3,080

A nickel plated elephant hatching from an egg, the base stamped L'Oeuf d'Elephant depose, circa 1920, 5½in. high. (Christie's) £660

A chromium plated Riley Ski Lady, circa 1930, 5½in. high. (Christie's) £440

A nickel plated Amilcar Pegasus, the base stamped Darel, circa 1920, 4in. high. (Christie's) £264

'Vitesse', a Lalique car mascot moulded as a naked female, 18.5cm. high. (Christie's) £5,500

CAR MASCOTS

A chromium plated Packard swan, 7in. high. (Onslow's)
£45

A chromium plated girl riding a goose, mounted on radiator cap, 4¼in. high. (Christie's)
£462

'The Dummy Teat', nickel plated mascot manufactured by J. Grose & Co., 1926, for the Austin 7 fondly known as the Baby Austin.
£300

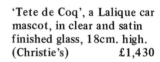

Grenouille, a Lalique glass car mascot, modelled as a small frog in crouched position, 6cm. high, signed R. Lalique, France, (Phillips London)
£12,000

A chromium plated charging Red Indian, 6in. long.
£100

'Tete de Coq', a Lalique car mascot, in clear and satin finished glass, 18cm. high. (Christie's)
£1,430

'Lady Skater', chrome plated Desmo mascot from the 1930's was for skating enthusiasts.
£150

'Sanglier', a Lalique car mascot in clear and satin finished glass, moulded as a boar, 6.5cm. high. (Christie's)
£715

Archer, a Lalique glass plaque moulded R Lalique mark, 13cm. high on chromium-plated base fitted to radiator cap. (Onslow's)
£1,000

CAR MASCOTS

A chromium plated Schneider Trophy seaplane, circa 1930, 6in. long. (Christie's)   £462

A brass 'Telcote Pup', circa 1930, mounted on radiator cap, 4in. high. (Christie's)   £242

'Perche', a Lalique car mascot in clear and satin finished glass, moulded as a fish, 9.5cm. high. (Christie's) £715

A bronze showroom display of a graceful winged speed goddess, with hair streaming in the wind, her base inscribed *Susse Frs. Ed. Paris, Cire Perdue,* and signed *Ch. Soudant,* 21¼in. high. (Christie's London)   £4,180

'Longchamps', a Lalique satin glass car mascot, moulded as the head of a racehorse with spirited expression, 12.70cm. high. (Phillips)   £3,200

A brass nymph holding a torch in front with leg raised and trailing scarf, 5¾in. high.   £120

'Falcon', a Lalique car mascot in clear and satin finished glass, 15.5cm. high. (Christie's)   £1,870

'Victoire', a good Lalique clear and satin glass 'Spirit of the Wind', car mascot in original Breves Galleries metal mount, 25.80cm. long. (Phillips)   £7,200

A nickel plated speed nymph clutching a scarf, by Lejeune, stamped Reg. AEL, 6in. high.   £250

CAR MASCOTS

'Longchamps', a Lalique car mascot, the clear and satin-finished glass moulded as a stylised head of a horse, 12cm. high. (Christie's) £8,250

'Tete de Paon', a frosted blue glass car mascot by Rene Lalique, 17.5cm. high. (Christie's) £36,324

A rare early 20th century English bronze statuette of the Spirit of Ecstasy, cast from a model by Charles Sykes, 60cm. high. (Christie's) £5,500

'Tete de Belier', a Lalique car mascot, the clear and satin-finished glass moulded as a ram's head with impressed signature R. Lalique, France, 9.5cm. high. (Christie's) £16,500

CHANDELIERS

The Art Nouveau period
threw up so many
extraordinary artists in glass
that it is not surprising that
many beautiful chandeliers
should have been produced in
that style.

The Art Deco period too
saw some stunning creations
being made, and these can
fetch just as much as their
earlier counterparts.

A Tiffany two tier Turtleback chandelier, the dome
shade composed of blue
iridescent green turtleback
tile border, 22in. diameter.
(Skinner)   £12,500

A Daum hanging shade overlaid with acid-cut
decoration of coral coloured berries and leaves.
(Christie's)   £2,200

One of a pair of Glenstone Hall hanging shades
designed by Sir Edwin Lutyens with three
vaseline glass beads, 32.6cm. diameter.
(Christie's)   £5,720

Tiffany bronze and favrile glass 'Swirling Leaf'
hanging lamp with raised rim and shaped beaded apron, 22in. diameter.
(Skinner)   £5,282

CHANDELIERS

A Roman key hanging chandelier, the whole overlaid with metal grid simulating leaded segments, 24in. diam. (Robt. W. Skinner Inc.) £650

Oak and slag glass chandelier, 20th century, square ceiling plate suspending five chains through oak cross brace with five shades pendant, 36in. diameter. (Skinner Inc.) £269

One of a pair of Dora Gordine four-branch chandeliers in hand-wrought tin of cruciform shape, inscribed 1932, 73cm. high. £2,000

An Art Deco two-tier chandelier in the style of Jacques Emile Ruhlmann, with gilt metal domed base and pendant bauble, 123cm. high. (Christie's) £2,200

A W.A.S. Benson brass and copper chandelier, the central copper circular fluted dish supported by a central brass rod with three brass arms, approx. 50cm. across. (Phillips) £1,450

An eight-light bronze chandelier cast after a design by Carlo Bugatti, circa 1910, 165cm. high. £1,750

A gilt-bronze and Schneider glass chandelier in the Art Nouveau style, 1920's. £500

A copper and amber glass lantern, style no. 324, by Gustav Stickley, circa 1906, 15in. high, globe 5¼in. diam. (Robt. W. Skinner Inc.)£4,054

A patinated wrought-iron and textured amber glass chandelier, attributed to Gustav Stickley, 28in. diam. £3,500

CHANDELIERS

Leaded glass ceiling lamp, with red and green swag border, mounted with tricon gilt metal chain and central hooked socket, 15in. diameter.
(Skinner Inc.) £257

Early 20th century hammered copper and bronze chandelier with seven Steuben shades, 20in. diam. (Robt. W. Skinner Inc.) £1,785

An Art Deco glass and chromium plated metal chandelier of star form, circa 1930, 71cm. wide.
(Christie's) £18,700

A hammered copper lantern with tinted amber glass, by Gustav Stickley, circa 1912, 22in. high. £2,500

A W.A.S. Benson three-branch electrolier, having ribbed vaseline glass shades of ogee form, approx. 70cm. high.
(Phillips) £1,500

Bird's Nest, a Lalique chandelier, the hemispherical form comprising twelve radial segments suspended from a circular frame, 49cm. diam.
(Christie's London) £1,980

A Lalique plafonnier, hemispherical clear and opalescent glass, 31.5cm. diam.
(Christie's) £1,100

An Art Nouveau brass six light chandelier, the circlet pierced with stylised flowers and whiplash motif, 102cm. high. (Christie's London) £605

A Sabino frosted glass chandelier, in three tiers, 1930's, 65cm. approx. maximum height. £1,500

CHINA

China of the Art Nouveau and Deco periods forms a complete departure from what had gone before. Farewell blue and white, delicate flower painting, gilded rims etc. The new age brought with it stunning bright colour combinations and a host of new and interesting glazes. There is little characteristic 'bone' china to be found from the period. More robust bodies were favoured, in keeping with the bold new decorative styles.

An Ault vase, designed by Dr. Christopher Dresser, with curling lip continuing to form two handles, streaked turquoise glaze over dark brown, 18cm. high. (Christie's) £935

One of a pair of vases, decorated in the 'Pomegranate' pattern in shades of pink, green and ochre on a dark blue ground, 8¼in. high. (Christie's) £605

A Pilkington's Royal Lancastrian lustre vase decorated by Gordon Forsyth, painted in red and gold lustre with bands of tudor roses, 1915, 8½in. high. (Christie's S. Ken) £352

Crown Ducal wall plaque, 1930s, 12½in. diameter. (Muir Hewitt) £75

A waisted cylindrical vase, of ribbed design with milled band around the centre, covered in a translucent flambé glaze over blue, 13in. high. (Christie's) £275

A cylindrical commemorative vase bearing the emblems of the Houses of York and Lancaster under a crown, 8½in. high. (Christie's) £308

A Phoebe Stabler 'Piping Faun' roundel, modelled as a young faun with pan pipes tripping through a circular garland of flowers and reeds, 40cm. diameter. (Phillips) £500

A baluster vase decorated with a band of anenomes, in shades of pink, blue and green on a shaded green ground, 15½in. high. (Christie's) £770

CHINA

A Pilkington's Royal
Lancastrian lustre solifleur
decorated by William S Mycock,
painted monogram and dated
1923, 6in. high.
(Christie's S. Ken)   £605

A George VI coronation mug,
of flared cylindrical form,
impressed factory marks and
facsimile signature, signed in
blue, 3¾in. high.
(Christie's)   £165

'Shy', an Ashtead pottery figure
modelled as young girl seated on
a pedestal draped with a garland
of flowers, 15¼in. high.
(Christie's S. Ken)   £715

A pear-shaped vase decorated with
a band of columbine, in shades of
mauve, purple, yellow and green
on a shaded blue ground, 7½in.
high.
(Christie's)   £115

A Gray's pottery tea for two,
painted with floral sprays in
blue, green, yellow and orange
on a black ground, height of
teapot 4½in.
(Christie's S. Ken)   £418

A solifleur of tapering ovoid
form decorated in the revived
'Cornflower' pattern, with
stylised sprays of purple and
yellow flowers with green
foliage, 5¾in. high.
(Christie's)   £900

A Pilkington's Lancastrian
moulded ovoid lustre vase
decorated by Richard Joyce, the
body embossed with wild
animals amongst grassland,
1915.
(Christie's S. Ken)   £770

Maling plate with stylized
Oriental decoration, 10in.
diameter.
(Muir Hewitt)   £195

An Ashtead lamp base, of ovoid
form moulded in relief on each
shoulder with the head of
gazelle, 11in. high.
(Christie's S. Ken)   £198

CHINA

A Martin Brothers vase, the writhen globular body with four handles modelled as snakes biting the rim of the vase, 1899, 27.5cm. high.
(Christie's)   £2,420

Late 19th century Chelsea Keramics Art Works pottery vase, Mass., 10½in. high. (Robt. W. Skinner Inc.)
                                        £1,428

Teco pottery vase with four handles, Terra Cotta, Illinois, circa 1910, squat, impressed twice, 6½in. high. (Skinner Inc.)   £802

Paul Revere Pottery decorated tea tile, Boston, Massachusetts, early 20th century, with central decoration of a cottage, 5³/₄in. diameter.
(Skinner Inc.)   £195

Late 19th century Grueby Faience Co. bust of 'Laughing Boy', based on a statue by Donatello, 11in. high. (Robt. W. Skinner Inc.)   £972

Dedham pottery plate with turtle alternating with scenic border, Mass., circa 1920, 10in. diam.
                        £320

Paul Revere Pottery decorated vase, Boston, Massachusetts, early 20th century, with incised and painted band of tree design, 8¹/₂in. high.
(Skinner Inc.)   £1,195

A Fulper pottery centrepiece on pedestal base, hammered olive-green on paler green glaze, circa 1915, 10½in. high. (Robt. W. Skinner Inc.) £864

A Morrisware pottery vase, decorated with peonies in mauve, crimson and olive-green against a sea-green ground, 16.5cm. high.
(Phillips)   £280

CHINA

A Pilkington Lancastrian lustre vase and cover decorated by Richard Joyce with a frieze of antelopes and stylised trees, 15.5cm. high. (Christie's) £550

A Pilkington Lancastrian deep bowl designed by Walter Crane and decorated by Wm. S. Mycock, date code for 1913, 21.6cm. high. £865

A Wadeheath pottery Walt Disney series novelty musical jug, the handle modelled as the Big Bad Wolf, printed factory mark and original paper label, 10in. high. (Christie's S. Ken) £495

A Pilkington Royal Lancastrian lustre charger decorated by William S. Mycock, decorated with a flamboyant armorial crest, dated 1924, 30.6cm. diam. (Christie's London) £352

A stoneware Martin Bros. grotesque double-face jug, dated 1903, 19cm. high. £1,190

Early 20th century Dedham pottery plate, stamped and dated 1931, 8¾in. diam. £1,330

George E. Ohr Pottery vase, Biloxi, Mississippi, circa 1904, fluted top on cylindrical form, midnight blue over cobalt glossy glaze, 5in. high. (Skinner Inc.) £442

Marblehead Pottery decorated vase, Massachusetts, early 20th century, with repeating design of parrots on branches, 7in. high. (Skinner Inc.) £831

A Newport pottery Bizarre 'Delicia' jar and cover, 1930's, 21cm. high. £440

75

CHINA

1930s football teapot with
footballer handle.
(Muir Hewitt)   £120

Arthur Wood wall pocket with
floral decoration, 8in. high.
(Muir Hewitt)   £30

Myott flower vase complete with
liner, 9in. wide on stepped base.
(Muir Hewitt)   £65

Honiton jug designed by
Collard.
(Muir Hewitt)   £60

Grays wall plate with stylized
flower decoration, 12in.
diameter, 1930s.
(Muir Hewitt)   £250

"Sweet Adeline" novelty
smoker's item.
(Muir Hewitt)   £35

Amusing dog-shaped pottery
container.
(Muir Hewitt)   £15

Racing car teapot by Sadler with
'OK T42' number plate.
(Muir Hewitt)   £120

"Elf" sugar shaker, 1930s.
(Muir Hewitt)   £20

1930s honeypot with bee finial.
(Muir Hewitt) £15

Bird napkin ring, 1930s.
(Muir Hewitt) £14

Rabbit napkin ring, 1930s.
(Muir Hewitt) £14

Biscuit barrel, 1930s, with floral
decoration.
(Muir Hewitt) £45

1920s figure, 'Souvenir of
Blackpool'.
(Muir Hewitt) £10

1930s budgie vase in green and
fawn.
(Muir Hewitt) £40

Dog shaped vase by Flaxman,
1930s.
(Muir Hewitt) £15

Humpty Dumpty teapot, 1930s.
(Muir Hewitt) £100

Stylized dog, 1930s, decorated
with red spots.
(Muir Hewitt) £25

CHINA

Grueby pottery two tile scenic frieze, Boston, circa 1902, depicting four cows in various states of grazing and repose. (Skinner Inc.)
£3,858

A large Louis Wain pottery vase, modelled as a seated cat, 25.4cm. high.   £1,190

A Newcomb College pottery high glaze mug, New Orleans, signed by Ada W. Lonnegan, circa 1901, 4¼in. high.   £950

A Gray's Pottery Art Deco spherical lampbase, painted in colours with a stylised scene of golfers, 6in. high. (Christie's S. Ken)
£770

A pair of Liberty jardinières on pedestals, each with shallow hemispherical bowl decorated with entrelac border in relief. 80cm. high. (Christie's)   £2,090

A Linthorpe vase, designed by Dr. Christopher Dresser, the gourd-shaped body with double angular spout and curved carrying-bar, streaked glaze of green and brown.
(Christie's)   £1,100

Grueby Faience Co. vase, Boston, Massachusetts, circa 1902, with bulbous vase moulded design, matte green glaze, 7in. high.
(Skinner Inc.)   £338

A terracotta twin handled oviform vase painted by Ruth Pavely with bluebirds and foliage between contrasting borders, impressed *CSA Ltd.* mark, 6½in. high. (Christie's S. Ken)   £660

A G. E. Ohr pottery vase, the concave-shaped mouth with elongated folded handles, circa 1900, 10in. high.   £2,360

CHINA

A Linthorpe vase, designed by Dr. Christopher Dresser, formed as a cluster of five pointed gourd shapes encircling a central funnel-shaped neck, 11cm. high. (Christie's) £1,430

A Charles Vyse figure of a ribbon seller on a square plinth, circa 1925, 30.5cm. high, including plinth. £650

Navy blue Grueby pottery vase, Boston, circa 1910, impressed and artist initialled (glaze imperfection and bubble bursts), 5½in. high. (Skinner Inc.) £1,173.

'Fantasy', a Charles Vyse pottery group, of a woman seated cross-legged on a grassy base, scantily clad with a turquoise and mauve robe, 21.50cm. high. (Phillips) £360

A Linthorpe pottery jug, designed by Dr. Christopher Dresser, with everted rim continuing to form an angled handle, terminating in a rippled design, covered in a streaky caramel, green and crimson glaze, 21cm. high. (Christie's) £1,980

A Louis Wain porcelain animal vase, the stylised figure of a dog bearing a shield, with shaped aperture on its back, 14.2cm. high. (Christie's) £990

A Pilkington Royal Lancastrian lustre vase and cover decorated by Gordon Forsyth, with two central reserves each surrounded by laurel leaves and flanked by two lions, 29cm. high. (Christie's) £3,300

A Rookwood pottery Indian squaw portrait vase, circa 1899, 11in. high. £450

A Ruskin high fired twin handled shouldered oviform vase, covered in a streaked lavender glaze flecked with green, 13¾in. high. (Christie's S. Ken) £385

CHINA

Maling plate with floral
decoration, 10in. diameter.
(Muir Hewitt)   £195

Sylvac dog, 4in. high, 1930s.
(Muir Hewitt)   £25

Hancock's Ivory ware Galleon
plate with shaped edge.
(Muir Hewitt)   £45

Burleigh ware Harvest jug, 8in.
high, 1930s.
(Muir Hewitt)   £50

Crown Ducal bowl with tube line
decoration, 10in. diameter.
(Muir Hewitt)   £45

Burleigh ware Pied Piper jug,
8in. high, 1930s.
(Muir Hewitt)   £120

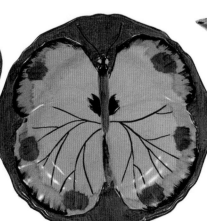

Burleigh ware lustre jug with
squirrel handle, 8in. high, 1930s.
(Muir Hewitt)   £60

Hancock's butterfly plate, 1930s.
(Muir Hewitt)   £50

Burleigh ware jug with parrot
handle, 8in. high, 1930s.
(Muir Hewitt)   £65

CHINA

Maling teapot, 1930s, with grapevine decoration. (Muir Hewitt) £35

Moorcroft Flambé vase, 10in. high, 1930s. (Muir Hewitt) £350

Crown Ducal tea pot, 1930s, with floral design. (Muir Hewitt) £30

Maling floral design jug, 1930s. (Muir Hewitt) £85

Maling hand painted bowl, 10in. diameter, 1930s. (Muir Hewitt) £120

Crown Ducal vase, 6in. high, 1950s. (Muir Hewitt) £35

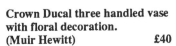

Crown Ducal three handled vase with floral decoration. (Muir Hewitt) £40

Stylized Art Deco style Sylvac jug, 1930s, 7in. high. (Muir Hewitt) £60

Hancocks ivory ware cottage jug, 1930s, 7in. high. (Muir Hewitt) £45

CHINA

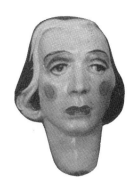

An amusing Newport pottery model of an owl wearing a suit, signed *M. Epworth*, 18.5cm. (Bearne's) £110

A Burslem ware ceramic wall plaque, the design attributed to Charlotte Rhead, decorated with stylised brown, and cream chrysanthemums with blue leaves and berries, 41cm. diam. (Phillips London) £220

A Susie Cooper wall mask modelled as the head of a woman with grey streaked black hair, 10¾in. long. (Christie's) £990

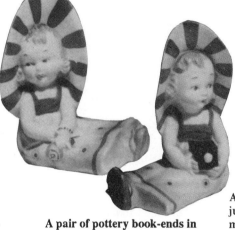

A Bizarre single-handled 'lotus' vase, 29.3cm. high. Newport, late 1930's. £350

A pair of pottery book-ends in the form of little girls sitting under sunhats, holding a camera and a rose, 5¾in. high, with the William Goebel crown mark. (Christie's S. Ken) £242

A Martin Bros. stoneware jug painted with fish and sea monsters on mottled blue ground, 10¼in. high, London and Southall 1897. £700

Fulper Pottery urn, Flemington, New Jersey, circa 1915, cucumber green crystalline glaze, vertical ink mark, 13in. high. (Skinner Inc.) £883

A Louis Wain porcelain lion vase, decorated in black, yellow, green and russet enamels, 11.8cm. high. (Christie's) £935

A Maw & Co. pottery vase of bulbous form with extended and flared neck painted with large stylised red floral buds, 33cm. high. (Phillips) £460

CHINA

A Louis Wain porcelain cat vase, decorated in white, green, russet and black enamels, with impressed and painted marks, 15.5cm. high. (Christie's)   £1,540

A Newport pottery Bizarre charger, 1930's, stylised foliate design in blue, orange and green with blue border, 33.5cm. diam.   £190

A Charles Vyse pottery figure of The Piccadilly Rose Woman, modelled as a plump lady, 10in. high.   £550

A Martin Brothers stoneware vase, painted in browns, white, black and blue with grotesque fish, an eel, a crab and a jellyfish, 23cm. high. (Phillips London)   £600

Three of five Art Deco Ashtead pottery wall plates. (Phillips)   £269

Pilkington's Royal Lancastrian lustre two-handled baluster vase decorated by William S. Mycock, 8.25in. high. (Prudential Fine Art)   £200

A decorated Marblehead pottery four-colour vase, Mass., circa 1910, 6in. high.   £1,300

An unusual ceramic and pewter inkwell, cast in the style of a Martin Brothers bird with the head forming the hinged cover, 4¼in. high. (Christie's S. Ken)   £220

A Grueby pottery experimental drip glaze vase, Boston, Massachusetts, circa 1905, with wide rolled rim and short neck, 11¼in. high. (Robt. W. Skinner Inc.)   £2,285

CHINA

Sylvac vase with lamb figure,
4in. high.
(Muir Hewitt)   £25

Crown Devon jug, 1930s, with
floral decoration.
(Muir Hewitt)   £25

Sylvac bunny match holder, 4in.
high, 1930s.
(Muir Hewitt)   £25

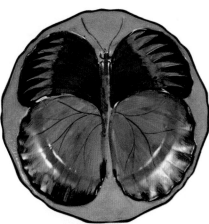

Sylvac rabbit, 4in. high, 1930s.
(Muir Hewitt)   £35

Hancock's Ivory ware butterfly
plate.
(Muir Hewitt)   £50

Burleigh ware miniature parrot
jug, 3½in. high, 1930s.
(Muir Hewitt)   £45

Shelley dripware vase 1930s, 9in.
high.
(Muir Hewitt)   £85

Shelley "Mode" shape part tea
service, 1930s.
(Muir Hewitt)   £120

One of a pair of Shelley Art Deco
vases with tulip decoration, 7in.
high.
(Muir Hewitt)   (Two)   £120

CHINA

Shelley Art Deco vase with
stylized floral decoration.
(Muir Hewitt)
£50

Royal Cauldon ware "Chang"
design wall plaque, 1930s,
17½in. diameter.
(Muir Hewitt)
£275

Crown Devon ceramic dog with
glass eyes, 4in. high.
(Muir Hewitt)
£20

Sylvac dog, 7in. high, 1930s.
(Muir Hewitt)
£45

Novelty Bridge marker, 1930s.
(Muir Hewitt)
£12

Crown Devon lamp base with
elaborate enamelled oriental
dragon design, 6in. high.
(Muir Hewitt)
£200

Royal Cauldon Chang pattern
vase, 8in. high.
(Muir Hewitt)
£50

Set of six 1950s liqueur bottles in
the form of a jazz band.
(Muir Hewitt)
£125

Royal Cauldon Chang pattern
jug, 8in. high.
(Muir Hewitt)
£50

CHINA

Decorated Marblehead pottery vase, Massachusetts, circa 1905, stamped with logo and incised with early *MP* mark, 5¾in. (Skinner Inc.)
£988

A Charles Vyse figure of a Shire horse, on rectangular base, 28.5cm. high. £300

A stoneware globular vase by Charles Vyse, covered in a lustrous mottled khaki and brown glaze with areas of crimson, incised *CV 1933*, 13cm. high. (Christie's London)
£484

A large S. Hancock & Sons Morrisware baluster vase, decorated with mauve and inky blue thistles on a greeny yellow ground, 32.9cm. high. (Christie's London) £990

Eight Dedham pottery Birds in Potted Orange Tree plates, Massachusetts, early 20th century, 8in. diam. (Skinner Inc.) £1,049

An Art Pottery matt green umbrella stand, early 20th century, the domed top with triangular cut-outs, unsigned, 26½in. high. (Skinner Inc.) £250

A Minton slipware jardinière, the inscription commemorating the 1911 Coronation, 16cm. (Phillips) £180

A Louis Wain ceramic animal model of a stylised dog with squared geometric features, coloured in green, red, black and blue, 13cm. high. (Phillips London) £440

Vance faience vase with moulded mermaid decoration, Ohio, circa 1905, with repeating figures and fish (some chips and roughness), 12½in. high. (Skinner Inc.) £184

CHINA

A rare Sabrina ware vase of pear shape, decorated with fish swimming among seaweed, 14cm., date code for 1931. (Phillips London) £120

A Wade Heath novelty teapot as Donald Duck in blue sailors outfit, printed marks, circa 1935, 8in. wide. (Christie's S. Ken) £968

Van Briggle Pottery vase, Colorado Springs, circa 1904, with moulded floral design, yellow and ochre semi-matte glaze, 8½ in. high. (Skinner Inc.) £442

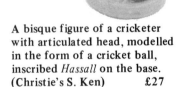

Admiral Beatty dressed in naval uniform, supporting a shell entitled *Dread-nought* between his legs, 26.5cm. high. (Phillips) £120

A five-piece Picard China Co. porcelain breakfast set, decorated with the 'Aura Argenta Linear' design, artist signed by Adolph Richter, circa 1910-30. (Skinner Inc.) £350

A bisque figure of a cricketer with articulated head, modelled in the form of a cricket ball, inscribed *Hassall* on the base. (Christie's S. Ken) £27

A Pilkington's Royal Lancastrian twin-handled vase decorated by Gordon Forsyth, 1908, 30.2cm. high. £190

A Louis Wain porcelain pig vase, decorated in green, yellow, russet and black enamels, with impressed and painted marks, 12.4cm. high. (Christie's) £1,540

Van Briggle pottery copper clad vase, Colorado, 5½in. high. £840

CHINA

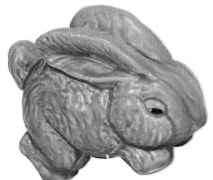

Stylized porcelain dog, 1930s, 2½in. high.
(Muir Hewitt) £7

Flaxman running hare, 5in. wide, 1930s.
(Muir Hewitt) £25

J.H. Cope & Co. wall mask, 6in. high, 1930s.
(Muir Hewitt) £90

Stylized elephant bottle, 1930s, 7½in. high.
(Muir Hewitt) £25

1930s stylized cottage teapot and milk jug.
(Muir Hewitt) £60

Porcelain figure of Pierrette, 1930s.
(Muir Hewitt) £50

Art Deco vase with stylized decoration, 8in. high, 1930s.
(Muir Hewitt) £50

Booths hors d'oeuvre dish decorated with a stylized country scene.
(Muir Hewitt) £175

Thomas Forrester & Sons dripware vase, 8in. high.
(Muir Hewitt) £45

CHINA

Royal Winton bee-hive biscuit barrel, 1930s, 6in. high. (Muir Hewitt) £95

"Bunny" teapot, 1930s. (Muir Hewitt) £110

Beswick vase with stylized palm tree decoration, 1950s. (Muir Hewitt) £30

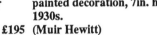

Pottery figurine, 1930s, 8in. high. (Muir Hewitt) £30

Susie Cooper coffee set with star decoration (coffee pot, sugar bowl, 4 cups and saucers). (Muir Hewitt) £195

Myott flower jug with hand painted decoration, 7in. high, 1930s. (Muir Hewitt) £45

Miniature vase with elf decoration. (Muir Hewitt) £15

Willow Art china vase with enamelled American Indian design, 6in. high. (Muir Hewitt) £85

Deco jug with stylized floral decoration. (Muir Hewitt) £20

Arcadian black boy in bath of ink, towel hanging at side, inscribed *How ink is made*, with arms of Torquay.
(The Crested China Co.) **£95**

A ceramic chamber pot with everted rim, decorated with a design by Christopher Dresser, printed in black, brown, beige and green, 23cm. diam.
(Phillips) **£260**

A Louis Wain porcelain Bull-dog vase, decorated in cream, yellow, green, russet and black enamels, 14.5cm. long.
(Christie's) **£935**

A Linthorpe twin-handled pottery vase designed by Christopher Dresser, the vessel of flattened oviform with bulbous neck, 20.8cm. high.
(Phillips) **£120**

Three Rookwood pottery standard glaze mouse plates, Cincinnati, Ohio, circa 1893, each depicting a mischievous mouse, 7in. diam. (Robt. W. Skinner Inc.) **£371**

A William de Morgan two handled baluster vase, decorated in green and purple with fruiting vines, the foot, handles and neck interior in turquoise, 27.3cm. high.
(Christie's London) **£1,320**

A good William de Morgan 'Persian-style' circular wall plate, painted by Charles Passenger, depicting in the sunken centre, a pair of dolphins, encircled with stylised floral and scale borders, 43.5cm. diam. (Phillips) **£5,200**

A Linthorpe vase, designed by Dr Christopher Dresser, decorated with four grotesque heads, each forming a handle, covered in a streaky green glaze, 22.5cm. high.
(Christie's) **£990**

A Carter Stabler Adams pottery dish, possibly a design by Erna Manners, painted in mauve, green and blue with stylised leaves and scrolling tendrils, 37.8cm. diam.
(Phillips) **£180**

CARLTON WARE

Carlton ware was the name given to the Staffordshire earthenware produced from 1890 at the Carlton Works, Stoke on Trent, by the firm which traded until 1957 as Wiltshaw & Robinson. From January 1958 it was retitled Carlton Ware Ltd.

The factory produced ornamental ware such as vases, characterised by bright enamelling and gilded floral and fanleaf decoration, black very often being used as the base colour. Early products normally bear a circular printed mark with *W & R Stoke on Trent* enclosing a swallow and surmounted by a crown.

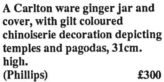

A Carlton ware ginger jar and cover, with gilt coloured chinoiserie decoration depicting temples and pagodas, 31cm. high.
(Phillips) £300

A Carlton ware twin-handled boat shape bowl on splayed cylindrical column painted with an exotic bird of paradise, 23.5cm. high.
(Phillips) £180

Shaped vase, 'Persian' design, marked with a gold star underneath, 280mm. high. £400

A Carltonware service decorated in polychrome enamels, coffee pot 20.4cm. high. £810

Pale pink shaped vase with Art Deco design, 195mm. high. £125

'Handcraft' design vase following the Arts & Crafts movement, using a white background with blue, beige, pink and purple stencilling, 225mm. high. £200

Carlton Ware lustre jug with gilt loop handle, the body painted and gilded with stylised floral and fan decoration, 5in. high. (Prudential Fine Art) £115

A leaf green Art Deco vase with large and small lustrous trees of unusual colours, black inside, 265mm. high. £250

CARLTON WARE

Carlton ware Australian design
salad bowl and servers, 8in.
diameter.
(Muir Hewitt)   £45

Carlton ware shell cruet, 1930s.
(Muir Hewitt)   £45

Carlton ware mushroom cruet
set.
(Muir Hewitt)   £45

Carlton ware stylized dog, 1930s.
(Muir Hewitt)   £50

Carlton ware dish, 1930s,
Kingfisher design on lustre
background, 9in. wide.
(Muir Hewitt)   £60

Carlton ware Australian
buttercup design dish, 8in. wide.
(Muir Hewitt)   £35

Carlton ware enamelled vase
with mallard decoration, 6in.
high.
(Muir Hewitt)   £80

Carlton ware salad dish and
strainer, 7in. wide, 1930s.
(Muir Hewitt)   £35

Carlton ware vase with raised
oak leaf decoration, 8$\frac{1}{2}$in. high.
(Muir Hewitt)   £70

CLARICE CLIFF

The legendary Clarice Cliff was born in 1899 in, perhaps inevitably, Staffordshire, where she started work at 13 in one of the local potteries, painting freehand onto pottery.

Her formal training comprised a year, when she was 16, at the Burslem School of Art, and a later year at the Royal College of Art, where she studied sculpture . At 17, she had gone to work at the firm of A.J. Wilkinson, and she remained with them, and their subsidiary the Newport Pottery, for the next two decades, ending up as Art Director and marrying the boss, Colley Shorter, when she was forty.

During the 1920's she painted Tibetan ware, large jars painted with floral designs in bright colours and gold, and she also transferred on to pottery designs by such distinguished artists as Paul Nash and Laura Knight.

In 1928, however, she painted 60 dozen pieces of her own design to test the market at a trade fair. These proved so popular that by 1929 the whole factory was switched to producing her Bizarre ware.

Cliff's style is character-ised by combinations of bright colours, such as orange, blue, purple and green, or black, yellow, orange and red. Her pieces are often angular in shape and strongly Art Deco in style. Major ranges, besides Bizarre, include Crocus, Fantasque, Biarritz and Farmhouse.

At the beginning of the Second World War, the factory was commandeered by the Ministry of Supply, and Wilkinson produced only a few white pieces. After the war, the market had changed and production was not resumed.

A 'Fantasque' Archaic vase, painted with blue centred orange flowers on a black ground, between blue and orange banding, 7in. high.
(Christie's) £880

A 'Bizarre' Bonjour biscuit barrel and cover with wicker handle, decorated in the 'Windbells' pattern, 6in. high.
(Christie's) £220

A 'Bizarre' Conical vase, decorated in the 'Honolulu' pattern, painted in colours, 6in. high.
(Christie's) £1,210

An 'Inspiration Bizarre' vase, shape No. 363, decorated in an Isnik-style pattern in shades of blue, yellow and green, 6½in. high.
(Christie's) £495

A 'Fantasque Bizarre' vase, shape No. 358, decorated in the seven colour 'Trees and House' pattern, 8in. high.
(Christie's) £605

A 'Latona Bizarre' spherical vase decorated in the 'Dahlia' pattern, painted in colours on a yellow ground, 6in. high.
(Christie's) £935

CLARICE CLIFF

An 'Appliqué' octagonal plate decorated in the 'Caravan' pattern, painted in colours, 11in. diameter.
(Christie's S. Ken) £2,200

A 'Bizarre' grotesque mask designed by Ron Birks, covered in a dark blue Inspiration glaze, the features picked out in red.
(Christie's S. Ken) £1,320

A Clarice Cliff 'Fantasque' ginger jar and cover decorated in the 'Melon' pattern, painted in colours, 8in. high.
(Christie's S. Ken) £572

A Clarice Cliff 'Fantasque' vase, shape No. 358, decorated in the 'Trees and House' pattern, painted in colours, 8in. high.
(Christie's S. Ken) £495

A pair of Clarice Cliff teddy bear book ends decorated in the 'Red Flower' pattern, painted in colours, 6in. high.
(Christie's S. Ken) £4,180

A 'Bizarre' Yo-Yo vase decorated in the 'Orange Luxor' pattern, painted in colours, 9in. high.
(Christie's S. Ken) £2,200

A Clarice Cliff 'Inspiration Bizarre' stick stand, decorated in the 'Caprice' pattern, in shades of pink, lavender and blue on a turquoise ground, 24in. high.
(Christie's S. Ken) £1,980

A pair of 'Bizarre' bookends, shape No. 406 decorated in the 'Honolulu' pattern, painted in colours, 6in. high.
(Christie's S. Ken) £495

A 'Bizarre' single-handled Lotus jug decorated in the 'Blue W' pattern, painted in colours between orange borders, 11¹/₂in. high.
(Christie's S. Ken) £2,200

CLARICE CLIFF

A 'Fantasque Bizarre' Dover jardinière decorated in the 'Trees and House' pattern, rubber stamp mark, 8in. high.
(Christie's S. Ken) £1,210

A 'Fantasque Bizarre' ginger jar and cover decorated in the 'Blue Autumn' pattern, painted in colours with contrasting banding, 7³/₄in. high.
(Christie's S. Ken) £935

A 'Fantasque' plate decorated in the 'Flora' pattern, painted in orange, yellow, green and black.
(Christie's S. Ken) £209

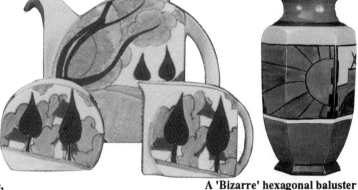

A Clarice Cliff 'Bizarre' vase, shape No. 342, decorated in the 'Sliced Circles' pattern, painted in orange, green and black, 7³/₄in. high.
(Christie's S. Ken) £605

A Clarice Cliff 'Fantasque Bizarre' Stamford trio decorated in the 'May Avenue' pattern, painted in colours, height of teapot 4¹/₂in.
(Christie's S. Ken) £2,420

A 'Bizarre' hexagonal baluster vase decorated in the 'Sunray' pattern, painted in colours between multibanded borders, 15in. high.
(Christie's S. Ken) £2,200

A 'Bizarre' single-handled Lotus jug decorated in the 'Lightning' pattern, painted in colours between orange borders, 11¹/₂in. high.
(Christie's S. Ken) £2,640

A pair of 'Bizarre' bookends, modelled as a pair of parakeets with green plumage on chequered base, 7in. high.
(Christie's S. Ken) £880

A 'Fantasque Bizarre' cylindrical biscuit barrel and cover decorated in the 'Blue Autumn' pattern, 6¹/₄in. high.
(Christie's S. Ken) £308

CLARICE CLIFF

Clarice Cliff Crinoline Lady wall pocket, 1930s, 7in. high. (Muir Hewitt) £175

Clarice Cliff cheese dish in Coral Firs pattern, 8in. long. (Muir Hewitt) £350

Clarice Cliff wall mask from the Bizarre series, 8in. high, 1930s. (Muir Hewitt) £450

'My Garden' vase from the Bizarre range by Clarice Cliff, 7in. high. (Muir Hewitt) £200

Clarice Cliff 'Flora' wall mask, 15in. high. (Muir Hewitt) £1,700

Clarice Cliff Inspiration double conical vase with hand written mark. (Muir Hewitt) £700

Clarice Cliff rare advertising dish. (Muir Hewitt) £600

Clarice Cliff, Bonjour shape sugar dredger in Coral Firs design. (Muir Hewitt) £275

Clarice Cliff conical bowl on foot in the Swirls design. (Muir Hewitt) £2,200

CLARICE CLIFF

'My Garden' vase from the
Bizarre range by Clarice Cliff,
5½in. high.
(Muir Hewitt)   £120

Clarice Cliff conical bowl in the
Secrets design, 9in. diameter.
(Muir Hewitt)   £1,200

Clarice Cliff vase with 'Orange
roof cottage' design, 7in. high.
(Muir Hewitt)   £550

Twin handled Isis jug by Clarice
Cliff, 10½in. high.
(Muir Hewitt)   £1,200

Clarice Cliff dish in 'House and
Bridge' design, 10in. diameter.
(Muir Hewitt)   £600

Clarice Cliff Bizarre sugar
dredger in Orange Chintz.
(Muir Hewitt)   £300

Clarice Cliff Isis shape vase in
Inspiration Caprice, 10½in.
high.
(Muir Hewitt)   £1,500

Clarice Cliff 1951 Teepee teapot
with "Greetings from Canada"
on underside.
(Muir Hewitt)   £750

Clarice Cliff 'Lotus' jug, Secrets
design from the Bizarre range,
12in. high, 1930s.
(Muir Hewitt)   £1,800

DE MORGAN

William Frend de Morgan
(1839–1917) was an English
ceramic designer, perhaps
now particularly remembered
for his tiles. His designs were
much influenced by his
friend William Morris and
include, birds, fish, flowers
and mythical beasts. He
established his own pottery in
Chelsea in 1872, producing
his own tiles, and
experimented with lustre
decoration in an attempt to
reproduce the red lustre of
maiolica painted in Gubbio.
He also designed dishes in
cream earthenware decorated
in red lustre, and the Sunset
and Moonlight suites
decorated in gold, silver and
copper. With Morris at
Merton Abbey he continued
to make tiles and dishes, and
also established a factory at
Fulham with Halsey Ricardo
producing tiles and murals.
He retired in 1905 and the
factory closed in 1907

A De Morgan lustre vase,
decorated in ruby lustre with
fish swimming against pale
amber waves, 15.6cm. high,
1888-97.   £375

A Craven Dunhill & Co. metal
mounted four tile jardiniere,
each tile decorated with a
design by William de Morgan,
21.2cm. high. (Christie's
London)   £682

A William De Morgan eight
inch tile forming part of the
Fan pattern, painted with two
stylised flowers. (Phillips
London)   £500

A De Morgan lustre vase,
decorated by Fred Passenger,
1890's, 32.6cm. high.   £880

A William de Morgan ruby
lustre twin-handled oviform
vase, painted with scaly carp
swimming in alternate
directions, 37cm. high.
(Phillips)   £2,100

A William de Morgan circular
plate, painted with a central
griffin-like creature and
bordered by a frieze of birds,
22cm. diam.
(Phillips)   £780

A William de Morgan 'Persian-
style' vase and cover, painted
with foliate fronds in turquoise,
blue and pale-green against a
white ground, 36cm. high.
(Phillips)   £4,600

DELLA ROBBIA

The Della Robbia pottery was established in 1894 at Birkenhead by H. Rathbone and the sculptor, Conrad Dressler. It produced vases, bottles, jars, plates and dishes with sgraffito decoration and sometimes elaborate modelled relief with a strong Italian maiolica influence. The factory closed in 1901, but reopened and continued until 1906. Their mark consists of *Della Robbia* with a ship device and the decorator's initials.

'The Third Day of Creation', a Della Robbia tile panel after a design by Edward Burne-Jones, 55.5 x 21.5cm. (Christie's) £2,860

'Water Avens Tile', a Della Robbia tile panel designed by Conrad Dressler and decorated by E. M. Wood, 51.5 x 34.2cm. (Christie's) £605

A Della Robbia twin-handled vase, decorated by Charles Collis, with eight circular medallions, each with a sea-creature whose long tail curls round on itself, 35.8cm. high. (Christie's) £660

A Della Robbia bottle vase, designed by Charles Collis, with piped slip decoration of peaches and leaves covered in pink and turquoise glazes, 33.5cm. high. (Christie's) £330

A Della Robbia pottery vase by Roseville Pottery, signed with Rozane Ware seal, circa 1906, 8¼in. high. (Robt. W. Skinner Inc.) £590

A Della Robbia twin-handled vase decorated by Charles Collis, with a broad decorative frieze of stylised Tudor Roses, 31.6cm. high. (Christie's) £660

A Della Robbia wall charger, the base incised DR with a sailing ship and artist's mono-gram, 47.5cm. diam. (Christie's) £378

A Della Robbia pottery vase, with marks of Chas. Collis, potter and sgraffito artist and G. Russell, Paintress, circa 1903/06, 11in. high. **£180**

DOULTON FIGURES

The first Doulton figures were made by George Tinworth, one of the original group of art potters who came to the company via the Lambeth School of Art. His output was small, however, and it was not until Charles Noke joined the firm in 1889 that figure making really became big business. Noke was inspired by the figures produced by Derby, Bow, Meissen and also, nearer home, by the Staffordshire figure making industry. Initially, the colours used tended to be rather dull, and the figures did not sell well, so their production was suspended until 1912, when a new range, including the famous 'Bedtime/Darling' by Charles Vyse, was introduced. (This was originally entitled Bedtime, but was rechristened after Queen Mary, seeing it while on a visit to the factory, exclaimed 'What a darling!') The new figures benefited from brighter colours, and a talented team of modellers now set to work. These included Leslie Harradine, Harry Tittensor and later Peggy Harper.

Sunshine Girl HN1344, designed by L Harradine, issued 1929, withdrawn 1938, 5in. high.
£850

Phyllis HN1420, designed by L Harradine, issued 1930, withdrawn 1949, 9in. high.
£200

Love Letter HN2149, designed by M Davies, issued 1958, withdrawn 1976, 5½in. high.
£165

Bather (Style two) HN1227, designed by L Harradine, issued 1927, withdrawn 1938, colour variation, 7½in. high.   £300

Young Miss Nightingale HN2010, designed by M Davies, issued 1948, withdrawn 1953, 9¼in. high.
£350

Sweet and Twenty (Style one) HN1298, designed by L Harradine, issued 1928, withdrawn 1969, 5¾in. high.
£120

Pied Piper HN1215, designed by L Harradine, issued 1926, withdrawn 1938, 8¼in. high.
£400

DOULTON FIGURES

Fairy, (Style One) HN1324, designed by L Harradine, issued 1929, withdrawn 1938, 6½in. high. £250

Negligee, HN1228, designed by L. Harradine, issued 1927-1938, 5in. high. £450

Coppelia, HN2115, designed by M. Davies, issued 1953, 7¼in. high. £275

Moira, HN1347, designed by L. Harradine. issued 1929-1938, 6½in. high. £850

Rhythm HN1903, designed by L Harradine, issued 1939, withdrawn 1949, 6¾in. high. £300

Mam'selle, HN724, designed by L. Harradine, issued 1925-1938, 7in. high. £500

Ermine Muff HN54, designed by C J Noke, issued 1916, withdrawn 1938, 8½in. high. £450

Sweet Anne HN1453, designed by L Harradine, issued 1931, withdrawn 1949, colour variation, 7in. high. £100

Bather (Style Two) HN773, designed by L. Harradine, issued 1925-1938, 7½in. high. £300

EUROPEAN CHINA

Flamboyance perhaps best characterises European china of the early part of this century. A host of very different talents flourished across the continent at this time, and none of them produced anything that could be classed as insipid or even terribly delicate! Some of the most avant-garde pieces were produced by the versatile Gallé and by Robj, also in France. Many whimsical, even impudent pieces were also made. Striking colours and arresting shapes were the keynote of this fascinating period.

Continental stylized China wall mask, 3in. high.
(Muir Hewitt)   £50

A Rozenburg pottery vase decorated in mauve, brown, green, blue and yellow, with an elaborate pattern of fleshy flowers, 30cm. high.
(Phillips)   £300

A Wiener Kunstkeramische two handled vase of irregular form painted in pastel shades with a loosely defined fairy-tale scene, 19½in. high.
(Christie's S. Ken)   £165

A School of Koloman Moser seven-piece porcelain tea service, designed by Jutta Sika, teapot 16.7cm. high.
                            £1,945

A Rozenburg glazed earthenware vase, painted with flowering creeper and butterflies, circa 1900, 43cm. high.
                            £330

A Robj porcelain jug, modelled as a rotund lady wearing a plum coloured dress, the spout modelled as an apron, 19.5cm. high. (Phillips London) £240

A pair of Gallé faience 'Origami' models each as an abstract folded creature painted with yellow and blue bands, 8cm. high. (Phillips)   £360

A Rosenthal ceramic sculpture by Gerhard Schliepstein, circa 1930, 50.8cm. high.
                            £1,405

EUROPEAN CHINA

An unusual Continental porcelain wall plate, the image based on a design by Alphonse Mucha for Sarah Bernhardt as La Samaritaine, 50cm. diam. (Phillips London)   £520

A Rosenthal porcelain figure, 'Korean Dancer', designed by C. Holzer-Defanti, 40cm. high, printed factory marks for 1929.   £400

A massive Clément Massier jardinière, of irregular tapering form, decorated in an overall lustre glaze of green, yellow, amethyst and amber, 56cm. high. (Christie's)   £770

A Clément Massier earthenware jardinière with a pedestal, decorated in relief with irises, the pedestal naturalistically moulded with a heron among bulrushes, 38cm. diameter of jardinière. (Christie's)   £270

An amusing Goebels ceramic decanter set comprising: a decanter modelled as a young man and a set of six liqueur goblets each painted in colours with the head of a girl. (Phillips London)   £380

A Gallé faience model of a cat, the creature sitting back on its haunches and gazing with glass eyes and whiskered grin, 34cm. high. (Phillips)   £900

'Reverie', a bisque and gilt-bronze bust of a lady cast from a model by Théophile François Somme, French, late 19th century, 10¼in. high. (Christie's East)   £496

A large pair of Turn porcelain figures of young women, each wearing a long dress, gathered at the waist, slight chipping, 62cm. high. (Bearne's)   £1,350

A Robj earthenware bowl and cover, formed as a Red Indian's head, with dark red glazed feather headdress, 20cm. high. (Christie's)   £440

EUROPEAN CHINA

Continental stylized negro head egg cup.
(Muir Hewitt)   £12

Gnome wall pocket by William Goebel.
(Muir Hewitt)   £95

Goebel stylized dog wall mask, 7in. high, 1930s.
(Muir Hewitt)   £75

Stylized Continental wall mask, 8in. high, 1930s.
(Muir Hewitt)   £275

Austrian Amphora mirror with stylized Art Nouveau figure, 1910, 13in. high.
(Muir Hewitt)   £295

Wall mask in Continental porcelain, 5in. high, 1930s.
(Muir Hewitt)   £85

Pincushion with half doll in Continental porcelain.
(Muir Hewitt)   £45

An earthenware plate decorated to a design by Marcel Goupy, painted in red, black and blue, 12$\frac{1}{2}$in. diameter.
(Christie's S. Ken)   £110

Czechoslovakian Art Deco bird jug, 1930s, 6$\frac{1}{2}$in. high.
(Muir Hewitt)   £25

FOLEY

The Foley pottery was established in Fenton, Staffordshire in the mid 19th century and was operated from 1903 by E Brain & Co. Its porcelain is noted for the simplicity of its design. That said, in the 1930's work was commissioned from leading contemporary artists such as Graham Sutherland and Laura Knight and is marked with the maker's name and the signature of the artist and decorator. The Foley marks include the brand name *Peacock Pottery*, with a peacock in a rectangle and Staffordshire knot.

A Foley Intarsio small oviform jardinière printed and painted in colours with a band of carp amongst waves, 4$^{1}/_{2}$ in. high.
(Christie's S. Ken)   £220

A Foley Intarsio cylindrical biscuit barrel with electroplate mount and cover, printed and painted in colours with panels of drinking scenes and flowers, 7$^{1}/_{4}$ in. high.
(Christie's S. Ken)   £750

A Foley Intarsio three-handled vase and cover, printed and painted in typical colours with panels depicting the Queen of Hearts, 8in. high.
(Christie's S. Ken)   £500

A Foley Intarsio single-handled spherical vase, printed and painted in colours with a band of buttercups and flowerheads on the shoulders, 6in. high.
(Christie's S. Ken)   £190

A Foley Intarsio miniature grandfather clock printed and painted in colours with Father Time and bearing the inscription *Time and Tide wait for no man*, 10in. high.
(Christie's S. Ken)   £500

A Foley Intarsio baluster vase printed and painted in colours with kingfishers perched on branches above a band of carp, 9in. high.
(Christie's S. Ken)   £280

A Foley Intarsio vase, printed and painted in colours with panels of seagulls in fiords, above a band of entrelac foliate motifs, 8$^{1}/_{2}$ in. high.
(Christie's S. Ken)   £120

A Foley Intarsio twin-handled baluster vase, printed and painted in colours with band of lavender and yellow flowers, 9$^{1}/_{4}$ in high.
(Christie's S. Ken)   £90

GOLDSCHEIDER

It was in 1886 that Friedrich Goldscheider founded his factory in Vienna. After his death in 1897, production continued there under the direction of his widow and brother Alois, until, in 1920, the business was taken over by his two sons Marcel and Walter. In 1927, however, Marcel broke away to form the Vereinigte Ateliers für Kunst und Keramik.

While such things as vases were produced, the factory is best known for the figures and wall masks which epitomised the Art Nouveau and perhaps even more, the Art Deco styles.

A Goldscheider figure of a woman with one hand on her hip, one on her hat, with artist's monogram, 33.5cm.high. (Christie's) .. £880

A Goldscheider terracotta wall mask modelled as the head of young girl holding a fan across her neck, 11in. high. (Christie's)   £300

A Goldscheider earthenware wall mask, 1920's, 17cm. high.   **£220**

A Goldscheider pottery figure of a dancer, in a floral lilac dress with bonnet, 12in. high, circa 1930. (Morphets) £280

Goldscheider pottery mask of an Art Deco lady, approx. 12in. (G. A. Key)   £360

A Goldscheider pottery figure of a young black boy, wearing a shabby brown jacket, greyish-brown trousers and a red and white striped shirt, 56cm. high, impressed maker's mark. (Phillips)   £1,100

Parisienne, a Goldscheider polychrome ceramic figure modelled by H. Liedhoff, printed factory marks, 13¾in. high. (Christie's S. Ken)
    £418

'Suzanne', a Goldscheider figure, the design by J. Lorenzl, the nude figure loosely draped with a patterned grey enamelled robe, 33.6cm. high. (Christie's)   £550

A Goldscheider pottery
figure, modelled as a sailor
holding a girl, 30cm. high.
£330

A small Goldscheider terracotta wall mask of the head,
neck and hand of a young
girl, 8in. high. (Christie's)
£200

A Goldscheider pottery group
after a model by Lorenzl, of
a flamenco dancer and a guitar
player, 17in. high.   £580

A Goldscheider pottery figure
of a dancing girl, designed by
Lorenzl, 16in. high.   £680

A Goldscheider pottery double
face wall plaque, the two
females in profile, 12in. high.
£385

A large Goldscheider 'Butterfly Girl', after a model by
Lorenzl, circa 1930,
48.5cm. high.   £1,650

A Goldscheider pottery
mask of a girl looking down,
Made in Austria, circa 1925,
23cm. high.   £325

A Goldscheider pottery figure
of a woman wearing a beaded
costume, on a black oval base,
18in. high.   £1,700

A Goldscheider pottery 'Negro'
wall mask, 26.5cm. high. £150

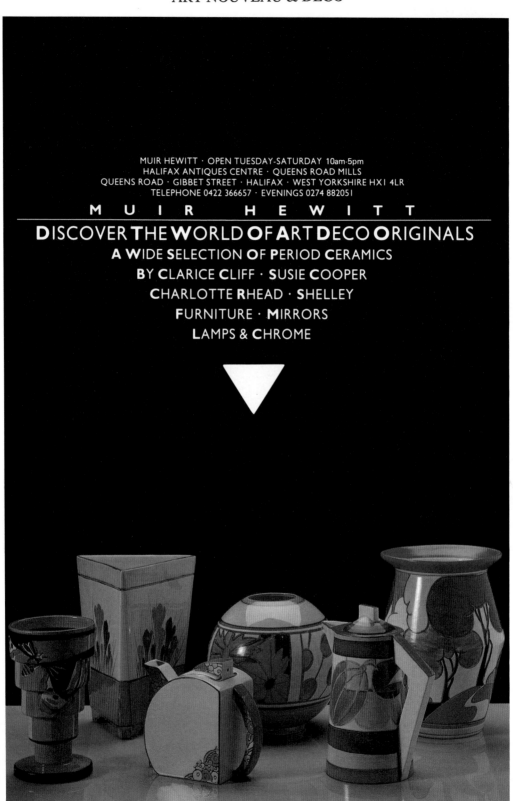

Photography by Keith Paisley

GOLDSCHEIDER

An unusual Goldscheider pottery wallmask modelled as Shirley Temple, painted in colours, 10in. long.
(Christie's S. Ken) £462

Goldscheider wall mask with stylized ringlets, terracotta, 8¹/₂in. high, 1930s.
(Muir Hewitt) £350

A Goldscheider terracotta wallmask modelled as an exotic woman partially concealed behind a mask, 14in. long.
(Christie's S. Ken) £263

A Goldscheider polychrome-painted pottery figure of a dancer, modelled by Dakon, wearing blue spotted bodice and floral divided skirt, 10¹/₂in. high.
(Christie's S. Ken) £528

Goldscheider porcelain figure by Lorenzl, 14in. high.
(Muir Hewitt) £800

A Goldscheider Art Nouveau pottery figure of a naked maiden supporting a circular mirror on her thigh, 30in. high.
(Christie's S. Ken) £1,100

A Goldscheider terracotta wall mask of a female profile painted with turquoise ringlets, orange-banded black hat and yellow scarf, 10in. long.
(Christie's S. Ken) £275

A Goldscheider terracotta wall hanging, modelled as a female bather standing amongst rushes, with towel draped over right forearm, 15in. long.
(Christie's S. Ken) £660

A Goldscheider terracotta wallmask, modelled as the stylised head of a woman with pierced eyes, orange hair and lips, 12in. long.
(Christie's S. Ken) £440

LENCI

The Lenci pottery was active in Turin during the 1930's, and produced three distinctive types of wares. The first, consisting of wall plaques in the form of female heads in scarves, as if going to Mass and figures of the Madonna and Child, were aimed at the domestic market. In stark contrast was the second group, made up of female figures, either nude or clad in contemporary costumes.

The third, and less well-known type, consists of vases and dishes decorated with Cubist-style painted scenes.

A Lenci earthenware box and cover, cover modelled with a dozing elf, dated 4.2.32, 21cm. £330

A Lenci centrepiece modelled as a young naked girl, 46cm. high. (Christie's) £880

A Lenci ceramic figure, of a nude girl wearing a chequered cap kneeling on the top of a globe, with a book in one hand and a dog by her side, with painted signature *Lenci, Made in Italy, Torino*, 48cm. high. (Christie's) £3,960

A Lenci bust of a father and baby, the sleekly groomed, dark-haired man clasping and kissing a rosy-cheeked, fair-haired and somewhat reluctant baby, 18cm. high. (Phillips) £680

A Lenci figure group, of a bare-breasted native woman wearing an abstract patterned wrap-around skirt in yellow, green and black, 44cm. high. (Phillips) £900

A large figure of a native girl, marked 'Lenci Torino Made in Italy', 1930's, 55.5cm. high. £440

A Lenci figure of a rooster, painted marks Lenci 1936 S.P., 29cm. high.(Christie's) £1,080

A Lenci pottery wall mask modelled as a young girl wearing a head scarf, 11½in. wide. £200

LENCI

A Lenci Art Deco ceramic figure, modelled as a girl wearing an orange hat, black jacket and black, white and grey chequered skirt, 37.5cm. high.
(Phillips)   £2,000

L Cacio Selle Colombe, a Lenci pottery figure modelled as a girl sitting with her floral and striped skirts spread out around her, 24.5cm. high. (Phillips London)   £580

A Lenci ceramic figure of a young peasant woman wearing black skirt, maroon floral shirt and yellow print scarf, 12½in. high.
(Christie's)   £640

A good Lenci ceramic group modelled as a mer-child holding a fish aloft, she kneels on the back of two open-mouthed fish, 51cm. high.
(Phillips)   £3,000

A Lenci ceramic group, modelled as a seated figure of a girl wearing a black dress, a coloured and patterned cape and a purple scarf, 34.8cm. high. (Phillips London)   £950

A monumental Lenci ceramic figure, the stylised female nude standing on a rock, covered in a cream slip, 99.2cm. high. (Christie's London)   £6,600

A Lenci Art Deco ceramic figure with box and cover, moulded as the head, shoulders and torso of a young woman, 21.4cm. high. (Phillips London)   £1,100

A Lenci polychrome ceramic figure of a mermaid and her baby astride a giant turtle, painted in shades of green and brown, 12¾in. high. (Christie's S. Ken)   £1,265

A Lenci ceramic head of stylised form, the hair and eye sockets painted in shades of blue and green, 14in. high.
(Christie's)   £990

MOORCROFT

When Macintyre's art pottery department closed in 1913, Moorcroft established his own pottery at Cobridge, employing his old colleagues. There, they made a wide range of items from pen trays to toastracks, from vases to brooches.

His flambé glazes were developed in the 1920s, and by the 1930s his range of motifs included fruit, birds, fish and boats. Matt glazes were introduced and his designs became increasingly simple. Moorcrofts signature always appears on his products, often painted in green until the 1920s and thereafter mainly in blue.

An octagonal bowl with everted rim, the interior decorated with alternate panels of peacock feathers and tulips, 10in. wide. (Christie's) £308

An ovoid vase with everted rim decorated with a band of frilled orchids, in pastel tones on a cream ground, 8½in. high. (Christie's) £275

A twin-handled square biscuit barrel and cover decorated in the 'Hazledene' pattern, in shades of green and blue, 6½in. high. (Christie's) £495

A pair of cylindrical candlesticks decorated in the 'Pomegranate' pattern, in shades of pink, ochre and green on a mottled green and blue ground, 8in. high. (Christie's) £990

A spherical vase decorated with stylised fish among waterweeds, in shades of red and ochre on a speckled salmon pink ground, the interior blue, 6in. high. (Christie's) £1,210

A baluster vase decorated in the 'Eventide' pattern, in shades of ochre, pink, green and blue, 13in. high. (Christie's) £682

A twin-handled tapering cylindrical jardiniere, made for Liberty, decorated in the 'Hazledene' pattern, in shades of blue and green, 8¼in. high. (Christie's) £550

A tapering cylindrical vase decorated with a bland of orchids, in shades of yellow, pink and purple on a graduated blue ground, 5in. high. (Christie's) £275

MOORCROFT

A twin-handled vase, decorated in Florian Ware cartouches of pink roses and green foliage on a blue ground, 8in. high. (Christie's)   £3,080

An oviform powder bowl and cover decorated with pansies, in shades of mauve and green on a deep blue ground, 3½in. high. (Christie's)   £286

A Florian Ware twin-handled vase, decorated with scrolling cartouches of peacock feathers and flowerheads, in shades of pale and dark blue, 8in. high. (Christie's)   £902

A twin-handled square biscuit barrel and cover, decorated in the 'Pomegranate' pattern, in shades of pink and blue on a sage green ground, 6¼in. high. (Christie's)   £440

A pair of Florian Ware baluster vases, decorated with scrolling cartouches of poppies and foliage, in shades of pale and dark blue, 12in. high. (Christie's)   £990

A large twin-handled vase, decorated with a band of plums and foliage, in shades of pink, mauve and green on a dark blue ground, 12½in. high. (Christie's)   £1,430

An oviform vase, decorated with a band of vine leaves and berries, in shades of yellow, pink and green on a deep blue ground, 12in. high. (Christie's)   £385

A pierced oval soap dish decorated in the 'Moonlit Blue' pattern, in shades of blue and green, 7¾in. long. (Christie's)   £308

A Flamminian vase made for Liberty, embossed on the shoulder with three foliate roundels, covered in a rose pink glaze, 6½in. high. (Christie's)   £187

POOLE POTTERY

The firm of Carter & Co was established in Poole, Dorset in 1873 to manufacture earthenware and tiles. The latter it often supplied for subsequent decoration, by, among others, William De Morgan. In 1895 they took over the nearby Architectural Tile Co.

Their range of earthenware, notably ornamental pottery, was developed principally by Owen Carter, the son of the proprietor. His experiments with glazes led to the creation of the matt, cream glaze which came to be associated with Carter Stabler and Adams. This amalgamation took place in 1921, when Owen Carter went into partnership with Harold Stabler and John and Truda Adams.

It was out of this partnership that the Poole Pottery, as it was renamed in 1963, grew. Poole Pottery products from all periods are much in vogue as collectables today.

A pottery oviform jug, shape no. 304, painted by Marjorie Batt with bluebirds and foliage in typical colours, impressed *CSA Ltd* mark, 5in. high. (Christie's S. Ken) £220

A pottery biscuit barrel and cover with wicker handle painted by Sylvia Penney, with stylised flowers and foliage, impressed *Poole*, 5½in. high. (Christie's S. Ken) £132

A pair of Pheobe Stabler earthenware figures modelled as a boy and girl, each draped with a garland of flowers, impressed *Hammersmith Bridge* mark, 7in. high. (Christie's S. Ken) £550

The Bull, a pottery group designed by Phoebe and Harold Stabler, modelled as two infants astride a bull in ceremonial trappings of swags and garlands, impressed *CSA* mark, 13in. high. (Christie's S. Ken) £2,310

A terracotta shallow bowl, decorated by Anne Hatchard painted with a deer in an open landscape, impressed *CSA* mark, painted insignia and *RG*, 9½in. diameter. (Christie's S. Ken) £242

A Phoebe Stabler plaster bust of a young girl with pigtails, painted yellow, inscribed *Phoebe Stabler 1911*, 15in. high. (Christie's S. Ken) £242

A pottery charger painted by Nellie Blackmore with a view of the ship the Harry Paye, by Arthur Bradbury, 15in. diam. (Christie's S. Ken) £605

A Carter red lustre flambé vase, with compressed base and lobed cylindrical neck, incised *Carter Poole 1905*, 11in. high.
(Christie's S. Ken) £110

A terracotta sculpture of a fully rigged galleon modelled by Harry Stabler, glazed in shades of blue, green, yellow and white, 20½in. high.
(Christie's S. Ken) £770

A Free Form Ware vase, shape No. 691, designed by A.B.Read, decorated with vertical lines of stylised foliage, printed *Poole Dolphin* mark, 11½in. high.
(Christie's S. Ken) £242

A pottery vase, shape No. 466, painted by Rene Hayes with a band of geometric pattern in typical colours on a white ground, impressed *CSA Ltd* mark and painted insignia, 5½in. high.
(Christie's S. Ken) £94

A pair of pottery bookends each modelled in full relief as leaping gazelles, impressed *Poole* and incised *831*, 8in. high.
(Christie's S. Ken) £440

A pottery candelabra, moulded with fruit and foliage and covered in a light blue glaze, impressed *Poole England* mark, 8½in. high.
(Christie's S. Ken) £66

A pottery vase, decorated with scrolling flowers and foliage, in typical colours on a white ground, impressed *CSA Ltd.* mark, 7in. high.
(Christie's S. Ken) £121

A pair of pottery doves designed by John Adams and modelled by Harry Brown, impressed *Poole England*, 8¼in. high.
(Christie's S. Ken) £275

A terracotta two-handled oviform vase shape No. 973, painted with flowers and foliage below geometric border, impressed *CSA Ltd.* mark, 7in. high.
(Christie's S. Ken) £440

CHARLOTTE RHEAD

Charlotte Rhead (1885-1947) came from a distinguished ceramics family. Her brother, for example, Frederick Rhead, made a name for himself in the States, designing for Samuel Weller and later for the Roseville Pottery. Charlotte worked as a decorator for three companies, Wood & Sons of Burslem, Burgess & Leigh, (Frederick also designed for a time for them) and, perhaps most notably, A G Richardson, where she was responsible for many designs in their Crown Ducal range.

Charlotte Rhead's work is highly characteristic. While the shapes she used were for the most part fairly conventional, consisting of standard vase, jug, bowl and plate forms, her decoration was very striking. Her main themes were floral or geometric, but painted big and bold in bright and interesting colour combinations.

A further feature which characterises much of her output was her predilection for tube lining. This technique consisted of thin outlines of slip trailed on the ceramic surface to control colour glazes, and had been in use from the late 19th century.

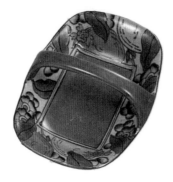

Bursley ware Charlotte Rhead pottery basket, 1930s.
(Muir Hewitt)   £85

Charlotte Rhead Art Deco vase, 5¹/₂in. high.
(Muir Hewitt)   £120

Pair of Charlotte Rhead Bursley ware vases, circa 1925, 7in. high.
(Muir Hewitt)   £450

Charlotte Rhead vase with stylized tube lined floral decoration, 1930s, 12¹/₂in. high.
(Muir Hewitt)   £350

Charlotte Rhead Crown Ducal Stitch pattern jug, 7in. high.
(Muir Hewitt)   £60

Charlotte Rhead Crown Ducal vase in Persian rose design, 10in. high.
(Muir Hewitt)   £195

Charlotte Rhead vase, 1930s, Crown Ducal, 8in. high.
(Muir Hewitt)   £140

CHARLOTTE RHEAD

Charlotte Rhead plate with floral decoration, Bursley ware, 1940s, 12½in. diameter. (Muir Hewitt) £275

Crown Ducal 'Golden Leaves' Charlotte Rhead jug, 10in. high. (Muir Hewitt) £160

Crown Ducal Charlotte Rhead 'Golden Leaves' wall plaque, 12½in. diameter. (Muir Hewitt) £175

Charlotte Rhead lamp base made by Bursley ware, 1930s. (Muir Hewitt) £175

Charlotte Rhead vase, Crown Ducal in stepped Aztec design, 7in. high. (Muir Hewitt) £175

Charlotte Rhead vase, 1930s, Bursley ware, 8in. high. (Muir Hewitt) £240

A Charlotte Rhead single handed oviform jug decorated with an undulating Chinese dragon, printed Crown Burslem mark, 8¼in. high. (Christie's) £294

Charlotte Rhead vase, 1930s, Crown Ducal, 8in. high. (Muir Hewitt) £200

Crown Ducal Charlotte Rhead jug, signed *C. Rhead*, 1930s, 9in. high. (Muir Hewitt) £195

ROYAL DUX

Royal Dux is the tradename of the Duxer Prozellanmanufaktur, which was established in 1860 in Dux, Bohemia, now Duchov, Czechoslovakia. It was noted at first for its portrait busts and extravagantly decorated vases, many of which were destined for the American market. From the 1920s onwards it produced Art Deco style figures, of single ladies, dancing couples etc. Marks include an *E* (for the proprietor Eichler) in an oval surrounded by Royal Dux Bohemia set on an embossed pink triángle.

A fine Royal Dux group of a classical Grecian horseman with his charges, 43cm. high, circa 1900.   £500

A Royal Dux porcelain bottle vase with applied rustic handle, 44.5cm. high.   £200

A Royal Dux porcelain group of a dancing couple in blue glazed and gilt Eastern costume, 12¼in. high. (Christie's S. Ken)   £352

A pair of Royal Dux book ends in the form of clowns, cream, green and brown designs with gilt work. (G. A. Key)   £290

A Royal Dux Art Deco porcelain figure, modelled as a girl with red hair, naked except for a blue cap tied with a ribbon at the side, 27.25cm. high. (Phillips)   £250

A Royal Dux centrepiece, the trefoil base with column modelled as three bare breasted girls kneeling and supporting lily-form bowl, 6½in. high. (Christie's S. Ken)   £198

A Royal Dux bust, the young Art Nouveau maiden gazing to the left, raised pink triangle mark, 20in. high.   £660

A Royal Dux porcelain figure group of a Roman charioteer, the chariot drawn by two rearing horses, 46cm. overall. (Henry Spencer)   £780

ART NOUVEAU & DECO

A Royal Dux group in the form of Pierrot kissing the hand of a young woman wearing a flowing ball gown, after a design by Schaff, 28.5cm.
(Bearne's) £560

A pair of Royal Dux bisque porcelain figures of a rustic boy and girl, the young boy wearing a green hat, the girl wearing a décolleté pink blouse, 17in. high.
(Spencer's) £480

A Royal Dux porcelain figural posy holder, in the form of a young girl in Kate Greenaway type dress, 25cm. high.
(Spencer's) £340

A Royal Dux bisque porcelain figure group of a traveller on a camel, the traveller wearing flowing robes, an attendant at the camel's feet, 17in. high.
(Spencer's) £600

A Royal Dux bisque porcelain figure of a bathing belle, seated wearing a green head scarf, and brown bathing costume, 16in. high.
(Spencer's) £750

A Royal Dux bisque porcelain Art Nouveau style flower holder, as a maiden draped in a brown robe seated upon a rocky outcrop, 27cm. high.
(Spencer's) £430

A pair of Royal Dux figures, one of a goat-herd wearing a bear skin over his tunic, his companion feeding a lamb from flowers, 52cm.
(Bearne's) £900

Royal Dux figure of Harlequin and female companion, on oval base, 19in. high. (Phillips Manchester) £250

A pair of Royal Dux bisque porcelain figures of harvesters after F. Otto, the young boy wearing a sou'wester, the young girl wearing a white blouse and purple bodice, 21in. high.
(Spencer's) £600

119

ROYAL DUX

A whimsical Royal Dux
porcelain group modelled as
small boy in swimming costume
squatting down to fondle his
devoted pet dog, 6¼in. high.
(Christie's)   £100

Royal Dux wall mask, 7in. high,
1930s.
(Muir Hewitt)   £180

A Royal Dux ceramic centrepiece modelled as a young
maiden draped on a conch
shell, 15in. high.
(Christie's)   £450

A Royal Dux ceramic
centrepiece, with two classical
maidens modelled in full relief,
15½in. high.
(Christie's S. Ken)   £715

A Royal Dux twin-handled
porcelain urn, on square
pedestal base, the cylindrical
body moulded in full relief with
two infants embracing above the
head of an old man, 14½in. high.
(Christie's)   £330

A Royal Dux ceramic
centrepiece, the base modelled
as roots and foliage supporting
maiden in flowing robes perched
between two shells forming the
bowls, 16¼in high.
(Christie's)   £880

A Royal Dux figure of a naked
female dancer poised on one
leg with a robe draped over her
thigh, 14½in. high.
(Christie's)   £600

A Bretby Pottery centre-piece
in the style of Royal Dux
modelled as a young maiden
in flowing robes perched
between conch shells, 15¼in.
high.   (Christie's)   £352

A Royal Dux ceramic figure of
a Greek youth wearing a toga
and sandals, painted in shades
of green sepia and gilt, 17½in.
high. (Christie's)   £200

RUSKIN

The Ruskin Pottery was founded at West Smethwick, Birmingham, in 1898 by William Howson Taylor (1876–1935) who had trained at the Birmingham School of Art. Throughout his career he was constantly experimenting with glazes and it is these which give his work its principal interest.

Initially, he made 'Soufflé' ware, where the predominant colours were blues, greens, purples, greys and celadons with a glaze in a single colour or mottled, clouded or shaded with a harmonising tone.

Lustre wares were also made in a wide range of colours and shades, and a pearl lustre was introduced, sometimes with a blistered texture and often with a kingfisher blue glaze. Flambé glazes with scattered viridian spots derived from the use of copper salts were produced, and after 1929 matt and crystalline glazes were added to the range. Taylor's High Fired wares featured dramatic colour contrasts, for example purple and black streaking on sea green, or black and green on cream.

With regard to the wares produced, many vases were made, some of which could be heavily potted and covered with blue, green, orange or crystalline blue with a frosted effect. The shapes were often based on Chinese styles. Other products included useful tableware, buttons, hatpins and cufflinks, some silver mounted.

Unfortunately Taylor took the secrets of his glazes with him to his grave, determined that his work should not be imitated. Production stopped at the factory in 1933.

Marks include Taylor's name up to 1903, after which *Ruskin* becomes usual, and the pieces are often dated.

A Ruskin high-fired stoneware vase, the oatmeal ground clouded with green and speckled with irregular areas of purple and blue, 1915, 21.cm. high. (Christie's) £1,100

A Ruskin high-fired stoneware bowl, the exterior glazed in deep red clouding over grey, the interior red speckled with purple and green, 1933, 24.5cm. diameter. (Christie's) £880

A Ruskin high-fired stoneware bowl, the oatmeal ground mottled overall in dove-grey overlaid with red and purple clouding, with green speckling, 31cm. diameter. (Christie's) £1,980

A Ruskin high-fired stoneware vase, pale ground mottled overall in purples and greens fragmented with random 'snake-skin' patterning, 1914, 32.3cm. high. (Christie's) £1,650

A Ruskin high-fired egg-shell stoneware bowl, with dark mottled red glaze clouding to green and purple towards the foot, 21cm. diameter. (Christie's) £1,100

A Ruskin high-fired stoneware vase, the mottled grey ground overlaid with a cloudy red, purple and grey, breaking into grey speckling, 1926, 31.5cm. high. Christie's £1,320

WEDGWOOD

Wedgwood moved with the times during the Art Nouveau/Deco periods to produce some pieces a world away from the traditional concept of typical Wedgwood. The fey quality of Daisy Makeig Jones's Fairyland lustre pieces are a case in point, as are some of the uncompromisingly stylised shapes and designs of the later Art Deco period.

Wedgwood

Zodiac Bull, a Wedgwood porcelain bull, designed by Arnold Machin, the cream glazed body with brown painted features, stars and signs of the Zodiac, circa 1945, 40.5cm. long. (Christie's London)   £605

A Wedgwood Fairyland lustre punch bowl, the interior decorated with The Woodland Bridge pattern, 28.5cm. diameter. (Bearne's)   £1,700

An Art Deco Wedgwood animal figure, modelled as a fallow deer, designed by J. Skeaping, 21.5cm. high.   £350

A pair of Wedgwood Fairyland lustre square vases decorated with panels of the 'Dana' pattern, 19.5cm. (Phillips)   £2,700

An Art Deco Wedgwood animal figure, modelled as a duiker, designed by J. Skeaping, 23.5cm. high.   £350

'Sun & Wind', a Wedgwood green and white Jasper plaque designed by Anna Katrina Zinkeisen, 12.5cm. diam. (Phillips)   £299

A Wedgwood black basalt vase designed by Keith Murray, of flaring cylindrical form with everted rim, 8in. high. (Christie's)   £1,980

A Wedgwood ceramic ewer and basin designed by George Logan, covered in a lilac glaze and decorated with stylised yellow floral designs, 29.6cm. height of ewer. (Christie's)   £770

ZSOLNAY

The Zsolnay earthenware pottery was established in 1862 at Pécs in Hungary by Vilmos Zsolnay, with the aim of shaping a characteristic national style.

Most of the output consisted of practical ware for everyday use, though some ornamental pieces were produced, often with Persian inspired motifs. Vases and bowls were made in Art Nouveau style with boldly coloured glazes and lustre decoration. These were the achievements of an experimental workshop under the direction of Vinsce Wartha which was operational around the turn of the century. Around that time too, vases with painted decoration designed by Josef Rippl-Rónai, also in Art Nouveau style, were produced.

The marks consist of versions of five churches with *Zsolnay*, and sometimes also with *Pécs*.

A Zsolnay ceramic jug, the handle formed as an Art Nouveau maiden with flowing hair and dress, 22.8cm. high. (Christie's) £220

A Zsolnay Pecs green lustre jug, the handle modelled as a nude maiden gazing over rim, 16in. high.
(Christie's S. Ken) £715

A Zsolnay Pecs lustre group, modelled as two polar bears on a large rock in a green and blue golden lustre, 4½in. high. (Christie's) £250

A large Zsolnay lustre vase covered with a violet/plum lustre glaze with random spots of gold/green/amber hues, 45.5cm. high. (Phillips London) £680

A small Zsolnay figural lustre vase decorated on the shoulders with the partially clad Orpheus with his lyre beside him and an amorous mermaid, 13cm. high. (Phillips) £680

A large Zsolnay lustre group, of two men possibly Cain and Abel, one lying prostrate on a domed rocky base with the other towering above him, 37.5cm. high. (Phillips) £550

A Zsolnay lustre figural ewer possibly designed by Lajos Mack moulded around its circumference with three sinuous Art Nouveau maidens, 35cm. high. (Phillips) £360

CHROMIUM PLATE

Chromium plate is a thin sheet of chromium which is electrolytically deposited on metal to increase its resistance to corrosion. It further imparts a brilliant silver sheen.

From its invention it was used for a wide variety of quality goods, such as car lamps and wristwatches. It also found favour with Modernist designers during the 1930s after its use for furniture was pioneered by such as Le Corbusier, Mies van der Rohe and Marcel Breuer in the 20s.

Chrome and wood cigarette box, 1930s.
(Muir Hewitt)   £30

Chrome yacht ash tray, 7in. high, 1930s.
(Muir Hewitt)   £25

Stepped chrome vase, 1930s.
(Muir Hewitt)   £25

Shell wall light of glass with chrome mount.
(Muir Hewitt)   £40

1950s chrome and plastic soda syphon.
(Muir Hewitt)   £25

Chrome ashtray with female figure, 1930s.
(Muir Hewitt)   £30

Chrome ashtray with stylized birds.
(Muir Hewitt)   £25

Chromium plated table gong, 1930s, 7in. high.
(Muir Hewitt)   £45

CHROMIUM PLATE

Chrome Angel figure table bell, 1930s.
(Muir Hewitt)   £15

Stylized chrome animal, 1950s.
(Muir Hewitt)   £12

Cocktail nibbles dish in chrome and plastic, 1930s.
(Muir Hewitt)   £20

Chrome cigarette case, 1930s, 6½in. long.
(Muir Hewitt)   £18

1950s Piquot ware tea set on matching tray.
(Muir Hewitt)   £75

Chrome companion set with Elizabethan figure support.
(Muir Hewitt)   £50

Chrome cake stand with stylized female support.
(Muir Hewitt)   £25

Chrome and glass tray, 1930s.
(Muir Hewitt)   £35

1950s chrome and plastic coffee percolator.
(Muir Hewitt)   £25

CHROMIUM PLATE

Pair of chromed metal candlesticks, early 20th century,
possibly Chicago, 3in. high.
(Skinner)   £54

Cocktail shaker, 1950s, complete
with instructions, 7in. high.
(Muir Hewitt)   £20

Beldray chrome plated vases
with Art Nouveau decoration.
(Muir Hewitt)   £45

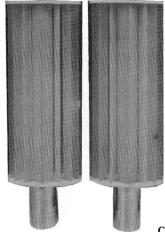

A pair of chromed steel and
acid textured glass wall lights,
circa 1940, 36.5cm. high.
(Christie's)   £600

Chrome and bakelite smoking
stand, Brooklyn, New York, circa
1930, with chrome topped ashtray and supports, 20¾in. high.
(Skinner)   £94

A pair of chromed steel directional
spotlights each on a rectangular
base supporting a box shade, stamped Desney, 15.8cm. high.
(Christie's)   £1,650

One of a pair of silver coloured metal frames, each
swivel mounted in angled
open supports, 31cm. high,
1930's.   £200

Pair of chromed metal candlesticks
by Salvador Dali, impressed signature, 14in. high.
(Skinner)   £556

A Modernist glass and chrome
metal fish tank, with polished
copper column supports at each
corner, on polished steel
rectangular base inset with
amber-tinted glass, 130.5cm.
high. (Christie's)   £4,620

CHROMIUM PLATE

Chrome cigarette lighter in the form of a bottle and two glasses. (Muir Hewitt) £35

Pussycat chromium cast money bank, with key, circa 1935. (Auction Team Koeln) £21

Chrome gong with stylized female figure, 1930s. (Muir Hewitt) £40

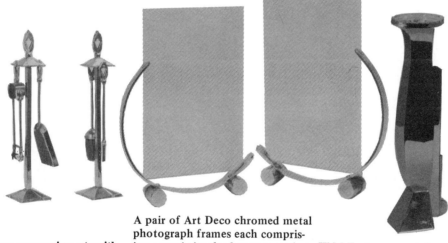

Chrome companion sets with shovel, tongs, brush and poker. (Muir Hewitt) £50

A pair of Art Deco chromed metal photograph frames each comprising a semi circular bar mounted at an angle, 17in. high. (Christie's) £308

W.M.F. chrome and glass vase, 1930s, 9in. high. (Muir Hewitt) £50

Chrome picture frame with picture of 1930's acrobats. (Muir Hewitt) £7

Chrome cake stand with two female figures support, 1930s. (Muir Hewitt) £30

Chrome frame complete with film star photograph. (Muir Hewitt) £15

CHROMIUM PLATE

Cream and blue glass table lamp with chromium plated fittings, 1930s, 16in. high.
(Muir Hewitt)   £75

Chrome and glass lamp with fern shade.
(Muir Hewitt)   £30

Chrome and glass lamp, 1930s, with amber shade.
(Muir Hewitt)   £40

Chrome and green glass lamp, 1930s, on stepped round base.
(Muir Hewitt)   £95

1930's chrome table lamp with black shade.
(Muir Hewitt)   £35

Art Deco lady lamp with chrome hoop and glass shade.
(Muir Hewitt)   £375

Chrome lamp 1930s with coat and dog decoration.
(Muir Hewitt)   £75

Table lamp in chrome with white glass shade.
(Muir Hewitt)   £75

Chrome and glass Art Deco lamp, 1930s.
(Muir Hewitt)   £120

CIGARETTE CASES

Cigarette smoking became popular in the late 19th century, and was at first essentially a male pastime. Thus early cigarette cases were quite weighty, and, many Continental examples also featured erotic scenes. It was not until after the First World War, when smoking had become socially acceptable for both sexes, that lighter, slimmer ladies' cases began to be made. Leading designers seized on this new accessory and Art Deco and Modernist examples from the 20s and 30s can be particularly attractive.

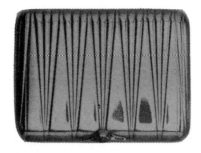

An oblong gold coloured cigarette case with cabochon bluestone pushpiece, with Swedish control marks, 3¼in. long. (Christie's)   £810

A gold and black enamel lady's cigarette case, with suede slip case, 1930's, 7.75cm.   £800

A stylish Art Deco cigarette case, formed by geometric segments of black, brown, brick-red and silver coloured metal, 10.7cm. (Phillips)   £150

A cigarette case, the cover cast with Napoleon mounted on a rearing horse, white metal, by Konstantin Skvortsov, Moscow, 1908-1917, 4½in. long, 204.6gr. (Christie's)   £440

An Art Nouveau hammered silver cigarette box, decorated in relief with an Art Nouveau maiden within a keyhole reserve, with Chester hallmarks for 1902, 12.5cm. long. (Christie's)   £286

An Imperial presentation gold cigarette-case, St. Petersburg, 1908-1917, 9.8cm. long.   £3,000

A French silver, black lacquer and crushed egg-shell cigarette case and a cigar piercer, London 1925, 11cm. wide.   £500

An Imperial presentation silver cigarette-case, St. Petersburg, late 19th century, 9.2cm. long.   £1,200

CIGARETTE CASES

An attractive German enamelled cigarette case, depicting a Titian haired beauty wrapped in a partly diaphanous shawl and seductively revealing a breast, 9.5cm. wide, 1906. (Phillips London) £1,150

A white metal and enamel cigarette case, the enamel by F. Zwichl, circa 1920. (Christie's) £1,944

A Victorian cigarette case, the cover enamelled with a nude girl lying beside a stream, Birmingham, 1887. (Phillips) £400

A Portuguese enamel cigarette case, the cover depicting a bare-breasted Classical girl, circa 1900. (Phillips) £380

A German Art Nouveau silver and enamelled cigarette case, depicting in naturalistic colours a Mucha-style girl, 8.50cm. long, maker's marks for Heinrich Levinger. (Phillips) £750

Late 19th century Austrian enamel cigarette case, the cover enamelled with an Ancient Egyptian scene, circa 1895. (Phillips) £600

An enamelled cigarette case decorated with a naked girl sitting on a wall catching water from a well in a bowl, 9cm. long, stamped *935.* (Phillips London) £420

A German cigarette case, one side engraved with an armorial, the lid enamelled with three naked women relaxing by a lake, London 1902, 3²/5in. (Christie's S. Ken) £1,045

A German enamelled cigarette case depicting a young woman wearing an off-the-shoulder dress and enjoying the amorous advances of her suitor in a boudoir setting, 8.7cm. long. (Phillips London) £850

CIGARETTE CASES

A German enamelled rect-
angular cigarette case,
maker's mark AW, circa
1910, 3¼in. wide.
£1,000

An Austrian white metal and
enamel eight-sided cigarette
case, the enamel by F. Zwichl,
depicting a Samson car in
black, red and cream.
(Christie's)   £540

A German enamelled
oblong cigarette case,
circa 1910, 3¼in. wide.
£1,000

An enamelled silver cigarette
case, probably German, circa
1910, thumbpiece missing,
3½in. high.   £440

An Austrian enamelled Art
Nouveau cigarette case, in
the style of Alphonse Mucha,
circa 1900. (Phillips) £650

A German .935 standard
cigarette case, signed
Reznicek.   £1,000

A Continental gilt lined
cigarette case, the lid
enamelled with a naked
woman rising from the sea,
3½in. (Christie's S. Ken) £385

A Continental cigarette case,
cover enamelled with a nude
lying on the edge of the shore,
with English import marks
for 1906. (Phillips)   £350

An enamelled curved rect-
angular cigarette case, probably German, circa 1910,
3¼in. high.   £1,200

CIGARETTE CASES

A French enamelled cigarette case by Eugene Grasset, circa 1900.
£600

A German Jugendstil cigarette case decorated in niello with sinuous linear banding, 9cm. long. (Phillips London)   £160

An Imperial two-colour gold and jewelled presentation cigarette case by Bok, St. Petersburg, 1899-1908, 9.7cm.   £3,000

A German enamelled oblong cigarette case, by Louis Kuppenheim, circa 1905, 3¼in. high.
£750

An Austrian enamel cigarette case, signed 'Schleiertanz', circa 1895. (Phillips)   £500

An enamelled oblong silver cigarette case, probably German, importer's mark M & C, Birmingham 1910, 3½in. high.   £1,200

A German enamelled curved oblong electroplated cigarette case, circa 1910, 3½in. high.
£1,000

A Soviet propaganda cigarette case, the foreground with crossed banners and Red Star, white metal, Moscow, 1927, 4½in. long, 162.8gr. gross. (Christie's)
£825

An enamelled oblong electroplated cigarette case, probably German, circa 1910, 3½in. high.
£1,200

CIGARETTE CASES

An enamelled oblong cigarette case, probably German, importer's mark S & Co., Birmingham 1910, 4in. wide. £900

Silver and enamel cigarette case by Raymond Templer, 1930. £2,000

An enamelled silver cigarette case, maker's mark A/Bros, Birmingham, 1907, 3½in. wide. £990

An Edwardian gilt lined cigarette case, polychrome-enamelled with a picture of a lady, R.C., Birmingham, 1905. (Christie's) £200

An enamelled cigarette case, probably German, circa 1910, oblong, painted in pastel shades, 3½in. high. £1,045

An enamelled cigarette case, German, circa 1905, 9cm. high. £352

A German enamelled cigarette case depicting a young girl wearing a lacy nightdress, falling from one shoulder, 9cm. long, stamped 935. (Phillips London) £780

A white metal rectangular hinged cigarette case, decorated in niello to a design by Gerard Sandoz, 5in. long. (Christie's S. Ken) £1,155

A German .935 standard cigarette case, 3¼ x 2¾in. £1,200

CIGARETTE CASES

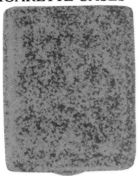

A Jean Dunand oreum and eggshell lacquer cigarette case, 1920's. £500

A jewelled guilloche enamel cigarette case, lilac enamel bands alternating with white plain enamel bands, marked Faberge, 1908-1917, 8.5cm. long. (Christie's) £3,300

Faberge rectangular silver-coloured metal cigarette case, 1899-1908, 3¾in. £1,500

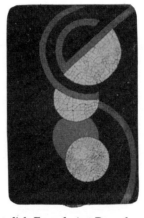

A 1930's cigarette case, silver and two-colour gold coloured metal, with stripes of black lacquer, 11.75cm. wide. £350

A stylish French Art Deco lacquered cigarette case, decorated with egg shell roundels, red roundel and curved bands, 12cm. wide. (Phillips London) £620

An Art Deco sterling silver cigarette case with black and silver ground in a crackle pattern with red enamel zigeraut decoration on one side. (Robt. W. Skinner Inc.) £161

A French Art Deco cigarette case, with black lacquered background, punctuated with random squares of golden coloured metal, 11.5cm. (Phillips) £90

A jewelled two-colour gold cigarette case, the reeded body set with diamonds, St. Petersburg, 1908-17, 9.8cm. £2,340

A French Art Deco lacquered and eggshell cigarette case, with broad band of crushed eggshell reserved against a black background, 10.3cm. (Phillips) £200

CIGARETTE LIGHTERS

The first cigarette lighters were introduced around 1900. Up to 1920 they worked on the flint principle. Dunhill and Orlik were notable early makers, and Dunhill examples are perhaps the most collectable of all. In the 1920s table lighters became popular, many of which were highly decorative and showed clear Art Deco inspiration. Some were even surmounted by dancing figures reminiscent of Chiparus and Preiss.

Silver cased petrol cigarette lighter by Tiffany & Co., New York.   £55

An 18ct. gold gas-burning lighter by Dunhill in original presentation case, 64mm. high. (Christie's S. Ken)   £308

Dunhill silver plated cigarette lighter, 1930s. (Muir Hewitt)   £75

Chromium plated 'Aeroplane' table lighter on a plated metal base.   £100

A Dunhill electroplated table lighter, stamped Made in England, patent no. 143752, 9cm. high. (Christie's)   £110

An unusual cigarette lighter mounted with a watch, signed 'The Golden Wheel Lighter', fitted with adjusted 6-jewel lever movement, signed Cyma, 52mm. high.   £400

1930's painted metal table lighter by Lorenzl, made in Austria, 8in. high.   £200

An 18ct. gold combined watch and lighter by Dunhill, engine-turned silvered Deco dial with Arabic numerals set in a hinged reeded octagonal frame, 1930, 49mm. high. (Christie's) £2,420

CIGARETTE LIGHTERS

A chromium plated cigarette lighter modelled as an **MG Midget**, circa 1933, 6¼in. long. (Christie's) **£198**

Ronson plated 'Dog Strike' table lighter, circa 1935. **£85**

MG Magic Midget George Eyston's Record Breaking Car, modelled as a silver petrol lighter, Birmingham, 1931, 7½in. long. (Onslow's) **£1,100**

1920's plated metal table lighter in the form of a dancing nude. **£75**

An Alfred Dunhill silver gilt and enamel cigarette box and lighter, London hallmarks for 1929. **£850**

Suzuki Optical Co., rare 5 x 8mm. 'Camera Lite' disguised camera with an f 8 lens, instant and bulb shutter. (Christie's) **£385**

'Mondain', a Dunhill patterned 9ct. gold petrol lighter, gold marks for 1950, 4.7cm. high. **£400**

A 9ct. gold combined cigarette lighter and watch by Dunhill, the base stamped Made in Switzerland, 5.3cm. high. (Lawrence Fine Art) **£605**

A Dunhill enamelled cigarette lighter, 5cm. high, stamped with maker's marks and Pat. No. 143752. (Phillips) **£280**

CIGARETTE LIGHTERS

A stylish Ronson 'Touch Tip' table lighter on a plated metal base, circa 1930. £75

A silver lighter by Dunhill, with false compartments enclosing powder tray, mirror etc., London 1928, 58mm. high. £400

An 18ct. gold lighter watch, with the 'Dunhill Unique' lighter mechanism, London, 1926. £1,430

1920's painted metal table lighter in the form of a dancing figure. £85

Dunhill cigarette lighter and cigarette case with enamelled decoration, circa 1929. (Habsburg Feldman) £3,890

A large 1930's gilded plaster table lighter in the form of a dancer. £175

A large white metal petrol-burning table lighter with clock mounted to the front, the matt gilt dial with stepped bezel, 10 x 8cm.(Christie's S. Ken) £165

A Tiffany & Co. Douglass petrol lighter, patterned yellow metal, stamped 14 Karat Solid gold, 5cm. high. £200

1930's Ronson 'Twentycase' table lighter in stylish black enamel. £100

CLOCKS

Most of the clocks produced during the Art Nouveau/Deco periods are of the mantel variety, perhaps reflecting the trend towards smaller houses. They come in all shapes and styles, from the elegance of Lalique glass to the most outré Art Deco examples, and many of the latter are electrically powered. Designs are never dull, and there are pieces to suit every taste and pocket.

Chrome plate electric clock by Smiths.
(Muir Hewitt)   £45

Late 19th century 'Coca Cola' walnut regulator timepiece, by Gilbert Clock Co., 30in. long.   £350

A chromium plated and gilt desk timepiece modelled as an Edwardian tourer, 8½in. high. (Christie's)   £450

Kneeling girl with clock, a bronze and ivory figure cast after a model by F. Preiss, 54.4cm. high. (Christie's)
£8,580

A Gustav Stickley oak mantel clock, early 20th century, the door with faceted cut-out framing brass dial, Seth Thomas movement, 13¾in. high. (Robt. W. Skinner Inc.) £1,714

A silver mounted and tortoiseshell pique desk timepiece, with a domed top, pique worked with foliage pendant from ribbon ties, 1908 by Harris Adelstein, 9.5cm. (Lawrence Fine Arts)   £506

A Liberty & Co. Tudric pewter 'Architectural' mantel clock, circa 1920, 7¼in. high. (Robt. W. Skinner Inc.)
£520

A gold mounted tortoiseshell miniature carriage timepiece, maker's mark CD, 1906, 9.5cm. high. (Lawrence Fine Art)
£902

CLOCKS

Chrome and black painted wood electric clock by Smiths. (Muir Hewitt) £40

A French Art Deco gilt bronze timepiece, the circular dial with gilded hands, 26.5cm. high, the case marked *G. Dunaime.* (Phillips London) £1,150

Ferranti electric clock, 1930s, with amber dial. (Muir Hewitt) £20

A Liberty & Co. Tudric pewter timepiece designed by Archibald Knox, embellished in relief with stylised plant forms, two buds set with blue enamel, 14cm. high. (Phillips London) £2,600

A silvered bronze Art Deco table clock, signed R. Terras, 34.5cm. high. (Christie's) £990

A Scottish Arts and Crafts ebony and silver timepiece with rectangular case in dark wood with flat metal top, signed 'J. H. McNair', 23.8cm. high. (Phillips) £8,000

A miniature tortoiseshell silver-gilt carriage timepiece, the backplate stamped *French made,* Roman and Arabic enamel dial signed *Drew & Sons Picc. Circus London. W.,* 3¹/₈ in. high. (Christie's) £440

1930s chrome and black electric clock. (Muir Hewitt) £50

An electroplated pewter presentation clockcase, surmounted by an Art Nouveau maiden standing contraposto, her arms raised against an elaborate pierced trellis superstructure, 50cm. high. (Christie's) £770

CLOCKS

An ebony and ivory inlaid
mantel clock, designed by
Josef M. Olbrich, circa 1902.
£16,500

Moineaux, a Lalique frosted
glass clock of domed outline,
the central dial enclosed by
nestling sparrows. (Phillips
London) £1,000

A square Nephrite travelling
timepiece with gold mounts,
by Cartier, circa 1920, 6.7cm.
£2,000

An Arts and Crafts copper
and brass mantel clock, the
pagoda style top with strapwork embellishment, 42cm.
high. (Phillips London)
£520

A silvered bronze mantel
clock, by Edgar Brandt,
30.6cm. high. (Christie's)
£3,080

A Liberty & Co. 'Tudric'
pewter and enamel time-
piece, embellished with a
stylised tree with leaves,
the roots tied in celtic knot.
(Phillips) £1,350

An Arts & Crafts mahogany
mantel clock with bevelled
glass, circa 1900, 12in. high.
(Robt. W. Skinner Inc.) £297

An unusual Jaeger LeCoultre
table clock in Art Deco style,
the straight line eight day movement jewelled to the centre with
monometallic balance, 7½in.
diam. (Christie's) £242

An Alfred Dunhill Art Deco
marble mantel clock and
cigarette case, 23.7cm. high.
£1,000

CLOCKS

An Art Deco marble and enamel timepiece, the corners set with cloisonne enamel panels decorated in black, brown, yellow, beige and white, 26.2cm. high. (Phillips) £260

An unusual French marine clock, modelled in the form of a shell with propellor fuse, inscribed *DUGHS CASTELNAUDARY*, 22in. high. (Christie's S. Ken) £462

A gold, rock crystal, onyx and enamel clock by Tiffany & Co. £3,500

Edwardian mahogany cased mantel clock with Art Nouveau shell inlay and striking movement behind an enamel dial. (G. A. Key) £155

'Deux Figurines', a Lalique moulded and engraved glass clock, of arched form, the clear and satin-finished glass moulded in intaglio with two scantily clad maidens, 38.7cm. high. (Christie's) £17,600

A fine hardstone and enamelled silver desk clock, signed Cartier, on agate base, 63mm. high. (Christie's) £3,391

Early 20th century grey marble and glass Art Deco mantel clock, France, 11in. high. £300

An Art Deco style circular pink mirror glass electric mantel clock. £350

A Swiss nickel keyless lever watch of very large size, the enamel dial with subsidiary seconds signed for J.C. Vickery, 13.5cm. diam. (Phillips) £350

CLOCKS

A silver miniature carriage timepiece with cut bimetallic balance to lever platform, the base stamped *Aspreys London* (London 1913); blue leather travelling case, 2⁷/₈in. high. (Christie's)　£495

A Lalique clock, the satin-finished glass moulded with two pairs of love-birds in blossoming branches, with brown stained decoration, 21.8cm. wide. (Christie's)　£880

A Liberty & Co. pewter and enamel clock, with scrolling decoration and four turquoise enamelled hearts, the circular face with Arabic chapters, 10.3cm. high. (Christie's London)　£220

An Arts and Crafts silvered metal mantel clock, the embossed circular dial with Arabic chapters, with stud decoration, 14½in. high. £220

A Foley 'Intarsio' earthenware clock case in the form of a miniature long-case clock, circa 1900, 33.8cm. high. (Lawrence Fine Art)　£484

A French Art Deco Van Cleef & Arpels small mantel time-piece, the lapis lazuli body with diamond chip surround and diamond set hands, 4in. high. (Tennants)　£20,000

An Aesthetic movement Elkington & Co. black marble mantel clock, with porcelain panels painted with stylised daisies, inscribed *Elkington & Co.,* 31.8cm. high. (Christie's London)　£1,100

'Inseparables', a Lalique opalescent clock, the clear and opalescent glass moulded with two pairs of budgerigars among prunus blossom, 11.2cm. high. (Christie's)　£1,980

A Liberty & Co. oak and enamel mantel clock designed by Archibald Knox, the circular dial with a red scrolling design on a mottled blue and green ground, 29.3cm. high. (Christie's London)　£1,320

An Ato Art Deco table clock with a pair of bronze owls perched on top, 41.5cm. high. (Christie's)   £495

Boston Beer Co. wall time-piece, manufactured by the New Haven Clock Co., circa 1900, 14in. diam.   £600

A carved wood Art Nouveau mantel clock, by the Chelsea Clock Co., Boston, circa 1920, 18¼in. high.   £750

A Liberty & Co. 'Cymric' silver and enamelled timepiece, embellished with a tree motif against a ground of coloured enamels, Birmingham marks for 1903, 11.5cm. high. (Phillips)   £5,200

A Liberty & Co. pewter carriage clock, the copper dial with black enamel chapters, on a mottled blue and green enamelled ground, stamped *English Pewter, Made by Liberty & Co.*, 12.2cm. high. (Christie's)   £605

Late 19th century ebonised mantel clock in the Arts and Crafts style with porcelain face and eight day movement. (British Antique Exporters)   £150

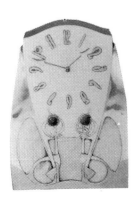

A Liberty & Co. 'Cymric' copper, mother-of-pearl and lapis clock, Birmingham 1903.   £8,000

An Art Deco green onyx mantel clock with ivory fig-ures carved after a model by F. Preiss, 25.2cm. high.   £2,500

Art Deco hardstone and cloisonne enamel desk clock, with 13J Swiss movement, 4.1/8in. high.   £1,200

CLOCKS

A Marchak & Linzeler Art Deco boudoir clock, circa 1925, 8cm. £3,000

A fine silver/gilt and enamel minute repeating timepiece by European Watch & Clock Co., for Cartier, in red leather travelling case, 2^{13}/$_{16}$in. high. (Christie's S. Ken) £5,500

Victorian oak hanging wall clock with pendulum, 1900 £150

A Liberty & Co. Tudric pewter clock, the stepped rectangular form with overhanging top, moulded with panels of foliate decoration, 18.3cm. high. (Christie's London) £286

A Jaeger-Le Coultre eight day mantel clock, with Roman chapters, the transparent glass discus-shaped body with chrome rim and foot, 23.3cm. diam. (Christie's) £528

A rare mixed metal mantel clock by Tiffany & Company, New York, 1880-1885, the front with mokume panels of silver mixed with niello, brass and red metal, 9in. high. (Christie's) £11,046

Cinq Hirondelles, a Lalique glass timepiece, moulded with five swallows in flight amid branches of blossom, 15cm. high. (Phillips London) £1,600

A Liberty & Co. pewter and enamel clock of domed rectangular outline, the circular dial centred in blue and turquoise enamels, 18cm. high, factory marks and '01156' to base. (Phillips) £520

A miniature tortoiseshell silver-gilt carriage timepiece, the backplate stamped *French made*, Roman and Arabic enamel dial signed *Drew & Sons Picc. Circus London. W.*, 3^{1}/$_{8}$in. high. (Christie's) £440

CLOCKS

A chromium plated Smiths electric mystery clock, inscribed Smith Electric, with dagger hands, 8in. high. (Christie's) £286

A gilt-brass mantel timepiece with alarm, the rectangular dial signed *Cartier 8 days alarm Swiss* with raised blued Arabic chapters, the movement signed *Concord Watch Co.*, 3½in. high. (Christie's) £1,320

Champleve and brass mantel clock, France, circa 1900, 8in. high. £800

L. & J. G. Stickley mantel clock, Fayetteville, New York, circa 1910, designed by Peter Heinrich Hansen, signed with Handcraft decal, 22in. high. (Skinner Inc.) £4,630

An Arts & Crafts square oak mantel clock, by Seth Thomas Clock Co., 20th century, 12½in. high, 10½in. wide. (Robt. W. Skinner Inc.) £648

A Liberty and Co. hammered pewter clock, the body decorated with stylised tree and foliate panels, the copper clock face with black enamel Roman chapters and turquoise enamel centre, 18.2cm high. (Christie's) £660

A German 'Secessionist' plated timepiece, the circular dial with gilded hands mounted in a face with pointed and pierced top, 44.5cm. high. (Phillips) £680

An attractive strut timepiece with square agate surround, the frosted gilt movement with bimetallic balance and lever escapement, engraved to the dust cover *Cartier*, 3¾in. square. (Christie's S. Ken) £1,100

A Liberty & Co pewter timepiece, designed by Archibald Knox, with copper coloured numerals, 8in. high. (Christie's) £2,090

DOMESTIC INSTRUMENTS

It is sometimes hard to remember that many of the domestic gadgets which we take for granted today have really only been in existence for a few decades. Technological advances have been so rapid that early examples of hairdriers, vacuum cleaners and the like are now almost unrecognisable as such, and this gives them an exoticism which makes them eminently collectable.

Aluminium and metal butterfly electric fire, 1930s. (Muir Hewitt) £195

A Mitrella toaster with bake-lite base, 1935. (Auction Team Koeln) £27

A very early AEG table fan, circa 1925. (Auction Team Koeln) £25

A French desk telephone by Ch. Ventroux Paris, wooden base and stand, receiver and extra receiver marked P. Jacquesson Paris, circa 1920. (Auction Team Koeln) £158

A fully automatic Morison's wooden washing machine, complete with tub, Belgian, circa 1900. (Auction Team Koeln) £122

A W. Feldmeyer spirit iron, with transverse tank and wooden handle, 1905. (Auction Team Koeln) £51

A nickel plated Friho-Sol hand held hairdrier of contemporary angular form, circa 1920. (Auction Team Koeln) £27

An Omega chromium toaster, circa 1935. (Auction Team Koeln) £29

DOMESTIC INSTRUMENTS

A moulded bakelite Siemens hand held hairdrier, circa 1930. (Auction Team Koeln) £16

A porcelain screw-in lamp valve and porcelain insulator, circa 1922. (Auction Team Koeln) £9

PhiliShave 6 dry electric razor by Philips, Holland, with bakelite case and plug in original box, circa 1938. (Auction Team Köln) £35

A German bakelite Forfex hand held hairdrier by Eisemann, circa 1935. (Auction Team Koeln) £43

A 1920s Morrisharp Art Deco style electric pencil sharpener, accompanied with letter of authenticity from Peter Noble, stating that the composer Max Steiner used the pencil sharpener when writing the score for the film Gone With The Wind. (Christie's S. Ken) £198

A CAL coffee grinder with ceramic holder and glass dispenser, circa 1925. (Auction Team Koeln) £52

Graeztor electric fire, black enamel with copper housing, 30 x 50cm., circa 1930. (Auction Team Köln) £99

A curious vacuum cleaner blower attachment with heating coil, in bakelite casing, circa 1935. (Auction Team Koeln) £19

Libelle fan with green hammer finish bakelite propeller, by Schoeller & Co Frankfurt, circa 1955. (Auction Team Köln) £50

DOMESTIC INSTRUMENTS

German Bing No. 2 type bar typewriter, 1925. (Auction Team Koeln) £110

A heavy duty iron with replaceable wooden handle, circa 1920. (Auction Team Koeln) £12

An Ozonomat wall hanging air purifier, circa 1955. (Auction Team Koeln) £30

A wooden coffee grinder with coloured tinplate sides and harvest thanksgiving motif, circa 1900. (Auction Team Koeln) £148

An early Kadus hairdrier, on cased movable stand, circa 1930. (Auction Team Koeln) £331

Prometheus Model WRS 4 toaster, 4 slice parallel tip mechanism, adjustable for 2–4 slices with control light and bakelite base, chrome, circa 1955.
(Auction Team Köln) £107

Katalyt 'Sun in Winter' paraffin heater, circa 1930.
(Auction Team Köln) £66

1950s "Frost" electric fan with green base.
(Muir Hewitt) £75

Nilfisk vacuum cleaner, an early industrial cleaner in original box with tools, circa 1935.
(Auction Team Köln) £49

DOMESTIC
INSTRUMENTS

An Alexanderwerk bread cutting machine, circa 1910. (Auction Team Koeln) £43

An Art Nouveau nickel plated cast iron stapler, circa 1890. (Aution Team Koeln) £37

A Dual dynamo pocket lamp, aluminium cased, circa 1940. (Auction Team Koeln) £12

An OBM Mokkadomat coffee machine, circa 1920. (Auction Team Koeln) £183

A Rolls Patent razor in plated case, circa 1910. (Auction Team Koeln) £14

A World Patented Mechanical Darner beard cutter, with adjustable levels and bakelite housing, English, circa 1930. (Auction Team Koeln) £16

An American Candlestick desk telephone by Stromberg-Carlson, circa 1920. (Auction Team Koeln) £197

A 127-film blue Kodak Petite camera with cloth covered body, by Eastman Kodak Co., Rochester, NY, U.S.A. with 'flash' pattern baseboard and original blue bellows. (Christie's S. Ken) £526

An original Miele mangel with wooden rollers, restored, circa 1910. (Auction Team Koeln) £50

FANS

The day of the fan as an essential fashion accessory has, for the present at least, passed away. It lasted, however, into the first years of this century, long enough for some pretty Art Nouveau examples to be produced, and these now fetch hundreds of pounds.

Later examples tend to take the form of gimmicks, often for advertising purposes, rather than the real thing, and their relative inferiority is reflected in the prices which they fetch.

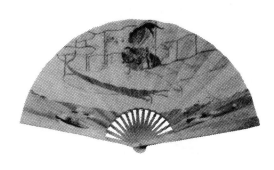

Parfum Pompeia, L.T. Piver, a chromolithographic fan of a lady in a flying machine, published by Maquet, 9in., circa 1918. (Christie's S. Ken) £352

A French fan designed as a peacock, signed A. Tomasse, the reverse inscribed Duvelleroy, in a box labelled Duvelleroy, circa 1900's, 25.5cm. long. (Phillips) £340

A fan, the shaped leaf painted with a woman wearing a violet trimmed bonnet, signed Jebagnes, 9½in., circa 1905. (Christie's) £1,650

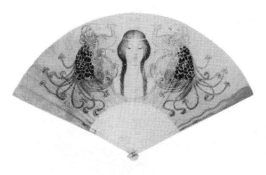

A fan, the leaf painted with a buste of a girl in medieval dress flanked by two peacocks embroidered with blue sequins, signed *G. Darcy*, 10½in., circa 1900. (Christie's S. Ken) £770

A fan with carved pierced blonde tortoiseshell sticks, decorated with mother-of-pearl and carved with foxgloves and convolvulus, 28cm. long, circa 1900s. (Phillips West Two) £850

FANS

He shoots the Hippopotamus with bullets made of platinum [Belloc], an unmounted fan leaf painted on silk by John Kettlewell, 10in. x 21in., circa 1918.
(Christie's S. Ken) £660

An Arts and Crafts fan, the dark blue leaf painted with pairs of dragonflies in silvered paint, 11in., circa 1890. (Christie's S. Ken) £1,045

Advertising fan with parrot design.
(Muir Hewitt) £20

E. Mercier, a chromolithographic menu fan in the shape of a champagne bottle opening twice, first to reveal a menu, secondly to reveal a handscreen, published by Chambrelant, circa 1910.
(Christie's S. Ken) £330

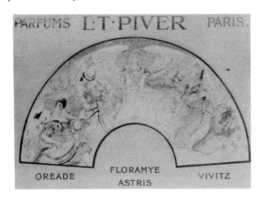

A design for a fanleaf by A. Willette, with an allegorical scene with France Ancient and other figures, 1906, the mount an advertisement for L.T. Piver.
(Christie's S. Ken) £154

Advertising fan, 1930s, with wooden sticks.
(Muir Hewitt) £25

A 14ct. gold engine turned Swan pen with vacumatic filling, inserted ball clip and original No.2 nib, circa 1920.
(Christie's S. Ken) £440

A shagreen Parker desk set with two lapis blue Parker Duofold pens with vulcanite tapers and gold Duofold nibs.
(Christie's S. Ken) £165

A 9ct. engine turned barleycorn design, lever filled Waterman's pen, with ball clip, circa 1920–29.
(Christie's S. Ken) £385

A gold coloured Parker 51 with grey nib section, the cap inscribed 18K., in an original retailers box.
(Christie's S. Ken) £187

A lapis blue streamlined Parker Duofold junior pen with two cap bands and ball clip, circa 1927–28.
(Christie's S. Ken) £99

A dark green vacumatic filling Parker 51 with 'Icicle' pink and gold caps inscribed 14K and a matching propelling pencil, circa 1944.
(Christie's S. Ken) £715

A mandarin yellow hard rubber Parker Duofold Lucky Curve Senior pen with two narrow cap bands and ball clip, circa 1928–29.
(Christie's S. Ken) £440

A gold filled Hick's 'Detachable' pen, with telescopic barrel fitting into barleycorn decorated casing with ribbon ring, in original box with instructions in the base.
(Christie's S. Ken) £66

Dunhill-Namiki: a Taka Maki-E lacquer pen, decorated with three carp swimming amongst green aquatic plants, signed by the lever, circa 1937.
(Bonhams) £1,250

A 9ct. 'barleycorn' panel and spotted patterned engine turned overlaid Waterman's Ideal lever filled pen, circa 1915–29.
(Christie's S. Ken)   £352

A sterling silver 'Gothic' design overlaid Waterman's lever filled pen, circa 1926.
(Christie's S. Ken)   £143

An emerald pearl Parker vacumatic standard pen and pencil set with three narrow cap bands and original Canadian arrow nib, circa 1933–36.
(Christie's S. Ken)   £154

A heavily chased and scrolled sterling silver eyedropper Swan over fed pen, in original presentation box with red velvet lining, circa 1900–1908.
(Christie's S. Ken)   £605

A sterling silver 'filigree' design overlay eyedropper Waterman's 12 pen, circa 1900–03.
(Christie's S. Ken)   £286

A gold filled scrolled and twisted design overlay eyedropper Swan pen with over/under feed nib, circa 1908–12.
(Christie's S. Ken)   £550

A Pelican self feeding reservoir pen by Thomas de la Rue, hallmarked *London 1897*.
(Bonhams)   £5,500

A fine lacquered Dunhill Namiki lever fill pen, with Maki-E design of a Japanese fisherman wearing large hat, carrying rod and bait basket on the barrel, with original Dunhill Namiki no. 20 nib.
(Christie's S. Ken)   £2,420

Dunhill Namiki: a gold dust Maki-E lacquer pen, decorated with a small wood surrounding a lake with an erupting volcano in the distance, with 18ct. gold top.
(Bonhams)   £750

FURNITURE
BEDS

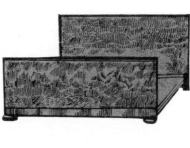

An Art Deco grand lit en lac d'or, 179cm. wide. £2,000

An Art Deco walnut day bed made in Austria, circa 1930, fitted with a compartment 'at one end', 92in. long, 37in. wide. £1,250

A large sycamore bed, circa 1955, signed by Louis Sognot. £3,000

American maple faux bamboo bed, circa 1880, headboard, footboard, side rails, turned finials, incised details, 72½in. long.
(Skinner Inc.) £451

A Leleu Art Deco three-piece bedroom suite, comprising: a grand lit with arched headboard and two bedside tables, with circular overhanging tops, 191cm. long measurement of bed.
(Christie's) £6,050

A tubular brass child's cot, circa 1910, 3ft. 8in. long. £750

An Art Deco burl and ash bed, American, circa 1930, 4ft. 6in. wide. £350

Child's metal cot by Theodore Lambert, 1910, 133cm. long. £600

BEDS

An Ebene de Macassar single bed designed by Emile Jacques Ruhlmann, mounted on chrome plated plinth bases, 109cm. wide. (Christie's London) £2,750

Lifetime Furniture day bed, Hastings, Michigan, circa 1910, shaped crest rail over nine vertical slats at each end joined by seat and lower rail forming three arches, 77³/₄in. long. (Skinner Inc.) £881

An Arts & Crafts inlaid bed, attributed to Herter Bros., oak burl and other veneers, 26½in. wide. **£1,000**

PEL chromed tubular steel B4 single bed with double-hoop bed head, 1930's, 90.5cm. wide. **£600**

A Wylie and Lochead mahogany bed, the design attributed to George Logan, the toprail inlaid with mother-of-pearl and wood peacock-eye motifs, 122cm. high. (Phillips) **£580**

An English Art Deco Egyptian style bed, the tall headboard with beaten copper panel of Egyptian style foliage, 108cm. wide. (Christie's) £550

A late 19th century mahogany double bed head and foot board in the Art Nouveau style. £500

BOOKCASES

Six section Globe Wernicke cabinet, 1880. (British Antique Exporters) £292

A Morris & Co. oak bookstand, the sloping rectangular rest sur-mounted with carved and tur-ned ball and foliate finials, above panelled sides and open recess, 185.5cm. wide. (Christie's) £4,400

A Sidney Barnsley walnut bookcase on two stepped trestle ends, 106.8cm. wide. (Christie's) £7,700

Late Victorian mahogany library bookcase with ogee moulded cornice, 3ft.6in. wide. (Capes, Dunn & Co.) £580

Display unit of oak with black painted facings, 1930s. (Muir Hewitt) £260

An unusual Edwardian mahogany inlaid bureau bookcase, the breakfront cornice with chequer inlaid frieze, 126cm. wide. (Phillips) £1,700

An Aesthetic ebonised and inlaid cherrywood book-case by Herter Bros., N. Y., circa 1880-85, 63½in. wide. £7,500

Oak bookcase, 20th century, gallery top, shelf with double keyed tenon over median shelf with single keyed tenons, 28⅛in. wide. (Skinner Inc.) £122

Shop of the Crafters inlaid bookcase, Cincinnati, Ohio, 1906, with pierced detail over two glass doors, 28¼in. wide. (Robt. W. Skinner Inc.) £1,043

CABINETS

A Sue et Mare rosewood, ebonised and marquetry music cabinet on elongated ebonised legs, 95.2cm. wide. (Christie's) £3,024

A side cabinet, the chromium plated metal frame supporting two walnut shelves, 125cm. wide. (Christie's) £220

An Art Deco coal box attributed to S.S. Henry, of cuboidal form, the front door opening from the top to reveal a metal coal bucket, 80cm. high.
(Phillips) £440

Early 20th century carved oak Belgian style linen fold cabinet, 32½in. wide. £630

A Rowley walnut and marquetry cabinet and stand, the design attributed to Frank Brangwyn, with two marquetry panels inlaid in various fruitwoods with toiling farm labourers, 85.1cm. wide. (Christie's) £770

Cassina laminated cabinet, inspired by Piet Mondrian, 1970's, 162.5cm. high. £1,000

An Art Nouveau oak dresser, the mirrored superstructure having a crest with two supports, 1.68m. high.
(Phillips) £750

A Wm. Watt ebonised side cabinet designed by E. W. Godwin, 197.4cm. high by 128.6cm. wide. (Christie's) £5,400

An Ernest Gimson cedar wood cabinet, the interior fitted with sliding shelves, 116cm. high. (Lawrence Fine Art) £770

CABINETS

An Aesthetic influence mahogany music cabinet, circa 1880, 3ft. 7in. high. £750

An Art Nouveau stained wood cabinet carved with tulips and ducks, 4ft.8in. high. (Anderson & Garland) £470

An inlaid mahogany music cabinet attributed to Christopher Pratt & Sons, circa 1900, 56.5cm. wide. £990

A fine Aesthetic Movement ebony and lacquer cabinet, set with lacquered rosewood panels of Japanese landscapes with parquetry borders, stamped Gregory & Co. 212 & 214, Regent St., London 944, 202cm. high. (Christie's) £1,870

A pair of fine Mercier Frères burr walnut Art Deco bedside cabinets, attributed to Eric Bagge, the overhanging rectangular top of each above a vase-form body, 58cm. high. (Christie's) £3,300

Art Nouveau mahogany cabinet, inlaid with other woods and mother-of-pearl, 3ft. 10¾in. wide. £2,000

An Art Deco wrought iron and zebra wood cabinet, carved signature J. Cayette, Nancy, circa 1925, 115cm. high. (Christie's) £1,404

Hoosier kitchen cabinet with metal fittings, 1920. £100

Romney Green walnut music cabinet, doors inlaid with lozenge-shaped panels, 1928, 119cm. high. £1,250

CABINETS

A Guild of Handicraft oak cabinet, designed by C. R. Ashbee, circa 1900, 105.5cm. wide. £19,800

Art Deco cabinet of various woods, 1930's. (British Antique Exporters) £600

Victorian oak hanging cabinet, 1880. (British Antique Exporters) £62

An Art Nouveau music cabinet, in mahogany, the central door with copper plaque embossed with stylised flower and quotation *If music be the food of love play on*, 1.50m. high. (Phillips) £820

A pair of Holland and Sons oak bedside cabinets, the chamfered rectangular top above cupboard doors, on chamfered and turned legs with gothic arch aprons, 93.6cm. high. (Christie's) £880

Romney Green Cuban mahogany photograph cabinet, doors inlaid with ebony, circa 1930, 76cm. wide. £1,500

An elaborate Art Nouveau dresser, possibly designed by Gustave Serurrier Bovy, in light oak, the superstructure having a central glass-fronted cupboard flanked by recesses, 206cm. high. (Phillips) £1,300

Victorian oak four-drawer filing cabinet, 1880. £270

An Austrian Secessionist black lacquer and pewter inlaid cabinet, the shaped rectangular top above bowed and glazed cupboard door enclosing red stained interior, 161.6cm. wide. (Christie's) £5,500

CHAIRS

A French Art Nouveau oak dining chair, designed by C. Plumet and A. Selmersheim. (Phillips) £340

An oak tub chair with open slatted back, circa 1900. £308

An adjustable back armchair, attributed to J. Young & Co., circa 1910, 31½in. wide. (Robt. W. Skinner Inc.) £476

A Plail Bros. barrel-back armchair, Wayland, N.Y., circa 1910, 33in. high. (Robt. W. Skinner Inc.) £562

Early 20th century wicker arm rocker, 31in. wide. (Robt. W. Skinner Inc.) £119

One of a pair of Valabrega open armchairs, each back with central shaped, upholstered and braided panel within a curved curvilinear, pierced framework. (Christie's London) Two £4,840

Fancy wicker armchair, by Heywood Bros. & Co., Mass., 39in. high. (Robt. W. Skinner Inc.) £838

Dental treatment chair by Koken St Louis, Art Nouveau metal fittings with white porcelain, without head support, with oil pressure height adjustment, circa 1910. (Auction Team Köln) £260

Plail Co. barrel back armchair, Wayland, New York, circa 1910, spring cushion seat over wide front seat rail, 40in. high. (Skinner Inc.) £556

CHAIRS

A Morris & Co. oak armchair to a design by Philip Webb, with horizontal spindles and arms supported by turned beaded spindles. (Phillips) £1,400

One of a pair of Valabrega sidechairs, each back of carved curvilinear pierced form. (Christie's London) Two £3,190

One of a pair of J. & J. Kohn 'Fledermaus' armchairs, circa 1907. £2,000

Plail Bros. barrel-back rocker, with spring cushion seat, N.Y., circa 1910, 31½in. high. (Robt. W. Skinner Inc.) £203

A tub armchair, with slats to floor, 1890's. £95

Early 20th century spindle-back lift seat hall bench, style no. 542, unsigned, 46in. wide. (Robt. W. Skinner Inc.) £265

A small Art Deco gilt and up-holstered salon chair attributed to Jules Leleu, the curved back and arm rests upholstered in beige fabric. (Christie's) £1,540

An oak chair designed by W. Cave, with drop-in rush seat, circa 1900. £750

Cassina 'chaise basculante', designed by Le Corbusier and Charlotte Periand, 70cm. wide, 1928-29. £650

CHAIRS

An oak open arm chair designed by Denham MacLaren, with shaped trestle ends, supporting deep upholstered black hide and zebra skin seat backrest. (Christie's London)   £2,860

A laminated mahogany arm-chair, circa 1900, 45in. high. (Robt. W. Skinner Inc.)   £354

One of a pair of Barcelona chairs, designed by Mies van der Rohe, with stainless steel, X-shaped frames. (Christie's)   £770

A child's spindle back arm rocker, unsigned, circa 1915, 24¼in. high. (Robt. W. Skinner Inc.)   £202

One of two Bruno Mathsson chairs, Sweden, circa 1940, laminated beech with upholstered webbing in brown, 33in. high. (Skinner Inc.) £349

An oak and oak veneered armchair with scenic inlay, circa 1910, unsigned, 37in. high. (Robt. W. Skinner Inc.)   £756

An upholstered oak armchair with cut out sides, circa 1905, 28¾in. wide. (Robt. W. Skinner Inc.)   £699

A mahogany carved chair in the form of a hand. (Christie's)   £432

One of a set of six Macassar ebony Art Deco armchairs, attributed to Paul Kiss, upholstered in brown hide. (Christie's)
Six   £6,050

CHAIRS

A rush-seated oak sidechair, by Joseph P. McHugh & Co., N.Y., circa 1900, 36in. high. (Robt. W. Skinner Inc.)
£187

A 'Paris' chair, by André Dubreuil, constructed of welded sheet steel, the shield-shaped backrest supported on triangular pillar. (Christie's) £1,430

A Maurice Dufrene giltwood bedroom chair, the arched back with wreath motif continuing into reeded decoration on arms. (Christie's) £440

An oak framed chair with carved narrow back and shaped arms. (Lots Road Chelsea Auction Galleries) £360

One of a set of six Wiener Werkstatte black stained limed oak dining chairs, designed by J. Hoffmann. (Christie's) £17,600

One of a pair of Italian perspex and chromium plated tubular steel chairs, designed by Harvey Guzzini, with original label. (Christie's)
Two £330

One of a pair of oak Bentwood open armchairs, each bearing a label 'Patent Pending 25597/1932, Regd Design 781, 637. (Phillips) £340

A Serrurier-Bovy 'Silex' dismantling mahogany chair, circa 1905. (Christie's) £216

Art Nouveau upholstered armchair, possibly Karpin Furniture co., early 20th century, carved fruitwood frame, 37½in. high. (Skinner Inc.) £370

COCKTAIL CABINETS

1930's cocktail cabinet in walnut veneer with centre glass covered shelf, 156cm. high.
£350

Art Deco bar cabinet, England, circa 1930, manufactured by George Berlin and Sons Ltd, Sureline Furniture, interior with lighted compartment, approximate height 48in. (Skinner Inc.)
£100

A brass and mahogany cocktail cabinet by Jacques Admet. £2,160

A good Art Deco sycamore cocktail cabinet, the twin doors with rounded corners enclosing two recessed shelves, 91.7cm. wide. (Phillips)
£1,450

1930s cocktail cabinet in walnut veneer. (Muir Hewitt)
£350

An Art Deco Epstein & Goldbart cocktail cabinet, mahogany veneered in sycamore, fitted interior, 60½in. high. (Christie's)
£500

A 1930's 'pop up' drum bar, 76cm. diam.
£100

An Art Deco cocktail bar trolley, the bar handle flanked by two inset clear and satin glass panels by Lalique, 88cm. wide. (Christie's) £6,480

A 1930's cocktail cabinet with curved doors, 91cm. wide.
£1,000

DESKS

An early John Makepeace, Andaman padouk and leather-covered desk, by M. Doughty, D. Pearson and A. Freeman, 199cm. wide, and a chair. (Christie's) £1,980

Edwardian oak fall-front desk cabinet, 1910. £100

A Maurice Dufrene semi-circular wooden desk, 31in. high, and a chair upholstered in red velvet, 32in. high, signed and dated 1935. (Christie's) £2,800

Prairie School style oak bureau with swivel mirror, Illinois, circa 1912, central portion with square posts and moulded cornice over vertical mirror, 87in. high. (Robt. W. Skinner Inc.) £982

Victorian oak desk with leather top, 1880. (British Antique Exporters) £153

An Edwardian mahogany writing table, interior fitted with a rising stationery rack and drawers, 26in. high. (Christie's) £2,035

Charles Rohlfs dropfront oak desk, Buffalo, New York, circa 1907, shaped gallery top above slant front, 25½in. wide. (Robt. W. Skinner Inc.) £1,472

Shop-O'-The-Crafters slant front desk, Ohio, circa 1906, style no. 279, signed with paper label, 42in. wide. (Robt. W. Skinner Inc.) £281

A lady's oak desk with fall-front, circa 1890, 28½in. wide. (Robt. W. Skinner Inc.) £320

DISPLAY CABINETS

An Art Deco walnut veneered circular display cabinet, with glazed doors enclosing glass shelves, 120.5cm. high. (Phillips) £300

An Edwardian Art Nouveau display cabinet in inlaid mahogany, 138cm. wide. £860

Art Nouveau style oak china cabinet, 1920. (British Antique Exporters) £150

A mahogany Art Nouveau display cabinet, the mirrored top with open canopy, 48in. long. £850

An Art Nouveau mahogany display cabinet, with recessed top shelf held by front supports heavily carved with fruit and leaves, 106.8cm. across. (Phillips) £750

An Art Nouveau oak vitrine with glazed cupboard, 62.3cm. wide, circa 1900. £1,300

A mahogany display cabinet with glazed doors and velvet covered shelving. £240

Oak Art Nouveau design display cabinet with two leaded glazed doors with inlaid decoration on shaped supports, 47¹/₂ in. wide. (Bigwood) £700

An Art Nouveau mahogany display cabinet in Scottish style, with bevelled mirror top above a single leaded glass door, 54in. wide. (Christie's) £650

DISPLAY CABINETS

Art Nouveau style oak display cabinet. (British Antique Exporters) £284

An Art Deco mahogany, maple and chromium plated display cabinet, on solid mahogany side supports united by an undertier. (Phillips) £1,000

Octagonal walnut display cabinet with two shelves, 1930s. (Muir Hewitt) £450

An Art Nouveau mahogany inlaid display cabinet, with glazed doors enclosing shelves, inlaid and coloured with stylised roses and leaves, 181cm. high. (Phillips London) £1,300

An Art Nouveau inlaid mahogany display cabinet, having a central bevelled mirror with an arched apron above with twin cupboards below, 1.45m. wide. (Phillips London) £1,900

An Edwardian Art Nouveau mahogany side cabinet with boxwood, satinwood and harewood stylised floral inlay, 4ft. wide. (Capes, Dunn & Co.) £440

A Wylie & Lochhead mahogany display cabinet, designed by E. A. Taylor, 88cm. wide. (Christie's) £1,728

An Art Nouveau mahogany display cabinet, 3ft.8in. wide, circa 1910. £715

A Christopher Pratt & Sons inlaid mahogany display cabinet, 192.6cm. high. (Christie's) £825

PIANOS

Bechstein Arts & Crafts period upright grand piano in mahogany case, 61in. wide.   £2,000

A chrome metal piano by Paul Henningsen, 1931.   £20,000

A Steinway upright oak piano, circa 1903, Serial 107781, decorated by Edwin Willard Deming. (Christie's)   £16,342

A baby grand piano, designed by Jacques Adnet, for Gaveau of Paris, of rosewood, on three tapering rectangular section legs, with matching upholstered stool. (Christie's)   £8,800

Eavestaff pianette mini-piano and stool, cream painted, 140cm. wide.   £1,000

Late 19th century flame mahogany and marquetry upright piano by S. Mercier, Paris. (Hôtel de Ventes Horta)   £2,000

PIANOS

An Art Deco sycamore and rosewood baby grand piano and stool by Steck.   £10,000

An Eavestaff Art Deco mahogany and satinwood baby grand piano, inlaid metal inscription Healy, circa 1930, 151.2cm. wide. (Christie's) £2,376

An Eavestaff overstrung under-dampered 'mini-piano' with green drag point slab shaped deco case, also matching stool.
£1,000

An Art Deco Strohmenger baby grand piano and stool, in bleached burr walnut, the semi-circular body having three arches under solid supports meeting at the pedals.
(Phillips)   £6,900

An upright grand pianoforte, iron framed, over-strung and underdamped movement, by R. Gors & Kallmann.   £1,000

A W. Menzel Secessionist piano, the mahogany case with elaborate brass mounts, circa 1900, 148.1cm. wide. (Christie's)   £715

SCREENS

John Pearson bronze and wrought iron firescreen, circa 1906, 27½in. high.
£500

An Arts and Crafts oak framed fire screen, the plain oak frame having a toprail pierced with oval shapes, 77.4cm. high. (Phillips)   £95

American leaded glass firescreen, circa 1900, 45¼in. high.   £2,000

A stained oak three-fold screen, 173cm. high, circa 1900.   £750

A wood and copper phone screen, circa 1910, 12in. high, 13in. wide. (Robt. W. Skinner Inc.)
£67

An ebonised and marquetry four-leaf screen inlaid in satinwood, beechwood, walnut and stained fruitwood, 190cm. high, 141cm. wide. (Christie's)   £1,540

20th century wrought iron firescreen in the gothic style. (British Antique Exporters)
£35

Victorian leaded light fire-screen, 1875. (British Antique Exporters)   £110

An Arts & Crafts oak fire-screen, the framework enclosing a panel of Morris & Co. fabric woven with 'The Tulip and Rose', 55.5cm. high. (Phillips)   £190

SCREENS

Giltwood and stained glass screen, circa 1900, 62in. wide. £1,000

Art Deco three-fold screen, signed Henri Etructure(?) and dated 4/23/30, 72in. high. £350

An Art Nouveau carved three leaf screen, the rectangular panels with bud finials, fluted borders and tapering legs, 135cm. wide. (Christie's London) £462

A four-fold screen, designed by Piero Fornasetti, one side depicting brightly coloured birds, the other showing guitars, each panel 200cm. high x 50cm. wide. (Christie's) £3,960

Arts and Crafts fireplace screen, circa 1910, triptych design comprised of three repousse copper panels decorated with stylized fish and naturalistic motifs, in hammered copper and riveted frame, 38in. wide. (Skinner Inc.) £249

Three-fold lacquer screen by M. Lattry, Paris, circa 1930, 165.5cm. high. £1,000

Victorian firescreen of polished copper, 1880. £105

A wrought-iron and pierced copper fire-screen, circa 1900, 34½in. wide. (Robt. W. Skinner Inc.) £162

A silk-embroidered firescreen, attributed to Morris & Co., 97.5cm. high. (Christie's) £220

SETTEES & COUCHES

A laminated birchwood chaise longue designed by Bruno Mathsson, Made in Sweden, 151cm. long. (Christie's)   £486

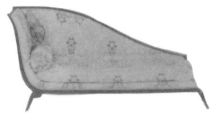

An Art Deco upholstered day bed with a black painted wood frame, on shaped legs, 180cm. long, circa 1925.   £1,000

A Modernist chromed tubular steel sofa, 1930's.   £485

'Anfibio', a white leather upholstered sofa bed designed by Alessandro Becchi, 240cm. wide. (Christie's)   £594

An Art Nouveau mahogany and marquetry settle on three arched trestle supports, circa 1890, 185cm. wide. (Christie's) £990

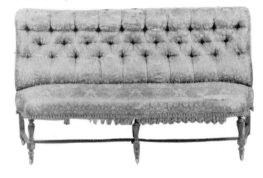

A Morris & Co. settle, designed for Stanmore Hall, the design attributed to George Jack, the rectangular button back and padded seat upholstered with 'flower garden' fabric, 76in. wide.
(Christie's S. Ken)   £1,760

Pine bench, probably circa 1900. (Lots Road Galleries)   £260

An Art Deco two seater sofa, upholstered in coloured velvet fabric depicting tigers walking through foliage, 166cm. long. (Phillips London)   £280

SETTEES & COUCHES

'Djinn series', an upholstered chaise longue designed by Olivier Mourgue, in green nylon stretch jersey, circa 1965, 170cm. long. (Christie's) £756

A 'lip' sofa, after a design by Salvador Dali, upholstered in red nylon stretch fabric. (Christie's) £1,155

A pair of chaises longues by De Sede fashioned as a pair of giant boxing gloves. (Christie's) £6,500

A carved mahogany tete-a-tete with scrolled and carved back over S-shaped arms above round upholstered seat, America, circa 1900, 41½in. long. (Robt. W. Skinner Inc.) £354

A.J. & J. Kohn bentwood two-seater settee, designed by Gustave Siegel, with woven rush seat, the back pierced with an array of arrow motifs, 122cm. wide.
(Phillips) £550

A Walter Cave oak settle, 136.5cm. wide, circa 1900. £880

A tubular chromium-plated chaise longue designed by Le Corbusier and Charlotte Perriand, the adjustable seat upholstered in brown and white pony skin, on black painted steel base.
(Christie's) £880

An Art Deco ebony, macassar and vellum covered day bed, the rectangular gondola-shaped form with vellum covered moulding on plinth base, with band of bone inlay, 81cm. wide. (Christie's) £5,500

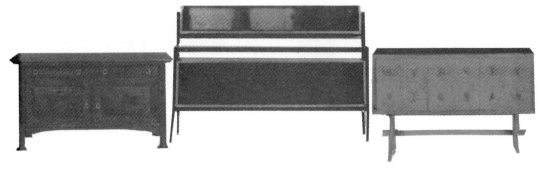

Oak straight front sideboard comprising two drawers and two cupboard doors, designed by August Endell, 188cm. wide, circa 1900. £2,000

A stylish metal and wood sideboard designed by Robin Day for S. Hille & Co. Ltd, 184cm. wide, circa 1950. £500

A stylish Italian sycamore sideboard on a trestle base, 150cm. wide, circa 1930. £400

A Shapland and Petter oak sideboard, the rectangular cornice overhanging a central reserve decorated with a copper relief panel of stylised flowers above shelf, 228cm. wide. (Christie's) £4,950

An English Art Nouveau mahogany display cabinet with bevelled mirror back, 71in. high x 53in. wide. (Christie's) £980

A 19th century Art Nouveau pollard oak sideboard, on sledge feet, 6ft.6in. wide. £1,500

20th century oak sideboard with cupboards. (British Antique Exporters) £70

A French Art Deco walnut veneered sideboard with mirrored back, 184cm. wide. £250

Part of an Art Deco dining room suite, comprising: a dining room table, a sideboard and four chairs with beige simulated leather upholstered seats. (Phillips London) £300

STANDS

Victorian brass gong and stand, 1880. (British Antique Exporters) £60

Victorian mahogany hall stand, 1860. (British Antique Exporters) £76

Victorian oak stickstand with brass plaque, circa 1900. (British Antique Exporters) £125

An Art Nouveau oak hall stand with circular mirror, stylish hooks and embossed copper panels, 36in. wide. (Lots Road Chelsea Auction Galleries) £350

A Gramophone & Typewriter Ltd 'Melba' gramophone pedestal, ebonised with gilt incised Art Nouveau floriate decoration, 39in. high, circa 1905.
(Christie's S. Ken) £1,540

Victorian brass banded oak fern stand, 1880. (British Antique Exporters) £78

A three-tiered muffin stand, by Charles Rohlfs, Buffalo, N.Y., 1907, 34in. high. (Robt. W. Skinner Inc.) £702

A Bentwood hall stand, possibly made by Thonet and possibly designed by Josef Hoffman, 194.5cm. high. (Phillips) £550

A mahogany plant stand, possibly by Ellwood, having four uprights with hemispherical finials, 93.2cm. high. (Phillips London) £150

An Aesthetic Movement ebonised rectangular chest-stool, decorated front and back with carved gilt emblematic roundels, 89.7cm. wide. (Christie's) £2,420

A turned ash bar stool with central footrest, 82cm. high, circa 1930. £60

Renouvin Art Deco music stool on turned legs with brass casters, 78cm. wide, circa 1930. £300

An Art Deco stained black and limed oak Ashanti style stool, possibly French, on five turned supports, 51.5cm. high. (Phillips) £240

An English Art Deco walnut and painted Egyptian style stool, the rectangular concave seat upholstered in brown leather. (Christie's) £264

Late 19th century pottery garden seat, probably France, whimsically depicting a cushion resting on a basket, 20in. high. (Robt. W. Skinner Inc.) £528

A Derby & Co. oak window seat, the cut-out armrests with spindle supports, circa 1910, 28in. high. (Robt. W. Skinner Inc.) £260

Pel chromed tubular steel bathroom stool with cork top, 1930's, 44.5cm. square. £125

An Edwardian mahogany framed stool with floral tapestry covered pad seat, 23in. wide. (Anderson & Garland) £290

SUITES

Three-piece Art Deco living room suite, by Collins and Alkman Corporation, circa 1929, wood mohair upholstery with wood veneer accents and feet, couch upholstery in shades of burgundy with gold piping. **£1,000**

A Limbert oak dining room set comprising a pedestal table with four boxed leaves, diameter 54in., and a set of four dining chairs, circa 1910.
(Skinner's) **£1,750**

Early 20th century **Plail & Co.**, barrel-back settee and matching armchairs, 46¼in. long.
(Robt. W. Skinner Inc.) **£2,857**

A seven-piece late Victorian mahogany salon suite upholstered in coral fabric, comprising a settee, two armchairs and four chairs. (Bonhams) £750

A rare Irish pearwood Art Nouveau three-piece suite by James Hayes, comprising; a two-seat sofa and two side chairs, each upholstered with brown leather, the frames carved with naturalistic forms, the shaped legs with carved feet reminiscent of cloven hooves. (Christie's) £6,050

Four piece suite of Heywood-Wakefield wicker seat furniture, a settee, armchair and two side chairs, raised on circular legs. (Skinner Inc.) £419

SUITES

Part of a four-piece Harden & Co. livingroom set, comprising: settee, rocker and two armchairs, settee 54in. wide, circa 1910. (Robt. W. Skinner Inc.)   £1,104

An English Art Nouveau three piece inlaid mahogany salon suite, each with inlaid fruit-wood roundels of buds, the tapering arms and padded seats on tapering legs, 104cm. width of sofa. (Christie's London)   £3,080

A mahogany sofa and two side chairs of horseshoe shape, designed by Josef Hoffmann, sofa 121cm. wide. (Christie's)   £3,780

An Art Deco burr-walnut and satinwood bedroom suite, comprising: a 'Lit Double', a pair of
bedside cabinets, a dressing mirror and a wardrobe with overhanging rectangular top.
(Christie's)   £1,650

An English Art Deco leather upholstered three-piece suite, the sofa with cloud-shaped arms
and back upholstered in grey leather with walnut stringing to arms, 162.5cm. length of sofa.
(Christie's)   £3,960

An Art Deco dining suite, probably Hille, veneered in light walnut, consisting of: a table, a
sideboard of geometric form, a small buffet and eight chairs en suite.
(Phillips)   £4,200

SUITES

An Art Deco three-piece suite, consisting of a three-seater settee with two matching armchairs, the solid wooden rounded geometric frame veneered with walnut, upholstered, with matching cushions, 175cm. long.
(Phillips) £1,900

An Art Deco maple dining room suite, comprising: a dining table, a similar side table, a set of six dining chairs with arched rounded back, a three tiered trolley and a glazed display cabinet.
(Christie's S. Ken) £1,980

An Art Nouveau pearwood salon suite, comprising a three seater settee, 175cm. long, two elbow chairs and four upright chairs. (Phillips) £2,600

TABLES

An Art Deco oak and painted dressing table, the red painted table surface with curved up ends, 1.66m. high, with stool en suite. (Phillips London)
£400

An Art Deco coffee table, circular parquetry top on four scrolling wrought iron legs, 79.6cm. diam. (Christie's)   £432

An ebonised occasional table by E.W.Godwin, on turned tapering legs united by an undertier, 66cm. high. (Phillips)   £220

A mahogany veneered side table, designed by Frank L. Wright, circa 1955, 21½in. wide, red decal on back. (Robt. W. Skinner Inc.)
˙£432

Bent plywood tea cart, mid 20th century, top fitted with beverage holder, centering tray, bent wood legs joined by lower median shelf, 20in. wide. (Skinner Inc.)   £122

Art Deco walnut veneer table with African influence. (Muir Hewitt)   £250

An Art Deco walnut dressing table, the removable shaped top having a glass cover and three drawers, 88cm. long. (Phillips)   £90

Oak Art Deco table with undershelf, 1930s. (Muir Hewitt)   £220

A maple side table, the design attributed to Ico Parasi, with plate glass top, 128.1cm. wide. (Christie's)   £1,540

TABLES

A circular oak table inlaid with herringbone banding, 50cm. diameter, circa 1900. £500

Occasional table in aluminium and walnut veneer, 1930s. (Muir Hewitt) £195

An Art Nouveau mahogany and inlaid dressing table with cartouche-shaped bevelled swing-frame mirror, 122cm. wide. (Phillips) £520

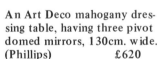

Carved Lotus centre table, executed by John Bradstreet, Minneapolis, circa 1905, original black finish, unsigned, 30in. diam. (Skinner Inc.) £15,432

An Art Deco mahogany dressing table, having three pivot domed mirrors, 130cm. wide. (Phillips) £620

An English Art Deco walnut centre table, the octagonal top on a pedestal base consisting of four shaped rectangular compartments with open recesses, 70.5cm. high. (Christie's) £660

An Arthur Simpson of Kendal dressing table, with three quarter galleried top, on square section tapering legs, stool en suite, 114cm. wide. (Christie's London) £715

A Salvatore Meli ceramic and glass centre table, 120.5cm. wide. (Christie's) £7,150

A bentwood coiffeuse manufactured by Jacob and Josef Kohn. £600

Burr walnut table with draw
leaves, 1930s.
(Muir Hewitt)   £375

Nest of walnut tables, 1930s.
(Muir Hewitt)   £240

An Art Deco veneered centre
table, having an oval top and
similar under shelf, 77cm. high.
(Phillips)   £250

Walnut veneer occasional table,
1930s, with undertiers.
(Muir Hewitt)   £100

A French Art Deco beechwood
writing desk on trestle ends,
105.4cm. wide.   £800

An Art Deco Macassar ebony
veneered dressing table,
120.5cm. wide, 1930's.
                               £1,250

A chromed tubular steel
desk, probably Pel, 114cm.
wide, 1930's.   £300

An Art Deco oval oak writing
table, the oval top inset with
green leather supports, the two
pedestals enclosing drawers and
a shelf, 69.6cm. high. (Phillips
London)   £320

A 1930's coffee table of
pale burr-wood, 60cm.
high.   £175

TABLES

A Guild of Handicraft oak dining table, designed by C. R. Ashbee, circa 1902, 97.5cm. wide. £1,000

Walnut veneer occasional table of stylized shape with glass top. (Muir Hewitt) £350

An Art Deco console table in walnut veneer, the rectangular top held by two splayed solid supports, 150cm. long. (Phillips) £360

One of a pair of console tables, circa 1930, 34cm. wide. £3,000

An Art Deco Macassar ebony dressing table on turned tapered legs, 47in. wide. £2,000

Modernist occasional table in sycamore veneer, 51cm. square, 1930's. £400

Victorian mahogany ornate occasional table, 1890. (British Antique Exporters) £168

Stylized Deco dining table in walnut veneer on 'U' shaped support. (Muir Hewitt) £850

Early 20th century oak occasional table. (British Antique Exporters) £35

WARDROBES

Victorian oak armoire in Art Nouveau style, 1900. (British Antique Exporters) £165

Mid 20th century Sellers pollard elm and burr-walnut wardrobe with three panel doors, 82in. wide. £1,000

An Aesthetic movement ash combination wardrobe and a similar dressing table, 43in. wide.(Reeds Rains) £320

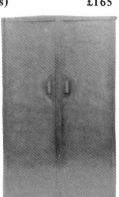

A Huntingdon Aviation & Co. aluminium wardrobe designed by P.W. Cow, with twin doors and amber plastic pulls, 122cm. across. (Phillips) £150

A fine Art Nouveau walnut wardrobe, designed by Georges de Feure, with shaped and carved pediment above twin central panelled doors, 200cm. wide. (Phillips) £5,000

A painted wardrobe, coloured in navy blue, red and green with linear decoration, combed wavy banding and roundels, 76cm. across. (Phillips London) £240

An Arts and Crafts oak wardrobe with broad everted top above a central mirrored door flanked by panelled sides, 198.5cm. high. (Phillips) £300

An Arts and Crafts mahogany wardrobe, attributed to Kenton & Co., possibly to a design by Arthur Blomfield, the doors enclosing drawers and shelves, 149cm. wide. (Phillips) £500

An oak wardrobe by E. P. Gardiner, having a plain cornice above twin panelled doors, raised on square legs, 1.275m. across. (Phillips London) £280

ALVAR AALTO

Hugo Alvar Henrik Aalto was born in 1898 in Finland and became one of the leading designers of the Art Deco movement. He worked in various media, designing for example asymmetrical vases in clear green glass for the Iittala Glass Works. It was however for his furniture that he is probably best remembered. His first important design, executed about 1930, was a sofa bed with a thick upholstered seat and adjustable back on a tubular steel frame. His was a seminal influence on 1930s design, particularly in his use of bent laminated birchwood.

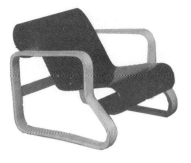

'Piamio', a laminated birch armchair designed by Alvar Aalto, the black painted back and seat formed from a single piece.
(Christie's)   £1,650

A Finmar tea trolley, designed by Alvar Aalto, raised on bent-wood supports with two large circular disc shaped wheels, 90cm. long. (Phillips London)
£977

One of a pair of armchairs designed by Alvar Aalto of Finland for Finmar, circa 1932.
(Bonhams)   £1,050

A Finmar laminated birch two tier table, designed by Alvar Aalto, painted black, the rect-angular tiers with curved sides supported by rounded square shaped trestle ends, printed manufacturer's label, 58.6cm. high; 60cm. wide; 50.1cm. deep.
(Christie's)   £285

One of a pair of Finmar laminated birchwood open armchairs designed by Alvar Aalto.   £1,750

A Finmar Ltd. plywood arm-chair, designed by Alvar Aalto.
£400

Finmar Ltd. sideboard, designed by Alvar Aalto, 1930's, 121.5cm. long.   £1,000

One of a set of six Finmar Ltd. plywood dining chairs by Alvar Aalto.   £1,000

ARTS & CRAFTS

The original inspiration behind the Arts & Crafts movement which flourished in late l9th century England was undoubtedly William Morris, who urged a return to medieval standards of design and craftsmanship in the face of their usurpation by industrialisation and mechanical processes.

The movement was characterised by craftsmen and designers organising themselves into cooperative associations rather in the style of the old Guilds. Indeed, The Century Guild and Charles Ashbee's Guild and School of Handicraft were both formed in the 1880s.

The ideas of the movement were much aired and documented in contemporary lectures, essays and books, and the firms of Morris Marshall, Faulkner & Co and later Morris & Co were formed to design and produce decorative objects in the Arts and Crafts style.

In the case of furniture, the ideals of the movement were reflected in simple, solid construction, using the natural beauty of the wood as the main decoration. Favoured woods were the traditional English oak, walnut and elm. More elaborate pieces were produced by the Guild of Handicraft.

The principles of the movement spread to influence designers both in Europe and America. In Europe, Serrurier-Bovy, Muthesius and the Deutsche Werkbund were among those so inspired, while in the US the work of Gustav Stickley, the Prairie School and Elbert Hubbard showed clear Arts and Crafts influence.

Charles Ashbee and Charles Voysey saw the movement into the 20th century.

An unusual Arts and Crafts side table, supported at the front on supports with three plant form branches, 1.11m. long. (Phillips London) £400

Arts & Crafts oak smoking cabinet with shaped copper hardware, circa 1910, 23in. wide. £220

An Arts & Crafts breakfront oak wardrobe by George Walton, 230.2cm. wide. (Christie's) £4,180

An Arts and Crafts oak writing cabinet, the shaped rectangular top with curved three-quarter gallery above open recess, fall flap and short drawers, 94cm. wide. (Christie's) £385

An Arts and Crafts oak tub chair, the curved toprail and rail below embellished with carved leaf motifs. (Phillips London) £310

Arts and Crafts bookcase, Jamestown, Ohio, circa 1912, cut out gallery flanked by two cabinet doors, 51^{1}/2in. wide. (Skinner Inc.) **£831**

ARTS & CRAFTS

An American Arts & Crafts oak reclining chair with reclining mechanism, in the manner of A. H. Davenport of Boston. (Phillips) £150

An English Arts & Crafts brass mounted mahogany, sycamore and walnut marquetry partner's desk, 129.6cm. wide. (Christie's) £2,484

An Arts and Crafts oak crib, the cylindrical barrel type rocking body supported by tall triangular rounded plank ends, 1.27m. high x 1.10m. long. (Phillips) £280

A Victorian Arts & Crafts carved walnut Masonic secretaire, 4ft.2in. wide. (Capes, Dunn & Co.) £600

An Arts & Crafts mahogany four-fold embroidered screen, 152cm. high. (Christie's) £825

An Arts & Crafts oak cabinet with repousse hammered copper panels, circa 1900, 31¾in. wide. (Robt. W. Skinner Inc.) £540

An Arts and Crafts inlaid oak card table, attributed to William Birch, the square top with four hinged triangular panels above arched aprons and plank legs, 74.6cm. high. (Christie's) £715

An Arts & Crafts painted cabinet and bookshelves (top missing), the figures drawn by M. Reed, 61cm. wide. (Phillips) £320

Arts & Crafts umbrella stand, probably Europe, early 20th century, shaped flat sides with spade trailing to circle cut-out, 22in. wide. (Skinner Inc.) £161

ARTS & CRAFTS

Arts and Crafts corner bar cabinet, circa 1910, with brass hinges, 22in. wide.
£500

An American Arts & Crafts stained oak rocking chair, in the manner of David Kendal for Phoenix Furniture. (Phillips) £90

An Arts & Crafts oak display cabinet with painted panel to the railed upstand, 107cm. wide. £540

An Arts & Crafts walnut wardrobe by Cope & Collinson, 188cm. wide. (David Lay) £1,050

A stained oak Arts & Crafts wardrobe, the panelled door having a beaten copper panel with a design of birds and trees towards its top. (Phillips) £380

An English Arts & Crafts walnut combination wardrobe with ebony crossbanding, 66in. wide. (Reeds Rains) £340

An Arts and Crafts oak secrétaire of tapering form, having twin-glazed doors, with drop-fronted bureau below. (Phillips) £600

An Arts & Crafts dressing table by George Walton, 134.2cm. wide. (Christie's) £605

An Arts & Crafts oak book-case, the cupboard doors with copper hinges, 101.3cm. wide. (Christie's) £374

ARTS & CRAFTS

An Arts & Crafts inlaid oak elbow chair, the central back splat inlaid with a flower motif in pewter and wood. (Phillips)   £120

An Arts & Crafts inlaid oak desk, the rectangular top with bow front, covered in red leather above three short drawers, 149cm. wide. (Christie's)   £1,540

An Arts & Crafts style walnut armchair probably Belgian.   £920

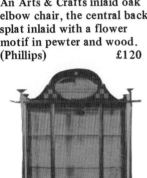

A mahogany display cabinet in the Arts & Crafts style, 53in. wide. (Prudential Fine Art)   £480

An Arts and Crafts writing table, the shaped superstructure with castellated back panel above a three-quarter gallery with over-hanging top, 111.2cm. wide. (Christie's)   £495

A late Victorian ebonised side cabinet in the Arts & Crafts style, 93cm. wide. (H. Spencer & Sons)   £550

An unusual ebonised and upholstered Arts and Crafts armchair, with upholstered drop-in seat, on curved back supports and turned front supports. (Phillips)   £300

An Arts and Crafts oak dres-ser, having a central mirror flanked by carved flowers, the base with twin drawers and cupboards, 1.55m. wide. (Phillips London)   £600

An Arts and Crafts mahogany armchair, having a cushion and seat upholstered in Liberty & Co. fabric. (Phillips London)   £320

191

M H BAILLIE SCOTT

Mackay Hugh Baillie Scott (1865–1945) was an English architect who also designed furniture, ceramics and metalwork. His furniture tended to be simple and linear in form often with colourful inlays in such materials as pewter, ivory, woods and copper and with elaborate metal mounts. One of his major commissions was to design pieces for the Palace of the Grand Duke of Hesse in Darmstadt, and these were executed by the Guild of Handicraft in 1898.

An oak dining table, designed by M. H. Baillie-Scott, of rectangular shape on two trestle supports, each composed of twin turned baluster columns on square plinths and shaped transverse base, circa 1897, 183cm. long. (Christie's) £3,520

A John Broadway & Sons oak 'Manxman' piano, designed by M. H. Baillie-Scott, with hinged overhanging rectangular top, circa 1899, 142.6cm. wide. (Christie's) £6,600

Oak sideboard, attributed to Baillie-Scott, circa 1900, 107cm. long. £1,500

A large oak buffeet designed by Baillie-Scott, the shaped rectangular top above shaped superstructure with beaten repousse copper panel, 327.9cm. wide. (Christie's) £3,520

An oak gate-leg writing cabinet designed by M. H. Baillie-Scott, rectangular top above fall-flap with pierced steel hinge plates designed by C. A. Voysey, 91.5cm. wide.(Christie's)£3,300

A. J. P. White 'Daffodil' oak dresser, designed by M. H. Baillie-Scott, the superstructure with rectangular top above two open shelves flanked by single cupboard doors, 153.5cm. wide. (Christie's) £5,000

A lead and stained glass window designed by M. H. Baillie-Scott in green, blue and puce-coloured glass, (1897-1898). (Christie's) £14,300

A. J. P. White oak inlaid dwarf cabinet designed by M. H. Baillie-Scott, a cupboard door with pewter and fruitwood inlay of stylised flowers and flanked on one side by open recess with fitted shelf, circa 1904, 50.8cm. wide.(Christie's) £1,540

MARCEL BREUER

Born in 1902, Marcel Breuer was a Hungarian architect and designer who joined the Bauhaus in 1920. He specialised in industrial and interior design and became 'Master of Interiors' there in 1926. He was influenced by Gerrit Rietveld, and designed wooden furniture and then the first tubular steel chair which was manufactured in 1925 by Thonet Brothers.

In 1930 he left the Bauhaus for Berlin, and then, as that became too uncomfortable with the rise of Nazism, came to Britain in 1935. He designed coffee tables and a noteworthy chaise longue for the firm of Isokon in bent plywood with latex foam upholstery.

A prototype plywood stool, attributed to Isokon, circa 1935, 45cm. high.   £400

An Isokon laminated plywood chaise longue, designed by Marcel Breuer, circa 1935–1936, the arms and legs of bent laminate.
(Christie's)   £1,760

One of two 'Wassily' chairs, designed by Marcel Breuer, in natural canvas, 1925, 70.5cm. high.   £275

A large sectional wardrobe designed by Marcel Breuer in a pale coloured wood, with drawers and hanging space, 186cm. wide. £1,000

An important oak lath armchair designed by Marcel Breuer for the Bauhaus, Weimar, 1924, constructed from vertical and horizontal strips of stained oak, 94.8cm. high. (Christie's)
                    £28,600

A nest of three Isokon stacking laminated plywood side tables by Marcel Breur, circa 1936, with original cream painted finish, 35.5cm. high.
(Christie's)   £2,000

Open cabinet with adjustable height shelf, designed by Marcel Breuer, 1920's, 36cm. wide.   £400

An Isokon book stand, white painted natural wood, with sloping book compartments, 40.3cm. high.   £300

CARLO BUGATTI

Carlo Bugatti (1855–1940) was a Milanese furniture designer and craftsman, who was notable for the originality of his designs. His early pieces, dating from around 1888, often featured diagonal back panels, asymmetrical uprights, tassels, fringes, stamped brass and vellum covered wood. He was also influenced by Japanese styles and decorated his pieces with asymmetrical stylized motifs and floral medallions.

A Carlo Bugatti ebonised and inlaid open armchair, the seat-rail covered in beaten copper, above carved supports inlaid with pewter and bone.
(Christie's)   £2,420

One of two Bugatti arm-chairs inlaid with pewter and copper, circa 1900, 72cm. high.   £2,000

A Carlo Bugatti ebonized, inlaid and painted vellum side chair, the uprights with turned finials, above a rope tied rectangular vellum panel.
(Christie's London)   £2,640

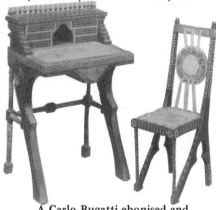

A Carlo Bugatti ebonised and inlaid writing desk inlaid with geometric patterns of bone and pewter together with a chair en suite.
(Christie's)   £2,090

A Carlo Bugatti side chair with an ebonised frame inlaid with pewter and having a studded back, circa 1900.   £2,000

Bugatti stand with stepped base, circa 1900, 130cm. high.   £2,500

A Carlo Bugatti vellum-covered and pewter inlaid centre-piece, the ebonised cross-shaped rotating superstructure inlaid in pewter with oriental motifs, with four end drawers, each with turned handle, 73cm. high.
(Christie's)   £3,960

An ebonised and rosewood Wellington chest, designed by Carlo Bugatti. £10,000

CARLO DUGATTI

A Bugatti selette with turned legs part wrapped in beaten copper, circa 1900. £990

A Carlo Bugatti two-seat sofa, the vellum-covered rectangular backrest painted with bamboo and arabic script and decorated with a beaten copper circular medallion, with tassel fringe. (Christie's) £3,080

A Bugatti side chair, the back inlaid in ivory and pewter, circa 1900, 90cm. high. £935

Small Bugatti side chair with tooled leather seat, circa 1900, 114cm. high. £2,500

A fine pair of side chairs designed by Carlo Bugatti. £7,500

A Carlo Bugatti ebonised and rosewood lady's writing desk with pewter and ivory inlay, 75.5cm. wide. (Christie's) £3,850

A Carlo Bugatti ebonised and inlaid table, the square top elaborately inlaid in pewter and bone, with circular and scrolling floral designs, on four turned and splayed legs, 74.5cm. high. (Christie's) £3,080

A Carlo Bugatti ebonized, inlaid and painted vellum table, the octagonal top with central vellum panel, painted with Arabic script, 74cm. high. (Christie's London) £7,480

A Carlo Bugatti ebonised and rosewood corner chair, the arched toprail on three turned columns with beaten brass panels and elaborate fringe. (Christie's) £1,430

CHARLES EAMES

Charles Eames was a leading American furniture designer whose work was much influenced by Bauhaus designs. In the 1940s he specialised in combining Bauhaus functionalism and new materials, such as plastics, to produce modern works which were typically American in spirit. Plywood too readily adapted itself to his designs, which tended to be moulded to follow the shape of the human body. Eames was one of several American designers working for pioneering manufacturers such as Herman Miller and Hans Knoll.

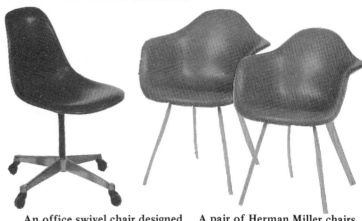

An office swivel chair designed by Charles Eames for Herman Miller, the orange shell upholstered with black leather. (Bonhams) £100

A pair of Herman Miller chairs with moulded fibreglass shells, designed by C. Eames. £200

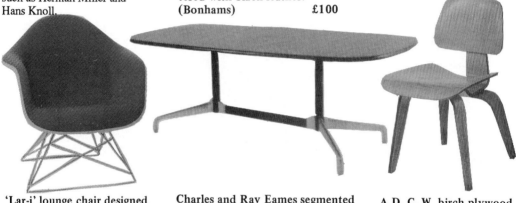

'Lar-i' lounge chair designed by Charles Eames for Herman Miller, the polyester shell seat with blue upholstery. (Bonhams) £500

Charles and Ray Eames segmented base table, design date 1972, manufactured by Herman Miller, rosewood veneer top, 78in. long. (Skinner Inc.) £323

A D. C. W. birch plywood chair designed by Charles Eames for Evans Products Company, 68cm. high. (Bonhams) £620

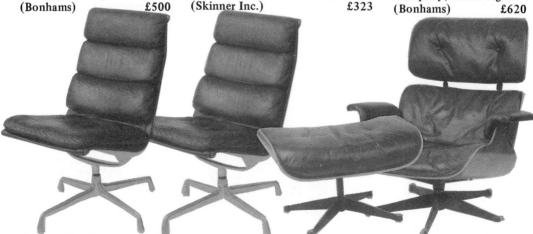

A pair of leather and aluminium lounge chairs, designed by Charles Eames for Herman Miller, the dark brown leather padded seat and back supported by an aluminium frame standing on a single swivel column. (Phillips) £500

A lounge chair and ottoman, designed by Charles Eames, the chair having black leather padded cushions supported by a moulded plywood frame, supported on a five-pronged pedestal, the ottoman of matching design, Herman Miller/Hille labels. (Phillips) £500

EMILE GALLE

While Emile Gallé is first and foremost associated with glass, from the 1880s he was also designing furniture. His pieces are often based on 18th century forms, and are characterised by their simple lines and naturalistic decoration. Plant forms are much in evidence, even for limbs and cross-section mouldings and Gallé also made much use of marquetry decoration in natural fruitwoods. His work is also sometimes inlaid with inscriptions, such as quotations from Baudelaire, and often titled.

A Gallé two-tier marquetry table, 87cm. high, circa 1910.   £375

A Gallé walnut and inlaid card table, the sides with halved panels depicting oriental figures representing the card suits, 66.6cm. high.
(Phillips)   £1,350

A Gallé marquetry sidetable, the rectangular tray top with two handles, inlaid in fruitwoods with a butterfly in a wooded landscape, 61.3cm. wide. (Christie's London)   £1,100

An Emile Gallé walnut and marquetry music stand, 90.4cm. high when not extended. (Christie's)   £972

A Gallé marquetry tray on stand, inlaid in various fruitwoods with five sailing boats, on carved trestle ends, 78cm. high.
(Christie's)   £880

A Gallé walnut and marquetry side table, the eared rectangular top inlaid in various fruitwoods with a spray of flowers, with inlaid signature Gallé, 73.1cm. high. (Christie's)   £550

A French marquetry etagere, the concave top inlaid with birds on flowering branches, on scroll supports, inlaid signature Gallé, 30½in. wide. (Christie's)   £1,540

A Gallé mahogany and marquetry two-tier etagere, signed in the marquetry Gallé, 59.3cm. wide. (Christie's)   £1,836

HEAL'S

While William Morris and his Arts & Crafts movement favoured a return to traditional handcraftsmanship, the middle classes also now wanted access to fashionable furniture, and this meant mass production. Their requirements were met by, among others, the firm of Heal's, whose head, Ambrose Heal (1872–1959) had begun to design furniture himself. It was Heal more than anyone who married the ideals of the Arts & Crafts movement with commercial expertise, and while Morris & Co's elegant designs were beyond the reach of all but the wealthiest, Heal featured good design at affordable prices in his Tottenham Court Road store.

His wares were publicised by means of illustrated catalogues, the first edition of which, Plain Oak Furniture, appeared in 1898. He named his styles after English seaside towns, and they had often a freshness and simplicity lacking in other commercially produced items. His beds, for example, were generally uncanopied, with plain, almost austere headboards and feet.

In 1900 Heal won a silver medal at the Paris Exhibition for a bedroom suite, and his success was assured. He was assisted by the fact that his furniture was eminently suitable for the growing number of suburban villas and houses which were being built in the new garden cities. His cottage bedsteads and later painted beds continued to couple simplicity of design with excellence of workmanship and he succeeded in his ambition to be remembered as having revived the true craftsmanship inspired by the ideals of Morris.

A Heal's oak writing desk, designed by Ambrose Heal, 152.3cm. wide. (Christie's) £2,640

A Heal's cherrywood dressing table and stool, the rectangular top with chamfered edge and shaped superstructure with triptych mirror, 130cm. high. (Christie's) £242

A mahogany four-poster bedstead, labelled Heal & Son, Makers of Bedsteads and Bedding, London W, 74in. wide, 92in. high. (Christie's) £3,520

A Heal's limed oak book-case table, of octagonal form, the top with stepped edge, above two shelves on trestle feet, 58cm. high. (Christie's) £220

A Heal & Sons Arts & Crafts oak wardrobe, with central mirrored door enclosing hanging space with single drawer below, 128.3cm. across. (Phillips London) £529

A small bedroom chair by Heal & Son covered in the original green and white linen, circa 1900. £150

HEAL'S

A Heal's oak blanket chest, the rectangular overhanging panelled top above plain panelled sides, on turned legs joined by plain stretchers, 93cm. wide. (Christie's London) £605

Heal & Sons fireside chair in weathered oak, with rush seat, circa 1930. £300

A Heal's sycamore kneehole desk, the rectangular top with semi-circular end, 133.4cm. wide. (Christie's) £440

Heal & Sons wardrobe in French walnut with hanging space in the centre section, circa 1930. £700

A Heal's oak book table, the hexagonal top on six gadrooned legs, 80.5cm. wide. (Christie's) £440

An Arts and Crafts oak dresser, attributed to Ambrose Heal, the plain sides extending to form the supports, 137cm. wide. (Lawrence Fine Art) £550

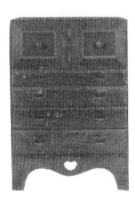

A Heal's painted 'Cottager's Chest', designed 1898-99, 106.5cm. wide. £2,000

Heal & Sons walnut framed settee with loose cushions and tapestry upholstery, circa 1930. £700

Heal & Sons escritoire in oak with ebony and pewter inlay, 3ft. 6in. wide, circa 1900. £1,000

LIBERTY FURNITURE

Furniture featured largely in the stock of Arthur Lazenby Liberty's London store.

He had formerly been manager of the Farmer & Rogers oriental warehouse in Regent Street, and it was therefore appropriate that he should continue to import eastern, Egyptian and Moorish furniture. He also commissioned designs for Moorish style smoking rooms, which owed much to the elaborate style of William Burges.

He later came under the influence of the Arts & Crafts movement and many Liberty pieces came to incorporate Quaint style features, such as unvarnished wood, or coloured wood inlays. The Quaint designer E G Punnett worked for Liberty, and some pieces were made by the noted chair makers, William Birch.

Liberty furniture was exported throughout Europe – in Belgium, for example, it was distributed by Serrurier-Bovy in Liège. Pieces were usually stamped or labelled Liberty & Co.

A Liberty & Co. tiled oak washstand, the tapering back and base similarly covered with narrow green tiles, 1.23m. high. (Phillips London) £650

A Liberty & Co. Ltd. oak sideboard, circa 1900, 137cm. long. £350

A Liberty & Co. walnut sideboard of bow fronted rectangular form on fine turned legs with shaped strecher shelf, 188cm. wide. (Christie's) £800

A Liberty & Co. oak washstand, the shaped superstructure with two tiled panels, above rectangular marble top flanked by two shelves, on bracket feet, 104cm. wide. (Christie's) £400

An Art Nouveau mahogany breakfront cabinet, probably made by Liberty, circa 1898, 139cm. wide. (Lawrence Fine Art) £550

One of a pair of Liberty oak folding stools, each consisting of ten slats forming X-shaped frames. (Christie's) £242

A Liberty oak dressing table with adjustable mirror, 132.6cm. wide with flaps extended. (Christie's) £432

LIBERTY

A Liberty & Co. walnut 'Thebes' stool, the square seat strung with brown hide. (Christie's) £880

A Liberty & Co. mahogany desk, the rectangular top having a drawer below flanked with three drawers on each side, 85.5cm. high. (Phillips London) £620

A Liberty and Co. oak stool with square curved seat, on straight square section legs joined by plain stretchers and diagonal struts. (Christie's) £605

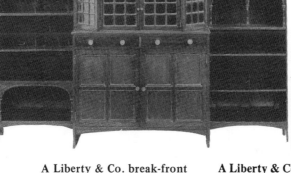

A Liberty & Co. oak corner cabinet, carved below the cornice with stylised leaves and foliage, with leaded glass doors enclosing shelves, 218cm. high. (Phillips London) £805

A Liberty & Co. break-front cabinet, shaped central glazed cupboard doors above rectangular top, flanked on each side with arched and columned open recesses and adjustable shelves, 122.5cm. wide. (Christie's) £550

A Liberty & Co. oak bookcase, the crested top having two leaded glass fronted doors, the base with two drawers above an enclosed cupboard, 1.21m. wide. (Phillips) £1,400

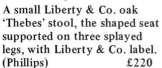

A small Liberty & Co. oak 'Thebes' stool, the shaped seat supported on three splayed legs, with Liberty & Co. label. (Phillips) £220

A Liberty & Co. inlaid mahogany armoire, England, circa 1905, 7ft. high. £750

An oak Liberty & Co. Moorish side chair, the back with tall turned finials, inset with three Moorish panels. (Christie's) £1,500

LIMBERT

Charles Limbert was a furniture designer and maker, working in Grand Rapids, Michigan, around 1900–10,. He must have been well acquainted with the two Stickley brothers, George and Albert, who were also active in the town at that period, and Limbert's output owes much to the inspiration of Gustav Stickley.

Limbert worked mainly in the Mission style, named from the furniture supposedly found in the Franciscan missions in California. His work is characterised by its simple, sturdy design, with exposed pegs and tenon ends often as the only decoration.

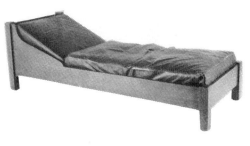

Limbert oak day bed, Michigan, circa 1910, shaped headrest and wide skirt accommodating spring cushions, square raised feet, 79in. long. (Robt. W. Skinner Inc.) £307

A magazine stand with cut-outs, Michigan, 1910, 20in. wide. (Robt. W. Skinner Inc.) £416

Limbert dining table, circa 1910, circular top over arched skirt connecting to four square legs, 51in. diameter. (Skinner Inc.) £571

Round table with caned pedestal base, probably Michigan, circa 1915, unsigned, (refinished), 36½in. diam. (Robt. W. Skinner Inc.) £215

Limbert double oval table with cut out base, Grand Rapids, Michigan, circa 1907 (bangs and stains on surface). (Robt. W. Skinner Inc.) £2,607

Limbert octagonal plant stand with cut-outs, Michigan, circa 1910, on box base with double trapezoidal cut-outs, 28½in. high. (Skinner Inc.) £926

Lifetime Furniture sideboard, Grand Rapids, Michigan, circa 1910, mirrored backboard, three central drawers flanked by cabinet doors over long lower drawer, 60½in. wide. (Skinner Inc.) £260

A cane-sided plant stand, probably Limbert, circa 1910, 23in. high, the top 16in. sq. (Robt. W. Skinner Inc.) £282

LIMBERT

A Limbert mirrored oak sideboard, Michigan, circa 1910, 54in. wide. (Robt. W. Skinner Inc.) £583

Limbert open-arm adjustable back rocker, circa 1910, no. 518, flat-arm over elongated corbels, original upholstered spring cushion seat, branded mark, 36¾in. high. (Skinner) £611

Limbert oak window bench, Grand Rapids, Michigan, 1907, with original leather cushion, branded mark (minor nicks), 24in. wide. (Skinner Inc.) £6,790

Three pieces of Limbert furniture, Grand Rapids, Michigan, circa 1910, open arm rocker, and matching armchair, both with straight crest rail, open-arm settle, with straight crest rail. (Skinner Inc.) (Three) £648

Limbert open book rack, Michigan, circa 1910, flat sides centring three open shelves, 28in. high. (Robt. W. Skinner Inc.) £399

Limbert round tall pedestal, circa 1906, no. 267, 32½in. high, 14in. diam. (Robt. W. Skinner Inc.) £630

A Limbert oval table with cut-out sides, Grand Rapids, Michigan, circa 1907, no. 146, 45in. long. (Robt. W. Skinner Inc.) £648

LIMBERT

A Limbert single door china cabinet, no. 1347, Grand Rapids, Michigan, circa 1907, 34¼in. wide. (Robt. W. Skinner Inc.) £1,027

A Limbert sideboard with arched mirrored backboard with corbel detail, Michigan, circa 1910, 47¾in. wide. £700

Limbert cellarette, circa 1908, no. 751, rectangular top projecting over single drawer with square copper pulls, 24¾in. wide. (Skinner Inc.) £538

Oak liquor cabinet with copper slide, probably Michigan, circa 1910, with fitted compartments, unsigned, 40¾in. high. (Skinner Inc.) £340

Unusual Limbert sideboard, Grand Rapids, Michigan, circa 1903, gallery top, three short drawers over three cabinet doors, single long drawer below, round copper and brass pulls, 59¼in. wide. (Skinner) £889

Limbert miniature book-case with heart cut-out gallery, circa 1910, 24in. wide. £750

Octagonal plant stand with cut-outs, Michigan, circa 1910, probably Limbert, with double trapezoidal cut-outs, 28in. high. (Skinner Inc.) £364

A Limbert mirrored sideboard, no. 1453 3/4, circa 1910, 48in. wide. £450

Limbert octagonal plant stand, style no. 251, circa 1910, 24¼in. high. (Robt. W. Skinner Inc.) £699

CHARLES RENNIE MACKINTOSH

Charles Rennie Mackintosh (1868–1928) was one of the seminal figures of the Art Nouveau/Deco period. He was apprenticed as an architect in Glasgow, during which time he also studied at the Glasgow School of Art, winning a scholarship to visit France and Italy in 1890. After this, he also began to design furniture. In 1897 he won the competition to design and furnish the new Glasgow School of Art.

Mackintosh became the leading figure in what came to be known as the Glasgow School. Other members of the group were Francis Newbery, the headmaster of the School of Art, and his wife, Mackintosh's own wife Margaret MacDonald and her sister Frances who married the remaining member, the architect Herbert MacNair.

Mackintosh strongly influenced the Vienna Secessionist movement, and his work generally found more acclaim abroad, especially in Germany and Austria, than it ever did in his own country. The keynote of Mackintosh's designs was simplicity of form, with long straight lines complementing gentle curves. Chairs have long attenuated backs and low seats; tables have slender tapering legs. Decoration was never allowed to dominate a piece, as was often the case with Continental Art Nouveau. His colour schemes tended to be light and delicate, and pieces were often painted white. He used stylized decorative motifs again and again so that they became almost a hallmark of his work. His favourite was a stylized rose inlaid in glass or ivory; groupings of small squares of coloured glass were also common.

Mackintosh also designed metalwork.

A tub armchair by Rennie Mackintosh for the Ingram Street Tea Rooms in Glasgow. (Christie's & Edmiston's) £3,000

A dark stained oak dining chair designed by Charles Rennie Mackintosh, 1897. £12,100

A stained oak cabinet designed by Charles Rennie Mackintosh, with beaten brass door panels signed by Margaret Macdonald and dated 1899, 182cm. wide. (Phillips) £115,000

A low back stained oak armchair designed by Charles Rennie Mackintosh, 1897. £5,000

An ebonized and painted corner cabinet, designed by Charles Rennie Mackintosh, with painted panels by Margaret Macdonald Mackintosh, the two cupboard doors with pierced hinge plates, circa 1897, 183cm. high. (Christie's) £13,200

An ebonised oak ladderback chair designed by Charles Rennie Mackintosh for the Willow Tearooms, Glasgow, the chair stamped number 24, the seat number 3, circa 1903, 41½in. high. (Christie's Glasgow) £21,450

LOUIS MAJORELLE

Louis Majorelle was born in France in 1859. He trained as a painter in Paris, but at the age of twenty took over his father's cabinet making business in Nancy, which had made 18th century reproduction furniture.

Majorelle however came under the influence of Emile Gallé, and began to produce Art Nouveau furniture in the Ecole de Nancy style, characterised by fluid, sculptural forms and often embellished with marquetry decoration and using local woods. He accepted many commissions for bedroom, dining room and drawing room suites, sometimes with ormolu decoration, and also produced some giltwood pieces. One characteristic feature of his designs is that flat surfaces such as table tops etc often curve upwards at the rim. After 1906 his furniture became much heavier in design.

Majorelle's factory also boasted a metalwork section, where mounts were made for the furniture and also for Daum vases and bowls.

A Louis Majorelle Art Nouveau walnut and rosewood vitrine, 188cm. high. (Phillips) £2,600

A Majorelle marquetry beech occasional table, the trefoil top inlaid in tulip and rosewood, 74.8cm. high. (Phillips) £520

Majorelle mahogany bed with semi-circular bed head, circa 1900, 201cm. wide. £1,000

Mahogany and burl walnut double bed by Louis Majorelle, circa 1897, 68½in. wide. £7,500

A Louis Majorelle inlaid and carved kingwood, mahogany and amaranth cabinet, the shaped overhanging top with three-quarter gallery above a single curved cupboard door, 59cm. wide. (Christie's) £22,000

A Majorelle side table, the top inlaid with floral marquetry, having three curved and sinuous moulded legs, with further leaf below, 90cm. high. (Phillips) £2,200

A Majorelle Etagere, in mahogany, on three legs, the front of sinuous organic form bifurcating to support the top shelf, the back solid with sinuous outline. (Phillips) £2,200

MISSION FURNITURE

The Mission Style of furniture which was immensely popular around the beginning of the 20th century was essentially the major American expression of the Arts & Crafts style which had recently evolved in England.

Its name derives from the fact that it was supposed to reflect the style of furniture found in the old Franciscan missions of California, and it was seen as a revival of medieval and functional designs.

Most pieces were made in oak, and the forms were rectilinear and as simple and functional as possible. Obvious signs of handiwork, such as exposed mortice and tenon joints were characteristic of the style. Mission furniture was often used in furniture schemes alongside Tiffany glass, Navajo rugs and Morris chairs.

The style flourished until around 1920, and mass-produced pieces are often found.

Mission oak double bed with exposed tenons, circa 1907, 58½in. wide. (Robt. W. Skinner Inc.) £1,351

A Mission oak magazine/wood carrier, circa 1910, 18in. high, 15¼in. wide. (Robt. W. Skinner Inc.) £267

Mission rectangular oak sideboard, circa 1910, 72in. wide. £750

Early 20th century Mission oak magazine stand with cut out arched sides, 49in. high. (Robt. W. Skinner Inc.) £312

Mission oak two-door china closet, no. 2017, circa 1910, 46½in. wide. (Robt. W. Skinner Inc.) £218

One of a pair of mahogany Mission oak beds, possibly Roycroft, circa 1912, 42in. wide. (Robt. W. Skinner Inc.) £406

Mission oak 'knock-down' table, unsigned, circa 1910, 30in. diam. (Robt. W. Skinner Inc.) £140

GERRIT RIETWELD

Gerrit Rietweld (1888–1964) was a Dutch furniture designer whose ideas revolutionised 20th century chair design. He used only rectangular, circular and cubic forms painted in primary colours and believed that design should reflect structure uncluttered by ornamentation. His Red and Blue Chair of 1917 was one of the landmarks of modern style.

From 1919 he joined De Stijl Group, whose theories were set out in De Stijl magazine.

He went on to design the asymmetrical chair (1923), with a flat arm rest on one side and an upright board on the other, and the Zigzag chair in 1934.

ROYCROFT

Elbert Hubbard (1856–1915) was an American soap manufacturer who became fired with enthusiasm for the Arts & Crafts movement after a visit to Britain in 1894. In 1895 he established the Roycroft shops, a craft community based in East Aurora, NY, to produce pieces in the Arts & Crafts style.

Thus they were one of the major manufacturers of Mission style furniture, mainly in oak and mahogany, often with leather seats and copper studs on armchairs. They also produced, between 1905–12, a kind of deck chair, with three slats in the back, which was known as the Morris chair. Their pieces were known as Aurora colonial furniture from 1905. In 1908 a copper workshop was set up, making bookends, trays, inkwells etc. Following his visit to England, Hubbard also bought a printing press, on which he printed some fine books, such as The Song of Songs, on handmade paper.

The '1919 Armchair' designed by Gerrit Rietweld of black painted bar construction. £10,000

'Military chair' by Gerrit Rietveld, the white painted rectangular back and seat on black painted bar frame, on rectangular section legs. (Christie's) £11,000

A Roycroft oak piano bench, N.Y., circa 1910, signed with logo, 36in. long. (Robt. W. Skinner Inc.) £1,428

Roycroft magazine pedestal, circa 1906, no. 080, overhanging square top, canted sides with keyed tenons, five shelves, carved oak leaf design, 64in. high. (Skinner) £1,989

Roycroft pedestal base lamp table, East Aurora, New York, circa 1910, with four curving legs joining in the middle, 29½in. high. (Skinner Inc.) £1,049

A Roycroft oak library table, East Aurora, New York, circa 1910, having two drawers and square tapered legs with shaped feet, 48in. wide. £1,000

ROYCROFT

Roycroft oak upholstered footstool, New York, circa 1910, no. 048, needlepoint cover, 10in. high. (Skinner Inc.) £230

A Roycroft oak bridal chest, East Aurora, New York, circa 1912, with extended serpentine sides, 36½in. wide. (Robt. W. Skinner Inc.) £3,857

Roycroft pedestal base dining table, East Aurora, New York, circa 1910, signed with logo, no leaves, 48in. diam. (Robt. W. Skinner Inc.) £1,288

Roycroft Little Journeys book stand, circa 1910, rectangular overhanging top over two lower shelves, keyed tenons, 26¼in. wide. (Skinner) £250

Roycroft "Ali Baba" bench, circa 1910, oak slab seat with some exposed bark underneath, plank ends joined by long centre stretcher, 42in. long. (Skinner) £833

Roycroft mirrored dressing table, East Aurora, New York, circa 1910, with swing handles, tapering MacMurdo feet, signed with orb, 39in. wide. (Skinner Inc.) £556

Roycroft oak chiffonier, East Aurora, New York, circa 1907, signed with *Roycroft* across front, 42in. wide. (Skinner Inc.) £3,704

Unusual Roycroft sewing table, East Aurora, New York, circa 1910, incised with logo, (some stains, one knob broken) 30in. wide. (Robt. W. Skinner Inc.) £982

Roycroft oak umbrella stand, East Aurora, New York, circa 1910, signed with logo, (finish partially removed) 29¾in. high. (Robt. W. Skinner Inc.) £307

GORDON RUSSELL

Sir Sydney Gordon Russell (b. 1892) was a famous English furniture designer and master craftsman, who established the Russell Workshops in Broadway, Worcs. making machine made versions of such traditional English designs as rush-seated, ladder backed chairs.

He specialised in the use of English woods such as oak and yew with the wood grain emphasising the linear design. From c 1930 onwards his work had a major influence on the styles of the 50s and 60s.

A Gordon Russell three-seat settee with rush seat, circa 1930, 176.5cm. wide. £1,000

An oak blanket chest designed by Gordon Russell, the lid with three wrought-iron strap hinges terminating in 'fleur-de-lys', with carved borders top and bottom, dated 20.6.27, 166.5cm. wide. (Christie's) £4,180

A Gordon Russell oak drop leaf centre table, the twelve sided moulded drop leaf top above four octagonal legs joined by chamfered stretcher, with swivel gate leg, 1930, 55.9cm. wide. (Christie's London) £935

A Gordon Russell mahogany desk, with five short drawers and solid trestle end joined by moulded stretcher, with chair en suite 106cm. wide. (Christie's) £660

A Gordon Russell walnut side cabinet, with open top shelf above a panelled door enclosing shelves, 76cm. high. (Phillips) £360

A Gordon Russell walnut chest of drawers, dated 29.10.30. £1,500

A Gordon Russell satin birch dwarf chest of drawers, two short and two long drawers, with moulded ebonised handles and stringing, on stepped trestle ends, 83.5cm. wide. (Christie's London) £2,090

A walnut and mahogany writing cabinet by Gordon Russell. £4,000

GORDON RUSSELL

A Gordon Russell walnut linen bag and frame, with a linen bag suspended within, 82.5cm. high. (Phillips) £320

A Gordon Russell quartered oak dining table, with octagonal panelled supports and pierced cross stretcher, made by G. Cooke, 1923, 5ft. 6in. x 2ft. 9in.(Hobbs & Chambers) £2,400

A Gordon Russell oak armchair, lacking drop-in seat, 1930's. £300

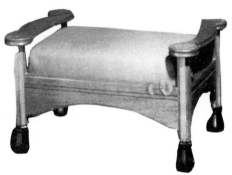

A Gordon Russell oak wardrobe, the moulded rectangular top above two panelled doors with brass ring drop handles, on rectangular legs, 136.5cm. wide. (Christie's) £2,530

A Gordon Russell walnut and ebony stool with shaped eared handles, on octagonal section legs with ebony chamfered bulbous feet. (Christie's) £3,630

A Gordon Russell oak wardrobe, together with an oak bed-head and end, 1930's, 138cm. wide. £1,500

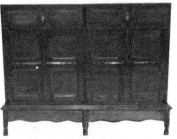

A mahogany side table, designed by Gordon Russell, with inlaid ebony and sycamore decoration, the rectangular top with undulating sides, 92cm. wide. (Christie's) £3,740

A Gordon Russell oak and chestnut sideboard, with chestnut tapering handles, shaped apron below, on octagonal supports, 1927, cabinet maker P. J. Wade, 4ft.5½in. wide. (Hobbs & Chambers) £1,700

A small Gordon Russell oak drop leaf gateleg occasional table with plank sides and pull-out supports, 51 x 82cm., extended. (Phillips) £650

GEORGE & ALBERT STICKLEY

Two of the famous Stickley family, George and Albert, set up their furniture workshop in Grand Rapids, Michigan in 1901. There, they produced furniture which owed much to the Craftsman style. (The Craftsman was a magazine published by their brother Gustav, which advocated the principles of the Arts & Crafts movement).

It was marketed as Quaint Furniture, and is generally inferior in terms of material, workmanship and design, to that turned out by their elder brother.

The Quaint, or Fanciful style was the name also given to the British trade version of the Art Nouveau style which flourished between c. 1895–1905. It combined elements of Anglo-Japanese, Arts & Crafts, Glasgow School and continental Art Nouveau furniture and was characterised by painted and inlaid floral motifs, heart-shaped apertures and ornate hinges.

With regard to decoration, 18th century forms were often used as the basic inspiration. Cabinets and armchairs had thin legs, and often six or eight of them, with low stretchers. Especially popular were versions of the Windsor chair and asymmetrical sofas. The woods used were mainly polished rosewood, fumed oak and cheap woods stained green or purple.

At its best Quaint furniture was restrained in form and decoration, whereas cheaper imitations tended to be over elaborate. Names of designers and manufacturers associated with the style include William Birch, George Ellwood, J S Henry and E G Punnett.

A Stickley Bros. sideboard, Grand Rapids, Michigan, 1912, 60in. wide. (Robt. W. Skinner Inc.)   £265

Stickley Brothers inlaid settle, Grand Rapids, Michigan, circa 1901, inlaid with flowers, leaves, grasses and other naturalistic motifs, unmarked, 51¾in. high. This settle, advertised in 1901, was influenced by the English Arts and Crafts movement. (Skinner)   £1,667

A Stickley Bros. slat-back settle, signed with paper label, Quaint, circa 1910, 72in. wide. (Robt. W. Skinner Inc.)   £2,432

GEORGE & ALBERT STICKLEY

Stickley Bros. set of drawers with swinging mirror, circa 1910, 38in. wide.   £400

Hinged oak box with glass lining, attributed to Stickley Bros., Michigan, circa 1910, 15½in. wide.   £400

Stickley Brothers chest of drawers, circa 1912, rectangular swivel mirror, two short drawers over three long drawers, 44in. wide. (Skinner Inc.)   £208

Stickley Bros. inlaid mahogany two-seater settee, Michigan, circa 1920.   £1,000

Stickley Brothers costumer, Grand Rapids, Michigan, circa 1914, no. 187, four iron hooks on post with corbelled cross-stretcher base, 68in. high. (Skinner Inc.)   £121

A Stickley Bros. spindle sided footstool, circa 1907, with stretchers centering seven spindles each side, unsigned, 20½in. wide. (Robt. W. Skinner Inc.)   £1,485

'Quaint Furniture' cafe table with copper top, Grand Rapids, Michigan, circa 1915, no. 2615, signed with metal tag, 18¼in. diameter. (Skinner Inc.)   £349

A marquetry panelled oak smoking rack, possibly Stickley Bros., Michigan, circa 1910, style no. 264-100, 22in. high, 24in. wide. (Robt. W. Skinner Inc.)   £81

Stickley Brothers flip-sided sewing table, Grand Rapids, Michigan, circa 1912, rectangular box with applied handle, 18in. wide. (Skinner Inc.)   £216

GUSTAV STICKLEY

The Arts & Crafts Movement found one of its greatest exponents in the USA in Gustav Stickley (1857–1942). He was the eldest of six brothers who all went into furniture making, though he at first trained as a mason.

In his youth he designed mainly chairs in the American Colonial style, but in 1898 he founded the firm of Gustav Stickley of Syracuse, New York, which specialised in the Arts & Crafts or Mission style of furniture (from the furniture supposedly found in the old Franciscan missions in California). He also published a magazine 'The Craftsman' which popularised this new style.

Like Art Nouveau, of which this was the American version, the style was seen as being a return to the simple functional style of the medieval period. Oak was the most popular wood, and construction was simple, often with obvious signs of handiwork, such as exposed mortice and tenon joints. Chairbacks were usually constructed as a series of flat vertical or horizontal boards.

Interestingly five of the brothers went into the same line of business, and the relationship between them seems to have been a highly political one. George and Albert worked in Grand Rapids, Michigan from 1891, and formed the firm of Stickley Bros. Co. around 1901. Their furniture is similar to the Craftsman style, often characterised by through tenons, but it was generally inferior in quality in terms of wood, design and finish. It was marketed as Quaint Furniture. They also produced independent designs similar to English cottage furniture.

A Gustav Stickley oak bed, designed by Harvey Ellis, 59½in. wide. (Robt. W. Skinner Inc.) £16,666

Gustav Stickley oak and wrought iron secretary, designed by Harvey Ellis, circa 1904, 56in. wide. (Robt. W. Skinner Inc.) £9,090

An inlaid oak three-panelled screen, designed by Harvey Ellis for Gustav Stickley, circa 1903-04, 66¾in. high, each panel 20in. wide. (Robt. W. Skinner Inc.) £10,714

An oak wastebasket, by Gustav Stickley, 1907, 14in. high, 12in. diam. (Robt. W. Skinner Inc.) £1,000

Gustav Stickley two-door wardrobe, circa 1907, two panelled doors with copper pulls opening to reveal two compartments, 34⅛ in. wide. (Skinner Inc.) £2,597

A three-sectioned oak screen, by Gustav Stickley, circa 1913, each panel 21½in. wide, 66in. high. (Robt. W. Skinner Inc.) £5,000

GUSTAV STICKLEY

The other two brothers, Leopold and J. George, were at first employed by Gustav but left his employment to found L. & J.G. Stickley at Fayetteville, in 1900. They too based their designs on Craftsman furniture, sometimes using veneers and laminated members, and their pieces are identifiable by the name L. & J.G Stickley in red. They were open to other influences, however, which may help to account for their survival, and made furniture designed by Frank Lloyd Wright, the Morris chair, and by 1914 were turning out reproduction furniture as well.

When one refers to 'Stickley' it is undoubtedly Gustav who springs most readily to mind. Certainly he was the most original designer of the family, he was also the purist, and his pieces are often austere in their unadorned simplicity. His brothers were perhaps more realistic in seeing that their products also had to find a market, and they were readier to compromise in terms of putting some embellishments on the basic style. It may have been Gustav's unwillingness to compromise his ideals that led to the break with Leopold and J. George, and it may also be why, by 1915, he was bankrupt. He attempted to soldier on, selling new lines based loosely on 18th century styles, or in bright colours, but to no avail. It was left to L. & J.G. to buy him out in 1916, when the business became the Stickley Manufacturing Co. Under this name it is still active, chiefly producing American Colonial reproduction furniture in cherrywood.

A Gustav Stickley spindle-sided baby's crib, no. 919, circa 1907, 56½in. long. (Robt. W. Skinner Inc.)
£833

A Gustav Stickley plate rack, circa 1904, 48in. wide. £1,500

Pair of Gustav Stickley oak twin beds, 40in. wide. (Robt. W. Skinner Inc.)
£2,500

A Gustav Stickley oak music cabinet, the ten pane single door with amber glass, circa 1912, 47¼in. high. (Robt. W. Skinner Inc.) £1,597

Gustav Stickley one door china closet, circa 1907, no. 820, 36in. wide. (Robt. W. Skinner Inc.) £902

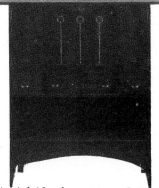

An inlaid oak secretary, designed by Harvey Ellis for Gustav Stickley, circa 1903-04, 42in. wide. (Robt. W. Skinner Inc.)
£55,357

GUSTAV STICKLEY BOOKCASES

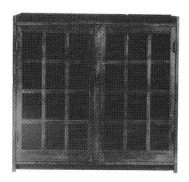

A two-door oak bookcase, twelve panels to each door, by Gustav Stickley, circa 1904, 48in. wide. (Robt. W. Skinner Inc.) £3,666

A Gustav Stickley oak bookcase, the door with wrought iron lock plate and drop loop handle, 98cm. wide. (Christie's) £1,296

A Gustav Stickley double-door bookcase, no. 719, circa 1912, 60in. wide. (Robt. W. Skinner Inc.) £2,142

Gustav Stickley leaded two-door bookcase, designed by Harvey Ellis, circa 1904, no. 716, 42¾in. wide. (Robt. W. Skinner Inc.) £1,539

A rare and important Gustav Stickley inlaid two door bookcase, designed by Harvey Ellis, circa 1903-1904, signed with red decal in a box, 55¾in. wide. (Robt. W. Skinner Inc.) £27,428

Gustav Stickley two-door bookcase, circa 1910, no. 716, gallery above eight-pane doors, 42in. wide. (Robt. W. Skinner Inc.) £1,329

A Gustav Stickley two-door bookcase, no. 718, signed with large red decal, circa 1904-05, 54in. wide. (Robt. W. Skinner Inc.) £2,250

Gustav Stickley leaded single door bookcase, designed by Harvey Ellis, circa 1904, no. 700, 36in. wide. (Robt. W. Skinner Inc.) £5,245

Gustav Stickley double door bookcase, Eastwood, New York, circa 1907, gallery top over two doors each with eight panes, 48in. wide. (Skinner Inc.) £1,224

GUSTAV STICKLEY CHAIRS

Rare Gustav Stickley oak Eastwood chair, circa 1902-1904, signed with a red decal in a box, 36in. wide. (Skinner Inc.) £11,728

A Gustav Stickley child's arm rocker, no. 345, signed with small red decal and paper label, circa 1904-06. (Robt. W. Skinner Inc.) £297

A Gustav Stickley willow armchair, circa 1907, 39in. high, 31in. wide. (Robt. W. Skinner Inc.) £277

Gustav Stickley mahogany bow armchair, circa 1907, no. 336, 36in. high. (Robt. W. Skinner Inc.) £1,110

A tall spindle-back armchair, no. 386, by Gustav Stickley, 49½in. high. (Robt. W. Skinner Inc.) £6,486

A Gustav Stickley bird's-eye maple wide slat cube chair, circa 1903-04, no. 328. (Robt. W. Skinner Inc.) £1,785

Gustav Stickley fixed back armchair, circa 1907, no. 324, flat arm over six vertical slats, 39in. high. (Robt. W. Skinner Inc.) £491

A Gustav Stickley slat-sided cube chair, no. 331, circa 1910, 25¼in. wide. (Robt. W. Skinner Inc.) £3,125

A Gustav Stickley bow arm-chair, no. 335, circa 1905, signed with small red decal, 37½in. high. (Robt. W. Skinner Inc.) £3,437

GUSTAV STICKLEY CHAIRS

A tall back, slat sided rocker with leather spring cushion by Gustav Stickley, 41½in. high.   £460

Rare leather sling seat arm chair, Toby Furniture Co., Chicago, circa 1900, design attributed to Gustav Stickley, unsigned, 33in. wide. (Skinner Inc.)   £1,790

A Gustav Stickley spindle-sided cube chair, no. 391, circa 1907, 26in. wide. (Robt. W. Skinner Inc.)   £9,523

Gustav Stickley revolving office chair, no. 361, circa 1904, signed with decal in a box, 28in. wide. (Robt. W. Skinner Inc.)   £909

Two of a set of five Gustav Stickley dining chairs with rush seats, circa 1907, 37in. high. (Robt. W. Skinner Inc.)   £1,062

A Gustav Stickley willow arm-chair, circa 1910, the tall back with square cut-outs centred by flat arms, unsigned, 42¾in. high. (Robt. W. Skinner Inc.)   £2,000

A bent arm spindle Morris chair, no. 369, by Gustav Stickley, with adjustable back, 24in. high. (Robt. W. Skinner Inc.)   £7,567

A Gustav Stickley oak 'East-wood' chair with original rope support for seat, circa 1902. (Robt. W. Skinner Inc.)   £16,666

One of a set of six Gustav Stickley dining chairs, including one armchair, circa 1907, 18in. wide. (Robt. W. Skinner Inc.)   £2,238

GUSTAV STICKLEY CHAIRS

A Gustav Stickley adjustable back drop armchair, no. 369, circa 1907, signed with red decal, 38in. high. (Robt. W. Skinner Inc.)   £2,812

Gustav Stickley inlaid oak side chair. £1,070

Gustav Stickley Morris chair, circa 1910, no. 332, adjustable back, five vertical slats, straight seat rail, unsigned, 40in. high. (Skinner Inc.)   £2,043

A leather upholstered dining chair, no. 355, by Gustav Stickley, circa 1910, 33¼in. high. (Robt. W. Skinner Inc.)   £513

Two of six V-back dining chairs, complete with dining table, by Gustav Stickley, circa 1907. (Robt. W. Skinner Inc.)   £2,333

A leather upholstered dining armchair, by Gustav Stickley, circa 1910, no. 355A, 36¼in. high. (Robt. W. Skinner Inc.)   £972

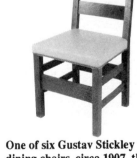

Gustav Stickley 'rabbit ear' armchair, 1901-02, signed, 41½in. high. (Robt. W. Skinner Inc.)   £385

A Gustav Stickley bent arm spindle Morris chair, circa 1907, with spring cushion seat. (Robt. W. Skinner Inc.)   £7,738

One of six Gustav Stickley dining chairs, circa 1907, three horizontal slats, new seats in cream coloured leather, 37½in. high.
(Skinner Inc.) (Six)   £1,610

GUSTAV STICKLEY CHESTS

A nine-drawer tall chest with cast bronze faceted pulls, by Gustav Stickley, circa 1904-06, 36in. wide. (Robt. W. Skinner Inc.) £3,783

An experimental Gustav Stickley cedar-lined chest, circa 1901-02, 27¾in. wide. £5,357

Gustav Stickley six-drawer chest, circa 1907, no. 902, reverse V splashboard, two half-drawers over four graduated drawers, signed with red decal, 52½in. high. (Skinner Inc.) £2,285

Gustav Stickley chest of drawers, circa 1907, two half drawers over three long drawers, 37in. wide. (Robt. W. Skinner Inc.) £1,166

Early Gustav Stickley six-drawer chest, circa 1902-04, no. 902, reverse V splashboard, two half-drawers over four graduated drawers with square wooden pulls, 40in. wide. (Skinner) £2,361

A Gustav Stickley work cabi-net, circa 1905-7, with two cabinet doors over two drawers with square wooden pulls, 36in. high. (Robt. W. Skinner Inc.) £8,000

Gustav Stickley smoker's cabinet, circa 1907, over-hanging top above single drawer and cabinet door, 20in. wide. (Robt. W. Skinner Inc.) £920

A Gustav Stickley nine-drawer tall chest, no. 913, circa 1907, 36in. wide, 50in. high. (Robt. W. Skinner Inc.) £2,500

A Gustav Stickley chest-of-drawers, no. 901, with wooden pulls, circa 1907, 37in. wide. (Robt. W. Skinner Inc.) £773

GUSTAV STICKLEY
DESKS

A Gustav Stickley drop-front desk, the doors opening to reveal a fitted interior, circa 1906, 38in. wide. (Robt. W. Skinner Inc.) £1,666

Early Gustav Stickley drop front desk, 1902-04, step-down gallery, chamfered drop front with copper strap hinges over two open shelves, 52in. high. (Skinner) £3,333

Gustav Stickley drop-front desk with cabinet doors, circa 1902-04, 32¾in. wide. (Robt. W. Skinner Inc.) £2,587

An early Gustav Stickley chalet desk, circa 1901-2, the arched gallery top with pierced corner cut-outs and keyed tenon sides, 45¾in. high. (Robt. W. Skinner Inc.) £914

Gustav Stickley slant lid desk, Eastwood, New York, circa 1907, gallery top, slant lid front over single drawer with brass v-pulls, 30in. wide. (Skinner Inc.) £489

An inlaid oak drop-front desk, designed by Harvey Ellis for Gustav Stickley, 1903-04, style no. 706, 30in. wide. (Robt. W. Skinner Inc.) £11,904

An oak drop-front desk, by Gustav Stickley, circa 1912, 32in. wide. (Robt. W. Skinner Inc.) £750

Gustav Stickley desk, circa 1912, letter file with two small drawers on rectangular top over two half drawers, 22¾in. wide. (Skinner Inc.) £343

A Gustav Stickley desk, no. 721, circa 1912, 29in. high. (Robt. W. Skinner Inc.) £252

GUSTAV STICKLEY
SETTEES & COUCHES

Gustav Stickley even arm settle, circa 1907, no. 208, straight rail over eight vertical slats on back, three on each end, with Southwestern designs, 76in. long. (Skinner Inc.) £4,570

Gustav Stickley knock-down settee, New York, circa 1907, 12in. wide horizontal back slat, 84in. long. (Skinner Inc.) £4,784

A Gustav Stickley panelled settle, no. 189, signed with large red decal with signature in a box, 1901-03, 84in. long. (Robt. W. Skinner Inc.) £3,720

An oak hall settle with leather covered spring cushion seat, by Gustav Stickley, 56in. wide. (Robt. W. Skinner Inc.) £1,750

A Gustav Stickley tall spindleback settee, no. 286, signed with decal, circa 1906, 48in. wide. (Robt. W. Skinner Inc.) £21,428

A Gustav Stickley slat-back settle, no. 206, circa 1904-06, 60in. wide. (Robt. W. Skinner Inc.) £8,928

A Gustav Stickley bird's-eye maple wide slat settee, no. 214, circa 1903-04, 50¼in. wide. (Robt. W. Skinner Inc.) £2,380

An early Gustav Stickley settle with arched slats, 1901-03, 60in. wide. (Robt. W. Skinner Inc.) £16,071

GUSTAV STICKLEY
SIDEBOARDS

Rare Gustav Stickley sideboard, circa 1902, the top shelf galleried on three sides, unsigned, 48in. wide. (Skinner Inc.) £1,882

Gustav Stickley desk, circa 1902-03, rectangular top over two banks of four short drawers, 54in. wide. (Skinner Inc.) £1,143

An oak chest with plate rack by Gustav Stickley, circa 1904, 69½in. wide. £2,750

Gustav Stickley oak sideboard, circa 1907, 56in. wide. £1,000

An oak sideboard, by Gustav Stickley, 1907, 66in. wide. (Robt. W. Skinner Inc.) £708

Gustav Stickley sideboard, circa 1907-12, no. 816, plate rack on rectangular top, long drawer over two central drawers, 48in. wide. (Skinner Inc.) £831

Gustav Stickley eight-legged sideboard, circa 1904, no. 817, with plate rack, 70in. wide. (Robt. W. Skinner Inc.) £4,895

Early Gustav Stickley sideboard, no. 967, with long copper strap hardware and square copper pulls, 60in. wide. (Robt. W. Skinner Inc.) £5,650

GUSTAV STICKLEY STANDS

A Gustav Stickley V-top bookrack, signed with red decal in a box, 1902-04, 31in. wide, 31in. high. (Robt. W. Skinner Inc.) £833

Gustav Stickley oak plant stand, circa 1903, 28in. high. £1,000

Gustav Stickley open slat-sided bookshelf, circa 1909, 27in. wide. (Robt. W. Skinner Inc.) £560

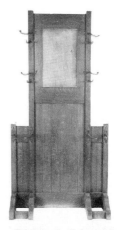

Gustav Stickley Toby magazine stand, circa 1904, square top with corbel supports, unsigned (top reglued), 43in. high. (Skinner Inc.) £368

Gustav Stickley inlaid tiger maple open music stand, circa 1904, no. 670, signed with Eastwood label, 39in. high. (Robt. W. Skinner Inc.) £5,069

Gustav Stickley hall tree, circa 1902–03, with four wrought iron hooks, 74in. high. (Skinner Inc.) £1,091

A Gustav Stickley three-drawer bedside stand, style no. 842, copper hardware with loop handles, circa 1907, 29½in. high. (Robt. W. Skinner Inc.) £763

An early Gustav Stickley leather fire-screen, 1902, 35in. high, 31in. wide. (Robt. W. Skinner Inc.) £1,190

A Gustav Stickley slat-sided folio stand, no. 551, 1902-03, 40½in. high, 29½in. wide. (Robt. W. Skinner Inc.) £1,785

GUSTAV STICKLEY
STOOLS

A Gustav Stickley mahogany footstool, no. 302, signed with red decal, 1905-05, 4½in. high. (Robt. W. Skinner Inc.) £562

Gustav Stickley footstool with cross stretcher base, circa 1902, no. 725, arched sides with leather upholstery and tacks, 16½in. wide. (Skinners) £667

A Gustav Stickley footstool with notched feet, style no. 726, circa 1902-04, 12¼in. wide. (Robt. W. Skinner Inc.) £378

A Gustav Stickley upholstered footstool with tacked leather surface, no. 300, circa 1905, 20½in. wide. (Robt. W. Skinner Inc.) £952

A Gustav Stickley mahogany footstool, circa 1904-1906, with upholstered seat, arched seat rail and exposed tenons, 20¼in. wide. (Robt. W. Skinner Inc.) £285

A leather upholstered footstool, no. 300, by Gustav Stickley, 20in. wide, circa 1905. (Robt. W. Skinner Inc.) £513

Gustav Stickley spindle-sided footstool, circa 1907, no. 395, 15in. high. (Robt. W. Skinner Inc.) £105

An oak piano bench with cut-out handles, by Gustav Stickley, circa 1907, 36in. wide. (Robt. W. Skinner Inc.) £916

A leather topped footstool, by Gustav Stickley, 20¼in. wide. (Robt. W. Skinner Inc.) £625

GUSTAV STICKLEY TABLES

A Gustav Stickley hexagonal leather-top table, no. 624, circa 1910-12, 48in. diam. (Robt. W. Skinner Inc.) £4,166

Gustav Stickley table, circa 1912–16, no. 626, round top on four legs, joined by arched cross stretchers with finial, 40in. diameter. (Skinner Inc.) £623

A Gustav Stickley round library table, no. 633, circa 1904, 48in. diam. (Robt. W. Skinner Inc.) £1,180

A Gustav Stickley square table with cut corners, no. 612, circa 1905-06, signed with small red decal, 29¾in. sq. (Robt. W. Skinner Inc.) £593

An occasional table with cut corners, possibly early Gustav Stickley, circa 1902-04, 29in. high. (Robt. W. Skinner Inc.) £594

An occasional table, no. 609, by Gustav Stickley, circa 1904-05, unsigned, 36in. diam. (Robt. W. Skinner Inc.) £486

Gustav Stickley tabouret, no. 603, circa 1907, round top on four square legs, cross stretcher base, 18in. diameter. (Skinner Inc.) £403

A leather top library table with three drawers, by Gustav Stickley, 66½in. wide. £1,500

Gustav Stickley round oak table, circa 1904, 24in. diam. £1,000

GUSTAV STICKLEY TABLES

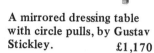

Gustav Stickley hexagonal top library table, circa 1904, no. 625, 48in. diam. (Robt. W. Skinner Inc.) £3,986

A mirrored dressing table with circle pulls, by Gustav Stickley. £1,170

A spindle-sided table with lower shelf, by Gustav Stickley, circa 1905, 36in. wide. £2,820

A Gustav Stickley round leather-top table, no. 645, circa 1907, 36in. diam. (Robt. W. Skinner Inc.) £1,250

Gustav Stickley table with twelve Grueby tiles, 1902-1904, four flat rails framing 4in. green tiles, 24in. wide. (Skinner Inc.) £12,346

Early Gustav Stickley table, circa 1902–03, no. 439, round top with four cut-in leg posts, 30in. diameter. (Skinner Inc.) £571

Gustav Stickley round library table, circa 1907, no. 636, with diagonal chamfered legs and arched cross stretcher with keyed tenons, unsigned, 48in. diameter. (Skinner Inc.) £753

An oak director's table with trestle base, by Gustav Stickley, 96½in. long. £9,166

A drop-leaf table, by Gustav Stickley, no. 638, circa 1912, 42in. long, 40in. wide, open. (Robt. W. Skinner Inc.) £1,513

GUSTAV STICKLEY

Gustav Stickley inlaid music cabinet, designed by Harvey Ellis, circa 1904, the flat overhanging top above the flat sides centering cabinet door with two inlaid recessed panels over four lower vertical sections, lower arched skirt, signed with decal in a box, 50in. high. (Skinner Inc.)   £24,285

The Eastwood chair was the largest production chair made by Gustav Stickley. It was first seen in the November 1901 edition of 'The Craftsman', and was still featured in Stickley's 1913 catalogue. Despite being in production for 12 years it remains one of the rarest Stickley pieces. (Skinner Inc.)   £16,666

GUSTAV STICKLEY

Rare and important Gustav Stickley inlaid two-door bookcase, designed by Harvey Ellis, circa 1903-1904 with single central vertical mullion and glass panels, centred by four square fruitwood floral inlaid medallions, 55¾in. wide. (Skinner Inc.) £27,428

Gustav Stickley table with twelve Grueby tiles, 1902-1904, the four flat rails framing four-inch green tiles over arched skirt and lower rectangular shelf with keyed tenons, slight splay to legs, dark finish, signed with red decal, 24in. wide. (Skinner Inc.) £12,346

L & J G STICKLEY

Leopold and J George Stickley were younger brothers of the famous Gustav, with whom they obviously enjoyed a somewhat complicated relationship. They were at first employed by him in his firm at Syracuse, New York, but in 1900 left to found their own establishment, L & J G Stickley at Fayetteville. Like Gustav, they based their designs on Craftsman furniture, sometimes using veneers and laminated members, and their pieces are identifiable by the name L & J G Stickley in red.

Unlike Gustav, however, they were also open to other influences, and were perhaps more realistic in seeing that their products also had to find a market. They were certainly readier to compromise in terms of putting some embellishments on the basic style. They later made furniture designed by Frank Lloyd Wright and by 1914 were turning out reproduction pieces as well.

They bought out their elder brother in 1916, when the firm, still in existence today, became the Stickley Manufacturing Co.

L. & J.G. Stickley davenport bed, circa 1912, no. 285, seat rail slides out opening to a bed, 77in. long.
(Skinner Inc.) £831

L. & J. G. Stickley oak double bed, Fayetteville, New York, circa 1910, signed, 50in. high, 58in. wide.
(Skinner Inc.) £3,241

L. & J. G. Stickley china closet, circa 1912, no. 746, overhanging top above two doors with six smaller panes above single glass panel, 62in. high.
(Skinner) £2,639

An L. & J. G. Stickley slatted double-bed, signed with red (Handcraft) decal, 58in. wide.
(Robt. W. Skinner Inc.) £5,952

L. & J. G. Stickley square drink stand, Fayetteville, New York, circa 1910, signed with Handcraft decal, 27in. high. (Skinner Inc.) £370

L. & J.G. Stickley settle, circa 1912, no. 216, straight crest rail, seven vertical slats across back, 72in. wide.
(Skinner Inc.) £1,195

L. & J.G. Stickley footstool, Syracuse and Fayetteville, New York, circa 1918, no. 397, signed with decal, 20in. wide.
(Skinner Inc.) £255

L & J.G. STICKLEY BOOKCASES

A double door bookcase, by L. & J. G. Stickley, circa 1912, 48¾in. wide. £1,500

L. & J. G. Stickley single door bookcase, circa 1907, no. 643, gallery top with exposed key tenons over single door, 36in. wide. (Robt. W. Skinner Inc.) £1,227

L. & J. G. Stickley three door bookcase, circa 1906, no. 647, gallery top and exposed key tenons over three doors, unsigned, 70in. wide. (Robt. W. Skinner Inc.) £2,454

An L. & J. G. Stickley two-door bookcase, no. 654, circa 1910, 50in. wide. (Robt. W. Skinner Inc.) £1,875

L. & J. G. Stickley narrow bookcase with adjustable shelves, circa 1912, no. 652, 22in. wide. (Robt. W. Skinner Inc.) £1,189

Onondaga double door bookcase, by L. & J. G. Stickley, circa 1902-04, 56½in. high. (Robt. W. Skinner Inc.) £1,328

L. & J. G. Stickley two door bookcase, Fayetteville, New York, circa 1907, unsigned, (escutcheons replaced) 42in. wide. (Skinner Inc.) £1,914

L. & J. G. Stickley two-door bookcase, style no. 645, circa 1912, 49in. wide. (Robt. W. Skinner Inc.) £1,748

L. & J. G. Stickley single door bookcase with keyed tenons, no. 641, circa 1906, 36in. wide. (Robt. W. Skinner Inc.) £1,500

L & J.G. STICKLEY

Rare L. & J.G. Stickley spindle 'Prairie' settle, circa 1912, no. 234, the broad even sided flat crest rail over spindles and seven arched corbels, two-section seat, unsigned, 86in. wide. (Skinner Inc.) £48,571

Stickley work cabinet, circa 1905-07, with two cabinet doors over two drawers with square wooden pulls, panelled sides, arched corbel centering lower shelf with exposed keyed tenons, 36in. high. (Skinner Inc.) £8,000

L & J.G. STICKLEY

L. & J.G. Stickley mantel clock,
Fayetteville, New York, circa 1910,
designed by Peter Heinrich Hansen,
with circular copper dial, applied
squares and pendulum window,
canted base, signed with Handcraft
decal, 22in. high.
(Skinner Inc.) £4,630

L. & J.G. Stickley Morris style
easy chair in oak with flat arms
enclosing rectangular panels
with vertical slats, having leather upholstery and cushion seat,
circa 1910.
(Skinner Inc.) £2,500

L & J.G. STICKLEY CHAIRS

An L. & J. G. Stickley adjustable back flat armchair, no. 412, circa 1909, 35in. wide. (Robt. W. Skinner Inc.)
£1,607

L. & J.G. Stickley rocker, circa 1910, no. 837, concave crest rail over four vertical slats, spring cushion seat, 39in. high. (Skinner Inc.)
£247

L. & J.G. Stickley adjustable back armchair, Fayetteville, New York, c. 1909, no. 470, flat arm with arched support, 27½in. wide. (Skinner Inc)
£496

L. & J. G. Stickley tall back armchair, with spring cushion seat, no. 837, circa 1907, 44in. high. (Robt. W. Skinner Inc.)
£350

Two of a set of six Stickley Bros. dining chairs, including one armchair, circa 1908. (Robt. W. Skinner Inc.)
£594

A slat sided armchair with cushion seat, by L. & J. G. Stickley, circa 1912.
£830

L. & J. G. Stickley fixed back armchair, circa 1912, with upholstered spring cushion seat with back cushion, unsigned, 32in. high. (Robt. W. Skinner Inc.)
£2,714

L. & J. G. Stickley slat-sided armchair, circa 1912, style no. 408, 26½in. diam. (Robt. W. Skinner Inc.)
£839

L. & J.G. Stickley fixed back armchair, Fayetteville, New York, circa 1910, no. 438, four horizontal back slats, 24½in. high. (Skinner Inc.)
£364

L & J.G. STICKLEY DESKS

Gateleg dropfront desk, circa 1912, arched gallery top and flat sides, branded *The Work of L. & J. G. Stickley,* 31½in. wide. (Robt. W. Skinner Inc.) £521

An L. & J. G. Stickley flat top writing desk, circa 1905, 40in. wide. (Robt. W. Skinner Inc.) £327

An L. & J. G. Stickley drop-front writing desk, no. 613, writing surface with fitted interior, circa 1910, 32in. wide. (Robt. W. Skinner Inc.) £406

L. & J. G. Stickley writing desk and chair, circa 1912, desk no. 610, chair no. 913, letter rail on rectangular top over single drawer, lower shelf with kneehole; chair with curved crest rail, both branded "The Work of L. & J. G. Stickley". £296

L. & J. G. Stickley single drawer desk, Fayetteville, New York, circa 1910, no. 520, rectangular top, single drawer with copper pulls, with short corbel supports, lower median shelf through-tenon, 36in. wide. (Skinner Inc.) £442

MAGAZINE RACKS

An L. & J. G. Stickley magazine rack, no. 45, circa 1912, 44½in. high. (Robt. W. Skinner Inc.) £812

L. & J. G. Stickley magazine and bookcase, circa 1910, 48in. wide. £1,000

An L. & J. G. Stickley slat-sided magazine rack, no. 46, circa 1910, signed with decal, 42in. high. (Robt. W. Skinner Inc.) £1,312

L & J.G. STICKLEY
SETTEES & COUCHES

Rare L. & J. G. Stickley spindle 'Prairie' settle, circa 1912, no. 234 the broad even sided flat crest rail over spindles, two section seat, unsigned, 86in. wide. (Robt. W. Skinner Inc.) £48,571

An L. & J. G. Stickley slat-back settle, style no. 281, with spring cushion seat, circa 1912, 76in. wide. (Robt. W. Skinner Inc.) £1,111

A panelled prairie settle with spring cushion seat, by L. & J. G. Stickley, circa 1912, 29in. deep. (Robt. W. Skinner Inc.) £7,500

L. & J.G. Stickley prairie settle, Fayetteville, New York, circa 1912, no. 220, wide flat arms and crest rail supported by corbels over inset panels, 84$\frac{1}{2}$in. wide. (Skinner Inc.) £9,870

SIDEBOARDS

L. & J. G. Stickley sideboard, circa 1912, panelled plate rail with corbels, (refinished, some stains and scratches) 54in. wide. (Skinner Inc.) £798

An oak sideboard with plate rack and slightly arched apron, by L. & J. G. Stickley, 54in. wide. (Skinner Inc.) £416

L. & J. G. Stickley sideboard, circa 1910, no. 738, rectangular plate rack on corresponding top, two long drawers flanked by cabinet doors, 60in. wide. (Skinner Inc.) £2,278

L. & J. G. Stickley sideboard, circa 1912, no. 734, plate rack with corresponding rectangular top over three drawers flanked by cabinet doors over single long drawer, 48in. wide. (Skinner Inc.) £1,056

L & J.G. STICKLEY STANDS

An open-sided music stand, possibly by Stickley, circa 1907, 39in. high. (Robt. W. Skinner Inc.) £245

L. & J. G. Stickley dinner gong, Fayetteville, New York, 1912, arched frame supporting circular bronze gong. (Robt. W. Skinner Inc.) £4,294

A drink stand, by L. & J. G. Stickley, no. 587, circa 1912, 16in. sq. (Robt. W. Skinner Inc.) £351

TABLES

An L. & J. G. Stickley occasional table, no. 543, circa 1912, 29¼in. diam. (Robt. W. Skinner Inc.) £187

A tabouret with cut corners, by L. & J. G. Stickley, no. 560, circa 1912, 16in. wide. (Robt. W. Skinner Inc.) £405

L. & J. G. Stickley oak server with open plate rack, circa 1912, no. 750, 48in. wide. (Robt. W. Skinner Inc.) £350

Ł. & J. G. Stickley dining table, circa 1912, no. 722, round top, straight apron cross stretcher base tenoned through square legs, with three leaves, 48in. diameter. (Skinner) £722

A library table with one drawer, by L. & J. G. Stickley, signed with Handcraft label, 42in. wide. (Robt. W. Skinner Inc.) £513

L. & J.G. Stickley dining table, no. 720, circa 1912, overhanging top supported by five legs, signed *"The Work of L. & J.G. Stickley"*, 54in. diameter. (Skinner Inc.) £1,290

GERALD SUMMERS

Gerald Summers (1899–1968) trained originally in London as an engineer. He first ventured into furniture design when he made some pieces for his wife's bedroom, and then, in the early 1930s, in partnership with her, formed the company known as The Makers of Simple furniture. They had a workshop off Tottenham Court Road and a showroom in Charlotte Street, and supplied such leading stores as Harrod's, Heal's and Fortnum's. Summer's bent plywood armchair is now seen as something of a milestone in English furniture design.

A laminated circular two tier low table by Gerald Summers, on drum base 40.2cm. high; 73.9cm. wide. (Christie's) £660

A Makers of Simple Furniture laminated beechwood kneehole desk designed by Gerald Summers, the overhanging rectangular top with D-end, 72.5cm. high. (Christie's) £495

A Makers of Simple Furniture laminated birch tea-trolley by Gerald Summers, consisting of three keyhole-shaped shelves, 43.9cm. (Christie's) £2,860

A white-painted plywood desk, the design attributed to Gerard Summers, circa 1930. £750

A Makers of Simple Furniture laminated birch armchair designed by Gerald Summers, cut and shaped to form a curved top rail with central splat and curved arms extending into plank legs. £5,500 (Christie's)

A Makers of Simple Furniture beechwood towel horse designed by Gerald Summers, the shaped form divided at the base, white painted, 77cm. high. (Christie's) £330

A laminated beechwood two-tier low circular table designed by Gerald Summers for The Makers of Simple Furniture, 73.3cm. diam. (Christie's) £1,620

One of a pair of birch laminated side chairs by Gerald Summers. (Christie's) £3,740

ROBERT (MOUSEMAN) THOMPSON

It was in the early years of this century that Robert Thompson went to work in his father's joinery in Kilburn, Yorkshire, serving the needs of the local farmers.

In the local churches and abbeys, however, Robert saw the magnificent work of the medieval craftsmen in wood, and became convinced that work of similar quality and style could be made for domestic use.

Only seven miles from Kilburn is the Abbey and College of Ampleforth, and when Father Paul Nevill wanted some furniture, he commissioned Robert Thompson to make it. It was the opportunity which was to make him famous.

Thereafter Thompson worked exclusively in English oak. He insisted on natural, out-of-doors seasoning, maintaining that kiln drying would destroy its character. His work is also characterised by the frequent use of the adze, used to produce the fine ripple effect on the surface of many of his pieces.

A Robert Thompson Mouseman oak cupboard, of rectangular two door construction with adze-finish, carved with a mouse, 108.5cm. wide.
(Lawrence Fine Art) £1,320

A Robert 'Mouseman' Thompson oak double bed, on casters, the panelled adze finished headboard carved with two rosettes and with three grotesque carved terminals, 152cm. wide.
(Christie's) £1,100

A Robert 'Mouseman' Thompson oak buffet, the rectangular top above a plain frieze, on octagonal section legs with platform shelf, 182cm. wide.
(Christie's) £1,980

A Robert 'Mouseman' Thompson oak chest of drawers, the rectangular, moulded and chamfered top above two short and three long drawers, 91.5cm. wide. (Christie's) £1,210

A Robert 'Mouseman' Thompson oak dresser, the overhanging rectangular top with carved frieze and inscription _J.M.C 1929_, on bracket feet, 169cm. wide.
(Christie's) £990

A pair of Robert 'Mouseman' Thompson oak armchairs, each with horseshoe arms and back, carved with two cats' heads and shaped terminals, dated 1928.
(Christie's) £1,980

A Robert 'Mouseman' Thompson oak dressing table, with rectangular cheval mirror on rectangular, moulded and chamfered top, on two pedestals each with three short drawers and eight octagonal feet, 106.7cm. (Christie's) £2,090

C F VOYSEY

Charles F Annesley Voysey (1857–1941) was an architect and prolific designer of furniture, textiles, carpets, tapestries, wallpapers, ceramics and metalwork. He set up his own practice in 1882 and the following year designed his first wallpapers and textiles. He was much influenced at this time by Arthur Mackmurdo of the Arts & Crafts Exhibition Society and the Century Guild. Voysey also exhibited at the former in 1893.

Voysey's furniture was much in the spirit of the Arts & Crafts Movement, rectilinear in form, with little embellishment, and executed mainly in oak.

A pair of oak side chairs designed by C. A. Voysey, each back splat pierced with heart-shaped motif, on square section legs joined by plain stretchers. (Christie's London)   £7,150

An Arts and Crafts oak armchair showing the influences of the designs of C. F. A. Voysey, the woven fabric 'slung' combined back and seat held by large brass hemispheres. (Phillips)   £340

A German oak green stained writing desk in the style of C. A. Voysey, 110.5cm. wide. (Christie's)   £3,520

An oak desk top stationery cabinet designed by C. F. A. Voysey, rectangular section, with single panelled cupboard door applied with shaped panel with pieced heart-shaped motif, 38.7cm. high. (Christie's)   £1,000

An oak side chair designed by C. F. A. Voysey, the back with arched back rail and square section finials, the central back splat pierced with heart-shaped motif. (Christie's)   £3,500

A set of four Pilkington six inch tiles, designed by C. F. A. Voysey. (Phillips London)   £440

A pair of oak armchairs by C. F. A. Voysey, circa 1898.   £15,000

A printed velvet curtain designed by C. A. Voysey, 262 x 239.5cm. (Christie's)   £2,592

PETER WAALS

Peter Waals (1870–1937) was a Dutch cabinet maker who worked mainly in England. He was employed first by S & E Barnsley and then, from 1901, by E W Gimson. Both of these were leading exponents of the Cotswold School, an association of furniture designers and craftsmen in Gloucestershire, which flourished from 1893. Their aim was to link traditional rural craftsmanship with the Arts & Crafts Movement. Waals rose to become foreman in charge at Gimson's establishment at Daneway House, Sapperton, and carried on the traditions after Gimson's death.

An oak wardrobe designed by Peter Waals, of rectangular form, the two cupboard doors each with four panels and wooden latch, 182.5cm. high. (Christie's) £2,200

Solid walnut breakfront wardrobe, designed by Peter Waals, with panelled cupboard doors. £3,000

A Peter Waals walnut dressing table with rectangular cheval mirror, 116.4cm. wide. £1,000

An oak bedside cabinet with bronze drop handles, by P. Waals assisted by P. Burchett, 1928, 78.9cm. high. (Christie's) £1,296

A Peter Waals rosewood bookcase, the lower part with two pairs of cupboard doors, on plinth base and bracket feet, 166cm. wide. (Christie's London) £1,100

An oak centre table framed by chequered inlaid lines executed by Peter Waals assisted by P. Burchett, 1928, 68.3cm. wide. (Christie's) £1,512

A Peter Waals ebony cabinet on stand, circa 1920, 73.5cm. wide, with key. £6,050

A walnut writing table by Peter Waals, with barber's pole inlay, on moulded tapering legs, 94cm. wide. (Christie's) £1,870

GLASS BOWLS

A Loetz iridescent glass bowl with an everted rim and having six loop handles, exhibiting a green, gold and mauve iridiscent skin, 21.3cm. diam. (Phillips) £900

'Lys', a Lalique opalescent bowl, the clear and satin-finished glass moulded with four lilies, the stems forming the feet of the bowl, 23.9cm. diameter. (Christie's) £990

A Daum acid-etched and enamel painted bowl, the mottled clear, green and yellow glass decorated with polychrome enamelled wooded landscape, 19.8cm. diameter. (Christie's) £2,200

'Ondine', a Lalique opalescent glass bowl, the under side moulded with six sea sprites, with wheel-carved signature *R. Lalique France*, 21cm. diameter. (Christie's) £880

An Orvit cameo glass, mounted punch bowl, cameo carved with four stylised designs of alternating grapes on vines and grape leaf clusters, 12in. high. (Robt. W. Skinner Inc.) £887

Libbey lovebirds cut glass bowl, shallow form in the Wisteria pattern with crosshatch border, 8in. diameter. (Skinner Inc.) £216

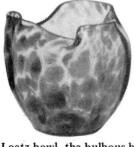

A Loetz bowl, the bulbous body with a drawn trefoil rim, the clear glass internally decorated with a pattern of blue and glittery-green spots, 14.6cm. high. (Christie's) £286

An Argy-Rousseau pate-de-verre bowl, with moulded decoration of three reserves with a ballerina in white taking her bow, surrounded by stylised rose border, on a mottled yellow ground, 6.3cm. high. (Christie's) £3,520

A Gabriel Argy-Rousseau pate de verre bowl, overlaid in shades of green and red with berried branches, 7cm. high. (Christie's London) £2,420

GLASS BOWLS

A Gallé twin-handled cameo glass bowl, the translucent body overlaid with orange glass acid-etched with sunflowers and foliage, 8.5cm. high.
(Phillips) £4,200

'Perruches'. A Lalique opalescent glass bowl moulded with love birds amid flowering prunus branch heightened with blue staining, 23.5cm. diameter.
(Phillips) £700

A Loetz white metal overlay bowl, clear glass splashes with golden iridescence, decorated with curvilinear flowers and foliage, 5^1/$_4$in. high.
(Christie's S. Ken) £209

A Lalique opalescent bowl with beads graduating inside and forming a swirling pattern, 20cm. long.
(Phillips) £275

An Almeric Walter pâte-de-verre cache-pot, modelled by H. Bergé, the mottled white and blue pot moulded with green and red leaves and berries, 13cm. high. (Christie's) £2,420

'Calypso', a Cristal Lalique opalescent glass bowl, moulded on the underside with five mermaids swimming amid angular waves, 35.5cm. diam.
(Phillips) £4,000

A Daum Art Deco glass bowl overlaid with olive-green transparent glass acid-etched with a geometric design of birds on foliate branches, 22.5cm. high. (Phillips) £1,900

A 'Le Verre Français' cameo glass jardinière, of yellow tone streaked with turquoise-green overlaid with red glass shading to reddish-brown, 17.50cm. high.
(Phillips) £900

A Gabriel Argy-Rousseau pâte-de-verre pedestal glass bowl, the exterior moulded with a green and blue vine leaf pattern, 13cm. diameter.
(Bearne's) £2,700

GLASS CANDLESTICKS

A pair of Venini black and white glass candlesticks each modelled as kneeling blackamoors holding baskets, 6³/₄ in. high. (Christie's S. Ken) £495

Tiffany Studios bronze and favrile glass candleholder, candlecup with seven green iridescent jewelled glass inserts, 8in. high. (Robt. W. Skinner Inc.) £932

Tiffany bronze and blown-out glass chamberstick, circa 1915, 6in. high. £450

Pair of bronze floriform candlesticks, attributed to Jarvie, Chicago, circa 1902, 14in. high. (Robt. W. Skinner Inc.) £1,675

A Tiffany Studios bronze candelabrum, with blown-out green Favrile glass in each holder, New York, 12in. high. (Robt. W. Skinner Inc.) £1,301

Pair of gold Aurene candlesticks, baluster and ring-turned shaft on cupped pedestal foot, 8¹/₄ in. high. (Skinner Inc.) £427

A Tiffany 'Favrile' glass candlestick in iridescent gold, 4½in. high. (Du Mouchelles) £180

A pair of Tiffany Favrile pastel candle holders, lavender opalescent optic pattern with squared bobeche rim, 3½in. high. (Robt. W. Skinner Inc.) £192

One of a pair of Venini candlesticks designed by Fulvio Bianconi, each modelled as a white jacket on a tripartite coatstand, 8¹/₄ in. high. (Christie's S. Ken)(Two) £1,430

GLASS DECANTERS

A Guild of Handicraft decanter, designed by C.R. Ashbee, the green Powell glass mounted with a hammered silver neck set with five chrysoprase, with London hallmarks for 1903, 23cm. high. (Christie's) **£1,980**

A Continental dark green faceted decanter with clear stopper and pierced silver foot mount, 1930, 29.5cm. (Osmond Tricks) **£85**

A Venini Vetro Pesante Inciso decanter and stopper, designed by Paolo Venini, of topaz glass cased in clear, 22cm. high. (Christie's London) **£264**

A Gallé enamelled decanter and stopper, the green tinted glass polychrome enamelled with the suit of hearts picture cards flanked by an ace and ten, 34.8cm. high. (Christie's) **£2,970**

A pair of silver mounted decanters, circa 1910, each of pinched quatrefoil section with facet cut spherical stopper, 27.5cm. overall, Sheffield, 1910. (Lawrence Fine Art) **£121**

A liqueur decanter and stopper by Moser of Karlsbad, decorated with floral motifs and trailing stems in mauve, ruby and green glass appliqués, 17.5cm. high. (Phillips) **£550**

A Hukin & Heath electroplated metal and glass 'crow's foot' decanter, designed by Dr. Christopher Dresser, stamped *H&H*, and with registration lozenge for 1878, 24cm. high. (Christie's) **£13,750**

A Hukin & Heath electroplated tantalus designed by Dr. Christopher Dresser, the open rectangular square-section frame with sliding and locking front stretcher, registration lozenge for 1879, 28cm. high. (Christie's) **£5,500**

A Hukin & Heath silver, glass and ivory decanter, the design attributed to Dr. Christopher Dresser, faceted cut glass, with London hallmarks for 1882, 22.5cm. high. (Christie's) **£1,870**

GLASS DISHES

A Gallé gilded and enamelled dish, the clear glass decorated with gilt and polychrome enamelled umbel flowers, 30cm. long.
(Christie's) £880

A glass dish attributed to H. P. Glashutte with enamel painted decoration of a purple clematis bloom, circa 1900, 23.5cm. diam. (Christie's) £172

An Almeric Walter pate-de-verre dish of lozenge shape, designed by H. Berge, 24.6cm. wide. (Christie's) £1,296

'Gorgette', a Lalique opalescent bonbonnière, the circular slightly domed cover moulded with three dragonflies, 21cm. diameter.
(Christie's) £2,200

An Almeric Walter Pâte-de-Verre dish of tri-lobed shape modelled in high relief and naturalistically coloured with a lizard clambering among ivy leaves, 17.5cm. wide.
(Phillips) £3,600

'Martigues', a Lalique opalescent glass dish the underside moulded in relief with a band of spiny fish, 14$^{1}/_{4}$in. diameter.
(Christie's S. Ken) £2,200

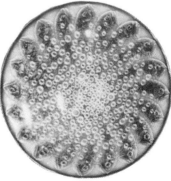

An Austrian Art Deco circular green glass dish, with silver deposit decoration of prancing horses, 12$^{1}/_{2}$in. diameter.
(Christie's S. Ken) £55

'Poissons', a Lalique opalescent glass dish, the underside moulded in relief with a spiralling pattern of fish, 11$^{3}/_{4}$in. diameter.
(Christie's S. Ken) £308

A Lalique opalescent dish, moulded with a radiating pattern of twenty fish and bubbles, with a slightly undulating rim, 35.2cm. diam. (Christie's) £715

GLASS DRINKING SETS

Lemonade set of jug and six glasses with blue glass decoration, 1930s. (Muir Hewitt) £175

Art Deco cameo cut beverage set, twelve tumblers and an ice bucket of frosted glass with red bamboo and stylised leaf decoration. (Skinner Inc.) £107

Stylized decanter and six glasses, 1930s. (Muir Hewitt) £75

A Loetz drinking set, designed by Richard Teschner, comprising a jug and five tumblers, the smokey white glass with polychrome applied decoration, 17.7cm. high. (Christie's) £308

A Stuart enamelled glass harlequin cocktail set, the shaker of tapering cylindrical form with chromed metal mount and cover, 8³/₄ in. high. (Christie's S. Ken) £99

A seventeen piece Lalique drinking set, each piece with moulded motif incorporating two male nudes, with acid-stamped and engraved signatures. (Christie's) £1,980

'Adam and Eve', an Orrefors cocktail set designed by Edward Hald in 1935, comprising cylindrical decanter with black applied foot and stopper, 8¹/₄ in. high. (Christie's S. Ken) £462

A Daum Art Deco glass decanter set, comprising: a bullet-shaped decanter, and six flared glasses en suite, each of pale orange-amber tone. (Phillips) £680

An Art Deco glass decanter set, comprising: a decanter of tapering, faceted form with six cylindrical, faceted glasses en suite. (Phillips) £360

GLASS FIGURES

An Art Deco frosted glass model of a naked female, in Venus de Milo stance, supported on square black glass base, signed *'Joz 30'*.
(Phillips)   £540

A Venini latticino stylised glass figure of a bird perched on a bell-shaped platform, 10³/₄in. high.
(Christie's S. Ken)   £550

Sirene, a Lalique opalescent glass figurine modelled as a mermaid with her legs drawn up, 10.3cm. high. (Phillips London)   £950

A Venini Commedia dell'Arte figure, designed by Fulvio Bianconi, of a clown, performing a handstand, on a circular black base.
(Christie's S. Ken)   **£1,870**

Chrysis, a Lalique presse papiers, moulded as a nude maiden with flowing hair, with acid stamped signature, 13.3cm. high. (Christie's London)   **£1,540**

An Italian clear glass sculpture of a pugilist standing with fists raised, 12in. high.
(Christie's S. Ken)   £385

'Suzanne', a Lalique opalescent glass figurine modelled as a naked girl, her arms outstretched to reveal a cascade of loose fitting drapery, 23cm. high.
(Phillips)   **£14,000**

'Source de la Fontaine, Doris', a Lalique clear and frosted glass luminaire, modelled as the statuette of a young woman, on rectangular wooden base, 24¹/₂in. high.
(Christie's S. Ken)   **£13,200**

An Art Deco polished glass luminaire by Gueron Cazeaux, modelled as a naked woman wearing batwing cape, on stepped wood base, 15in. high.
(Christie's S. Ken)   **£770**

GLASS JUGS

Carder Steuben gold Aurene pitcher, broad bulbous vessel with applied conforming handle, 9¾in. high.
(Skinner Inc.) £575

A Clutha glass jug, the tinted lime green glass striated with pink and with silver foil inclusions, 18.2cm. high.
(Christie's London) £3,850

Daum cameo glass pitcher with silver mounts, the frosted clear glass body layered in bright emerald green, cameo cut with lilies, buds and convoluted leaves, 12½in. high.
(Robt. W. Skinner Inc.) £2,795

A 19th century Arts & Crafts period claret jug, by Heath & Middleton, Birmingham, 1893.
(Peter Wilson) £240

A Gallé enamelled jug, of swollen form pinched at sides, with pulled lip and applied handle, the amber tinted glass with polychrome enamelled wild flowers and praying mantis, 18.2cm. high. (Christie's) £3,960

Silver overlay pitcher, with applied handle, decorated with silver rim and border panels centring cut floral designs, 10in. high.
(Skinner Inc.) £297

Mount Washington Royal Flemish pitcher, with extensive marine decoration including realistic fish, seashells and oceanic plant-life, 8½in. high.
(Skinner Inc.) £1,081

A Daum carved, acid-etched, and applied jug, with long pulled spout, the clear, blue and green glass overlaid with mottled brown, green and yellow leaves and berries, 17cm. high.
(Christie's) £9,020

An American Aesthetic Movement white metal hot water jug, the oviform body extravagantly applied with pine-needles, 7in. high.
(Christie's S. Ken) £528

MISCELLANEOUS GLASS

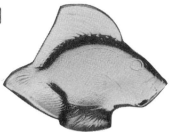

A Galle carved and acid etched cameo bonbonniere and cover, of compressed cylindrical form with swollen sides, 16.5cm. diam. (Christie's London)   £880

Six Figurines, a set of six Lalique liqueur glasses, moulded with rectangular panels enclosing classical maidens, stained pink, in original fitted box, 3¾in. high. (Christie's S. Ken)   £3,520

Gros Poisson, a large Lalique glass model of a carp, its body forming an arc and moulded with scale and fin details, 31.3cm. high. (Phillips London)   £3,200

A Tiffany 'Favrile' iridescent glass Seal moulded with the bodies of three scarab beetles, 4.5cm. high.
(Phillips)   £360

A pair of Almeric Walter 'Pâte-de-Verre' bookends designed by André Houillon as two dolphins with angular scaly bodies, 17cm. high.
(Phillips)   £1,250

Frosted cut glass ice bucket with metal swing handle, inscribed *Lalique, France* to base.
(G.A. Key)   £150

'Grenouille', a Lalique amethyst-tinted glass paperweight modelled as a seated frog, 2¾in. high.
(Christie's S. Ken)   £4,400

A Lalique clear and frosted glass presse-papier, the plaque intaglio moulded with the figure of St. Christopher carrying the infant Christ, 4½in. high. (Christie's)   £440

An Art Deco electroplated and cut-glass two-division tantalus with central locking carrying handle, 11½in. high.
(Bearne's)   £750

MISCELLANEOUS GLASS

Muller Fres scenic cameo glass jar, with conforming cover, layered in dark amethyst, cameo cut with birds in flight, trees and an ivy covered chapel, 5½in. diam. (Robt. W. Skinner Inc.) £683

A novelty duck amber glass bodied sauce bottle with silver head spout, the hinged cover set with glass eyes, 6¼in., Akers & Co. Birmingham 1919. (Woolley & Wallis) £420

Mid 19th century Bohemian overlay and enamelled casket, the body in opaque white, 5¼in. wide. (Bermondsey) £400

A Gallé gilt-bronze mounted, carved and acid-etched cameo brûle-parfum, the white glass globular body overlaid with dark amber anemones, mounted on a concave-sided triangular base, 17cm. high. (Christie's) £3,080

'Coutard, Masque de Femme No. 2', a Lalique square frosted glass plaque moulded in relief with the face of a young woman, 12½in. square. (Christie's S. Ken) £1,210

An important 'Whitefriars' glass, silver and enamelled centrepiece designed for James Powell and Sons by Harry Powell, 36cm. high. (Phillips) £9,800

A Galle cameo glass moon flask, with cup shaped rim and two small applied loop handles, cameo mark *Galle* with a star, 21cm. (Bonhams) £2,000

A Lalique frosted glass ice bucket, the exterior moulded in relief with naked Bacchanalian figures amongst foliage, 9in. high. (Christie's S. Ken) £462

An Austrian Art Nouveau iridescent glass tea caddy and cover, of clear glass covered in iridescent green splashes and applied with brown trails and spots, 6½in. high. (Christie's S. Ken) £176

SCENT BOTTLES

'Dans La Nuit', a Lalique spherical scent bottle and stopper, made for Worth, the body moulded in relief with stars and stained blue, 3in. high. (Christie's)   £198

Glass scent spray with chromium fittings, 1930s. (Muir Hewitt)   £35

'Sans Adieu', a Lalique emerald green scent bottle and stopper made for Worth, of cylindrical form with ribbed stopper. (Christie's)   £132

'La Joie D'Aimer', a Baccarat enamelled clear bottle for A. Gravier, of octagonal form, with swollen neck, enamelled in black and orange with an abstract pattern, 5¼in. (Bonhams)   £1,400

'Me Voici', a Baccarat enamelled clear bottle for A. Gravier, of shoe form, with faceted stopper, the bottle enamelled in green, blue, orange and yellow with Egyptianesque floral patterns, 4in. wide. (Bonhams)   £6,200

'Malice', a Baccarat enamelled clear bottle for A. Gravier, of squared baluster form, the grooved edges enamelled in blue, the front enamelled in black, 4½in. (Bonhams)   £1,800

'Fougères', a Lalique clear glass scent bottle and stopper, moulded in relief with an oval green stained panel centred with the head and shoulders of a woman in floral gown, 9.20cm. high. (Phillips)   £4,830

'Quatre Soleils', a Lalique amber-tinted scent bottle and stopper, the angular bulbous body moulded with four chrysanthemum flowerheads each with gold foil backing, 7.2cm. high.(Christie's)|£14,300

'Le Nouveau Gardenia', a Lalique clear glass perfume bottle and stopper for Coty, intaglio moulded to each facet with a fairy clutching at a long stemmed flower, 13.60cm. high. (Phillips)   £2,300

SCENT BOTTLES

A frosted glass scent bottle modelled as Bonzo the Dog, the features painted in brown and red, 2¾in. high. (Christie's) £66

'Volubilis', an Art Deco perfume bottle and stopper, of tapering design moulded in relief with flowers and foliage, 4½in. high. (Christie's S. Ken) £495

'Sans Adieu', a Lalique Art Deco green glass perfume bottle for Worth, the stopper formed as six graduated circular discs, 10.90cm. high. (Phillips) £550

'Pluie D'Or', a Baccarat enamelled clear bottle for A. Gravier, of triangular section, enamelled in black, orange, green and yellow with flower sprays, with triangular domed stopper, 5¾in. (Bonhams) £4,200

'Voltigy', a Baccarat clear bottle for A. Gravier, modelled as a butterfly with outstretched wings, the body stained in pink and black, 3½in. (Bonhams) £18,000

'Hantise', a Baccarat black enamelled pink opaque bottle for A. Gravier, of multi-faceted ovoid form, with gilt metal bullet-shaped stopper and circular foot, 4½in. (Bonhams) £3,400

'Cactus', a Lalique frosted glass scent bottle and stopper of spherical form moulded in relief with nodes enamelled in black, 4in. high. (Christie's) £200

A gilt metal cased glass scent bottle and stopper made for Rolex, modelled as a pocket watch, 2in. long. (Christie's) £300

A Cristallerie de Pantin cameo brûle-parfum, the yellow opalescent body overlaid in pink with pendant trails of fuschia, 6in. high. (Christie's S. Ken) £550

GLASS SHADES

Leaded glass lamp shade, of green graduated segments with four sets of blue squares at lower edge, 10¹/₂ in. diameter. (Skinner Inc.)   £9,000

A Tiffany bronze and leaded glass lamp shade, the irregular rectangular mottled green panes in vertical bands, stamped marks, 20in. diameter. (Christie's S. Ken)   £935

A Daum cameo glass lamp-shade, the body streaked with yellow and orange, overlaid with brown glass acid etched with Chinese lanterns and foliage, 19.5cm. diam. (Phillips London)   £2,700

A Sabino hanging light, the metal frame mounted in three tiers with satin-finished panels, each with moulded decoration, 60cm. high. (Christie's)   £1,650

A pair of Lalique wall light panels, moulded in high relief with a putto between floral friezes, 47cm. high. (Christie's London)   £4,400

Leaded glass hanging shade, attributed to Duffner & Kimberly, with green wreath and swag design incorporating red-amber flame designs, 24in. diameter. (Skinner Inc.)   £324

Boule de Gui, a Lalique green stained hanging shade, the clear and satin finished glass moulded with mistletoe, 44cm. high. (Christie's London)   £17,600

Deux Sirenes, a Lalique frosted glass plafonnier, moulded with two swimming water nymphs, their hair forming streams of bubbles, 39.5cm. (Bonhams)   £1,700

'Soleil', a Lalique opalescent glass shade, of semi-spherical form moulded in relief with interlocking sunburst motifs, 12in. diameter. (Christie's S. Ken)   £1,100

STAINED GLASS

One of a pair of Arts and Craft leaded and stained glass panels, with swallows before clouds in a border of stylised flowerheads in oak frames, 180 x 111cm. each panel. (Christie's London)
Two   £1,650

An Art Nouveau stained glass window by Muller Freres, fashioned from segments of stained glass supported with lead, signed, 111cm. high x 117cm. across. (Phillips) £900

A tinted glass panel, the centre section painted with a golfing scene, 1900s, 38¼ x 20½in. (Christie's S. Ken)   £2,200

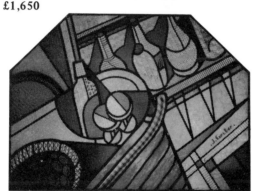

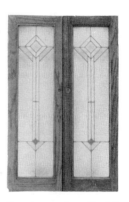

One of a pair of leaded glass windows, Midwest, circa 1910, two repeating arrow medallions in orange centring vertical strip, 48½in. high. (Skinner Inc.)   £309

An Art Deco leaded stained glass panel by Jacques Gruber, 70.2cm. wide, 50.3cm. high. (Christie's)
£3,520

Four tall and two short Prairie School style leaded glass windows, circa 1910, 40in. and 32in. high. (Skinner Inc.) £261

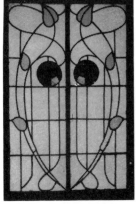

A leaded and stained glass panel by George Walton, after a design by Charles Rennie Mackintosh, 133.6cm. high, 91.4cm. wide. (Christie's)   £660

One of a set of three stained glass panels, possibly by Morris & Co., the pale yellow glass painted and stained in yellow and black, 18¼in. x 17¾in. (Christie's) (Three)   £418

A large rectangular glass panel by John Hutton, sand blasted and wheel engraved with Perseus before the Three Graces, 206.5 x 97cm. (Christie's)£1,650

VASES
DAUM

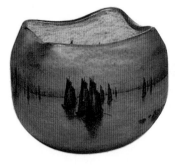

A Daum carved and acid-etched double overlay vase, the mottled amber and pink glass overlaid in mottled green and red with wheel-carved poppies, 23.5cm. high.
(Christie's)   £15,400

A Daum carved, acid-etched and enamel painted vase, the mottled amber and yellow glass decorated with brown enamel painted sailing boats, 11.5cm. high.
(Christie's)   £3,300

A Daum carved and acid-etched double-overlay vase, the mottled yellow ground cased in clear glass, and overlaid in brown and light amber hazelnut branches, 17.5cm. high.
(Christie's)   £1,650

A Daum carved-acid-etched and applied double-overlay vase, the mottled blue glass tending towards cobalt blue at the foot, with applied and wheel-carved yellow and white narcissus, overlaid with mottled green and amber leaves and stems, 16.4cm. high. (Christie's)   £8,800

A Daum carved, acid-etched and enamelled two-handled coupe, of bell shape on circular foot, the amber glass toning to cobalt blue at the base, carved in relief and polychrome enamelled on the body and applied handles with cornflowers. (Christie's) £7,150

A Daum, acid-etched and enamel painted vase, with mottled blue and white ground encased in clear glass, decorated with polychrome enamelled wooded river landscape, 11.5cm. high.
(Christie's)   £1,320

A Daum acid-etched and enamelled vase, the mottled clear, blue and green glass decorated with polychrome enamelled wooded river landscape, 12.1cm. high.
(Christie's)   £1,980

A Daum carved and acid-etched double-overlay vase, the mottled orange, red and clear glass overlaid in green and brown with a wooded river landscape, 31cm. high.
(Christie's)   £2,420

A Daum enamel painted and acid-etched opalescent vase, the blue-white glass decorated with black enamel painted Dutch river scene with sailing boats and windmill, 12cm. high.
(Christie's)   £880

256

VASES
GALLE

A Gallé double-overlay soufflé vase, the yellow glass overlaid in two shades of blue, with flowering clematis, 16.5cm. high. (Christie's) £6,600

A Gallé carved and acid-etched double-overlay vase, the swollen form overlaid in cobalt blue and amethyst with pendent flowers, 14.5cm. high. (Christie's) £4,620

A Gallé carved and acid-etched landscape vase, the milky-white and green glass overlaid in dark amber with a wooded river landscape, 32cm. high. (Christie's) £7,700

'Paysage Vosgien', a Gallé carved and acid-etched double-overlay landscape vase, the pale amber glass overlaid in purple and blue with a farm in a wooded mountainous landscape, 43.5cm. high. (Christie's) £39,600

A Gallé \entrecalaire, intaglio carved 'verrerie parlante' vase, the clear glass decorated internally with mottled green, yellow and amber oxide striations, overlaid in red, with intaglio decoration of a seahorse among various seaweeds, 11cm. high. (Christie's) £30,800

A Gallé carved and acid-etched double-overlay vase, the yellow glass overlaid with orange and amber flowering plants, 15cm. high. (Christie's) £2,860

'Vase à Pekin', a Gallé carved and acid-etched fire-polished vase, the jade-coloured glass overlaid with purple lotus flower, 21cm. high. (Christie's) £6,050

A Gallé carved and acid-etched double-overlay vase, the yellow glass overlaid with blue and purple flowering clematis, 12.5cm. high. (Christie's) £3,300

A Gallé carved, acid-etched, applied and fire-polished vase, the acid-textured butterscotch ground with gold foil inclusions overlaid with amber heavily carved sunflowers, 35.2cm. high. (Christie's) £9,350

LAMPS

LALIQUE

Réne Lalique (1860–1945) was one of the most versatile designers of the Art Nouveau/Deco periods, working in the varied media of jewellery, glass and silver.

As an apprentice in 1876 he studied at the École des Arts Décoratifs in Paris and became a leading Art Nouveau jeweller, receiving his first important commission from no less a person than Sarah Bernhardt. He became a freelance designer, and worked for Cartier and Boucheron. His favourite motifs were flower and insect forms, and he produced pieces using semi-precious stones, glass, gold, ivory, horn and enamel.

His interest in glass dated from the 1890s, when he first started to incorporate it into his jewellery. By 1914 he had all but abandoned jewellery and moved on to glass as his major medium. His work was strongly influenced by Gallé, and he experimented with unpolished statuettes and vases. In 1908 Coty commissioned him to design a range of perfume bottles, and shortly after this he acquired a glass factory. The 1920s and 1930s marked the period of his greatest success.

Lalique was noted for his innovative techniques. He developed an opalescent glass, first in milky white and then also in brown, blue and a soft peach. His designs often incorporated nude figures and animal forms and his predilection for flower and insect motifs continued throughout his career.

His marks include *Lalique France*, and *R Lalique France*, either engraved or stamped and etched.

Serpent, a fine amber glass vase, a serpent coiled around the body, the head with gaping jaws, intaglio moulded *R. Lalique*, 25cm. (Bonhams)
£8,000

'Actinia', a Lalique opalescent and blue-stained vase, decorated with heavily moulded and notched wavy lines, 21.7cm. high.
(Christie's)   £3,080

'Escargot', a Lalique amber glass vase, the milky-amber glass moulded with a spiralling shell motif, with moulded and engraved signatures *R. Lalique*, 25.5cm. high.
(Christie's)   £9,350

'Domremy', a Lalique black-stained vase, the satin-finished glass moulded with flowering thistles, with moulded signature *R. Lalique*, 21.5cm. high.
(Christie's)   £1,100

'Alicante', a Lalique electric-blue glass vase, the satin-finished glass moulded with three pairs of budgerigars in profile amongst ears of millet, 25.5cm. high.
(Christie's)   £38,500

'Bacchantes', a Lalique blue-stained vase, the flared cylindrical body moulded in relief with nude female dancing figures, 24.5cm. high.
(Christie's)   £10,450

LAMPS

LOETZ

The Loetz glass factory was established at Klostermühle in Bohemia in 1836, and was bought by Johann Loetz in 1840. During the 1880s it produced glass imitating onyx, jasper and other hardstones and cameo glass with simplified plant forms in blue and black.

It was in the following decade however, that it sprang to fame, when it started to produce glass in the Jugendstil (literally youth style) which was the German speaking world's equivalent of Art Nouveau.

Under the direction of Max Ritter von Spaun, Loetz's grandson, who was director from 1879–1908, this took the form of an iridescent glass which fell into two types. The first, Papillon, consisted of pearly spots covering a vessel, and the second, Phenomenon, consisted of glass threads undulating across a pearly surface. These Loetz pieces were noted for their rich colours and sensuous forms.

Shapes were often novel, twisted, pinched or goosenecked vases, three handled vessels, or some with applied decoration in the form of snakes or mounted in silver and bronze. Many were made in imitation of the Favrile glass which Tiffany were producing in the USA at that time. Many Loetz pieces found their way across the Atlantic, and at times were even more popular there than the home-grown examples on which they were based.

The factory ceased production on the outbreak of war in 1939.

Marks include various forms of two crossed arrows with stars in each intersection, and *Lötz, Lötz Austria* or *Klostermühle*.

An unusual Loetz iridescent glass vase, of shouldered globular shape with flared neck, the upper portion in speckled glass, 12.8cm. high. (Phillips) £850

A Loetz cased glass vase, the green glass decorated with a webbed silvery-blue design, 28.3cm. high. (Christie's) £550

A Loetz shell shaped iridescent vase, modelled as a conch shell resting on a spiky base, 21cm. (some chips) (Phillips) £400

A Loetz white metal mounted vase, decorated with an iridescent blue and green oil splashed pattern, 20cm. high. (Christie's London) £660

A important Loetz iridescent glass vase, the deep-blue body decorated with brick-red feathering and further decorated with a Secessionist appliqué of formalised plant forms, 28cm. high. (Phillips) £6,000

A Loetz vase, with two applied angular handles, the body of purple glass decorated with iridescent green and blue oil splashes, 21cm. high. (Christie's) £880

HAGENAUER

The Hagenauer workshop flourished in Vienna between 1898 and 1958. A definite house style began to emerge after the proprietor's son Karl joined the enterprise in 1919, and from the 1920s onward they produced figures, often either sporting or with a sporting motif, in metal and/or wood.

These were given a highly stylised, abstract, often whimsical interpretation, and their unique style makes them easily identifiable.

A Hagenauer wood and metal sail boat, circa 1920, 28.5cm. high.
£500

Hagenauer bronze vase, circa 1910, 11.5cm. high.
£500

A Hagenauer brass and copper bust of a woman, the stylised figure with lightly hammered surface, with applied beads to neck and curled and cut copper strips forming hair, 60.5cm. high. (Christie's) £6,050

'Man and Woman', a Hagenauer brass sculpture, of two stylised male and female figures, standing arm in arm, with curled strips at their feet in the form of grass, mounted on a triangular base, 98cm. high. (Christie's) £5,720

A Hagenauer brass twin branch candelabrum of interlaced form, the cylindrical sconces with gadrooned oval drip pans, decorated with a stylised dog, 35.5cm. high. (Christie's) £308

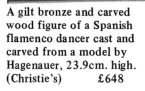

A gilt bronze and carved wood figure of a Spanish flamenco dancer cast and carved from a model by Hagenauer, 23.9cm. high. (Christie's) £648

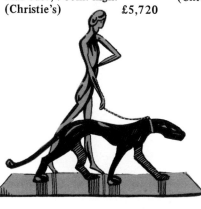

Austrian Hagenauer chrome lady with ebony panther, 1930. £1,500

A Hagenauer carved wood and metal bust of a woman in profile, 12½in. high. (Christie's) £880

HAGENAUER

A Hagenauer bronze, modelled as a sleek horse's head and
neck, mounted on a rectangular
bronze base, 31.5cm. long.
(Phillips London)   £900

A Hagenauer brass bowl, supported on a broad cylindrical
stem pierced with golfing
figures, 11cm. high. (Phillips)
                         £360

A Hagenauer chromium-plated
stylised figure of a polar bear,
20cm. long. (Christie's)
                         £770

A Hagenauer brass bust of a
young woman, lightly beaten
textured surface applied with
brass strips to form the flowing
hair and features, 47cm. high.
(Christie's)   £4,620

A wood and bronze cockerel,
in the manner of Hagenauer,
the stylised form having a
wooden body and bronze face,
39.5cm. high.   £450

A Hagenauer chromium plated
table mirror cast as a stylised
leaping deer, stamped monogram, 30.5cm. (Bonhams)
                         £800

A pair of Hagenauer bronze
Tennis figures, each one
fashioned in sheet bronze as
male tennis players wearing
flannel trousers and adopting
athletic poses, 22.4cm. high
and 25.8cm. high respectively.
(Phillips London)   £1,500

A pair of Hagenauer polished
steel and wood skiers, each
of stylised form, one in the
down hill position, the other
performing acrobatics, 33cm.
high. (Christie's)   £1,320

A Hagenauer brass figure of a
tennis player, the stylised male
figure in serving position, stamped marks Hagenauer, Wien,
wHw, Made in Austria, 27.5cm.
high. (Christie's)   £770

ART NOUVEAU & DECO

HAT PINS

The heyday of the hat pin was during the last few years of the last century, when the wearing of large, heavily decorated hats, perched on top of elaborate coiffures, made them indispensable. They were sold in pairs or in sets, and could be up to twelve inches long. (In America, at one time, a licence had to be obtained for any over 9" long, as they were classed as offensive weapons.) After the First World War, however, shingled heads and small, close fitting hats made the hat pin largely redundant, and examples produced after that time were generally of inferior quality to the exotic examples which had gone before.

Very unusual Victorian hat-pin, a bird's wing in burnished metal set with purple Vauxhall glass. £30

Silver and enamel dog rose, excellent condition. £30

Edwardian silver hatpin, dated 1906. £20

Silver butterfly, set with garnets, circa 1900. £35

Art Nouveau silver and imitation amethyst hat-pin by Charles Horner, 1916. £35

Unusual double-faced pierrot on long pin. £60

Silver Art Nouveau butterfly by Charles Horner, 1911. £60

Plastic Art Deco ram's horn. £20

Silver metal butterfly with pale blue and green painted wings. Body set with clear brilliants. £30

Edwardian painted glass hatpin. £4

HAT PINS

Fine hand-painted porcelain hatpin, early 20th century.
£40

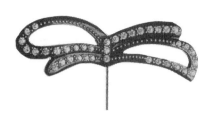

Art Deco jet and diamante bow, circa 1918.
£30

Pewter stag-beetle hatpin, circa 1918.
£45

Very fine gold and silver pique hatpin, early 20th century.
£75

Very popular golfclub hatpin in silver, 1912.
£20

Edwardian hatpin in pale blue and green enamel.
£18

Cut steel swallow with glass eye, on swivel, circa 1900.
£30

Stamped silver metal butterfly with swivel head.
£20

Delicate silver hatpin with marcasite decoration, circa 1900. £30

Large, attractive head in silver metal, mistletoe design, set with clear brilliants.
£25

Silver "Tennis Racquet" hatpin, 1912.
£35

Coiled silver wire and faceted amethyst glass, hallmarked FB, Chester, 1908.
£20

The Son of the Sheik, United Artists, 1926, half-sheet, unfolded, 22 x 28in.
(Christie's East) £1,458

Citizen Kane, RKO, 1941, half-sheet, unfolded, 22 x 28in.
(Christie's East) £2,041

The Jazz Singer, Warner Brothers, 1927, 24-sheet, linen backed, 9 x 20 feet.
(Christie's East) £9,911

Platinum Blonde, Columbia, 1930, three-sheet, linen backed, 81 x 41in.
(Christie's East) £2,449

Manhattan Melodrama, MGM, 1934, half-sheet, unfolded, 22 x 28in.
(Christie's East) £1,691

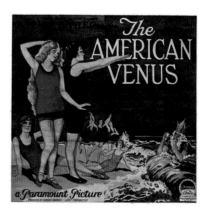

The American Venus, Paramount, 1926, six-sheet, linen backed, 81 x 81in.
(Christie's East) £1,982

HOLLYWOOD POSTERS

The Pilgrim, First National, 1923, six-sheet,
linen backed, 81 x 81in.
(Christie's East)   £6,705

Way Out West, MGM, 1937, half-sheet,
unfolded, 22 x 28in.
(Christie's East)   £1,691

The Cabinet of Dr. Caligari, Goldwyn, 1921,
one-sheet, linen backed, 41 x 27in.
(Christie's East)   £19,822

American Entertainment Co., ca. 1900, one-
sheet, linen backed, 28 x 41in.
(Christie's East)   £1,982

The Wizard of Oz, MGM, 1939, half-sheet,
unfolded, 22 x 28in.
(Christie's East)   £5,830

She Done Him Wrong, Paramount, 1933, six-
sheet, linen backed, 81 x 81in.
(Christie's East)   £3,032

Angel, Paramount, 1937, one-sheet, linen backed, 41 x 27in. (Christie's East) £1,516

The New Frontier, Republic, 1935, one-sheet, linen backed, 41 x 27in. (Christie's East) £3,032

Dimples, 20th Fox, 1936, one-sheet, linen backed, 41 x 27in. (Christie's East) £1,399

Her Wedding Night, Paramount, 1930, one-sheet, linen backed, 41 x 27in. (Christie's East) £1,749

Flying Pat, Paramount, 1920, one-sheet, linen backed, 41 x 27in. (Christie's East) £991

The Mysterious Dr. Fu Manchu, Paramount, 1929, one-sheet, linen backed, 41 x 27in. (Christie's East) £1,341

Red Headed Woman, MGM, 1932, one-sheet, linen backed, 41 x 27in. (Christie's East) £5,713

Shall We Dance, RKO, 1937, one-sheet, linen backed, 41 x 27in. (Christie's East) £3,207

The Young Rajah, Paramount, 1922, one-sheet, linen backed, 41 x 27in. (Christie's East) £1,807

HOLLYWOOD POSTERS

The Unknown, MGM, 1927, one-sheet, linen backed, 41 x 27in.
(Christie's East)   £6,413

The Grim Game, Paramount-Artcraft, 1919, one-sheet, linen backed, 41 x 27in.
(Christie's East)   £6,705

Go Into Your Dance, First National, 1935, one-sheet, linen backed, 41 x 27in.
(Christie's East)   £1,866

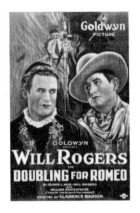

Doubling for Romeo, Goldwyn, 1922, one-sheet, linen backed, 41 x 27in.
(Christie's East)   £991

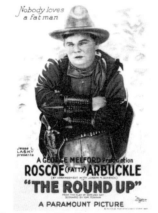

The Round Up, Paramount, 1920, one-sheet, linen backed, 41 x 27in.
(Christie's East)   £2,332

Tarzan and his Mate, MGM, 1934, one-sheet, linen backed, 41 x 27in.
(Christie's East)   £3,032

Son of the Golden West, FBO, 1928, one-sheet, linen backed, 41 x 27in.
(Christie's East)   £991

The Suitor, Vitagraph, 1920, one-sheet, linen backed, 41 x 27in.
(Christie's East)   £554

Prodigal Daughters, Paramount, one-sheet, linen backed, 41 x 27in.
(Christie's East)   £758

HOLLYWOOD POSTERS

What Do Men Want?, Lois
Weber Productions, 1921,
one-sheet, linen backed,
41 x 27in.
(Christie's East)   £3,032

The Toll Gate, Paramount-
Artcraft, 1920, one-sheet,
linen backed, 41 x 27in.
(Christie's East)   £1,399

The Siren Call, Paramount,
1921, one-sheet, linen backed, 41 x 27in.
(Christie's)   £525

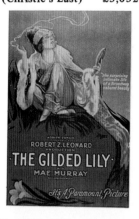

The Gilded Lily, Paramount,
1921, one-sheet, linen backed, 41 x 27in.
(Christie's East)   £933

Forbidden, Columbia, 1932,
one-sheet, linen backed,
41 x 27in.
(Christie's East)   £991

Victory, Paramount-Artcraft,
1919, one-sheet, linen backed,
41 x 27in.
(Christie's East)   £466

Know Your Men, Fox, 1921,
one-sheet, linen backed,
41 x 27in.
(Christie's East)   £875

A Dog's Life, First National, 1918, one-sheet, linen
backed, 41 x 27in.
(Christie's East)   £9,328

Minnie, First National, 1922,
one-sheet, linen backed,
41 x 27in.
(Christie's East)   £292

HOLLYWOOD POSTERS

The Big Parade, MGM, 1927, one-sheet, linen backed, 41 x 27in.
(Christie's East)   £1,516

Don't Shove, Pathe, 1919, one-sheet, linen backed, 41 x 27in.
(Christie's East)   £641

The Woman Alone, Gaumont British, 1936, one-sheet, linen backed, 41 x 27in.
(Christie's East)   £1,166

The Bait, Paramount, 1921, one-sheet, linen backed, 41 x 27in.
(Christie's East)   £554

The Wild Party, Paramount, 1929, one-sheet, linen backed, 41 x 27in.
(Christie's East)   £1,574

Charlie Chan's Chance, Fox, 1931, one-sheet, linen backed, 41 x 27in.
(Christie's East)   £1,166

An Amateur Devil, Paramount, 1921, one-sheet, linen backed, 41 x 27in.
(Christie's East)   £437

The Rough Diamond, Fox, 1921, one-sheet, linen backed, 41 x 27in.
(Christie's East)   £641

East is West, First National, 1922, one-sheet, linen backed, 41 x 27in.
(Christie's East)   £1,982

IRON AND STEEL

Iron and steel tend to be thought of as practical, rather than decorative materials, and the fireplace is about the only site which springs to mind where they are in common decorative use. Certainly the hearth was still the central point of the home in Art Nouveau period, and some very fine cast iron fire surrounds, screens and fireplace sets were produced in that style, both in Europe and America. Some iron and steel furniture was also produced and this in a way presaged the tubular chairs of Breuer, Aalto, and the like.

A pair of German iron candlesticks, circa 1910, 21 cm. high. £300

A cast iron panel by Hector Guimard for the entrance to the Paris Metro, 74 cm. high. (Christie's) £1,100

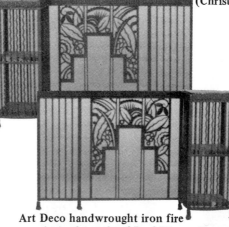

Hand forged steel rocker, 20th century, bent steel, with tufted upholstered suede back and seat, 45in. high. (Skinner Inc.) £122

Art Deco handwrought iron fire guards, in the style of Paul Kiss, circa 1925, in two rectangular sections with fluted crest rail over a series of square spindles and foliate work, 26in. high. (Skinner) £1,075

Four piece wrought iron fireplace set, attributed to Gustav Stickley, circa 1905, with strapwork log holder, unsigned, 33½in. high. (Skinner Inc.) £3,395

A wrought iron fire screen, in the manner of Edgar Brandt, with openwork form of stylised foliage, 91.5cm. high. (Phillips London) £300

A pair of iron and brass Fire-Dogs, possibly a design by Ernest Gimson, each tapering upright with raised sides, 68.6cm. high. (Phillips) £800

Victorian cast iron fire surround in Art Nouveau style, circa 1885. £500

IRON & STEEL

A wrought iron snake sculpture by Edgar Brandt, of a king cobra coiled in a circle with its head raised to strike, dark patina, stamped E. Brandt, 11.5cm. high. (Christie's)
£660

Early 20th century Art Deco cast and wrought iron parcel gilt pier table, France, 53in. wide. (Robt. W. Skinner Inc.)
£659

The Skier. Attributed to Manuel Felguerez Barra. Signed *"Felguerez"* on the figure, painted steel, 10in. high. (Skinner Inc.)
£161

A cold painted iron Vesta case in the form of a German soldier, standing wearing a spiked helmet, trench coat and rucksack, 3in. high. (Spencer's)
£85

An Art Nouveau cast-iron fire surround, the circular top moulded with a naked kneeling maiden in a cartouche, 1.70m. high. (Phillips)
£1,150

One of a pair of cast iron foliate andirons, attributed to E. Gimson, circa 1905, 22¼in. high. (Robt. W. Skinner Inc.)
£3,846

A Gordon Russell polished steel set of fire irons, the stand with square section column, arched legs and trefoil feet. (Christie's)
£880

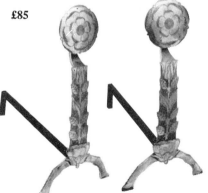

A pair of Arts and Crafts polished steel firedogs, designed by Ernest Gimson and made by Alfred Bucknell, 58.5cm. high. (Phillips)
£1,750

A wrought iron fire grate, in the manner of Ernest Gimson, the shaped back cast with stylised and entwined foliage, 105.5cm. high. (Phillips London)
£320

IVORY

Ivory became a hugely popular medium during the Art Nouveau period, thanks largely to the aggressive marketing policy of the Belgian government. The Congo was the personal possession of the King of the Belgians and ivory flooded the market as its resources were ruthlessly exploited. From 1894 artists were offered material free if they would work in the medium, and in 1897 the Brussels Exhibition featured a new 'chryselephantine' section to publicise their work.

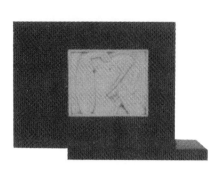

Profil de femme, an ivory plaque by Bela Voros, 11.2 x 14.4cm. £3,000

'Posing', an ivory figure carved from a model by Ferdinand Preiss, of a naked maiden, on a green onyx plinth, signed in the onyx *F. Preiss*, 10cm. high. (Christie's) £770

'Naked maiden', an ivory figure, carved from a model by Ferdinand Preiss, on a green onyx circular dish, 20cm. high. (Christie's) £1,760

'Dancing Girls', a pair of ivory figures carved from models by Ferdinand Preiss, on rectangular green and black onyx bases, 13.5cm. high. £2,500

'Ecstasy', an ivory figure by Ferdinand Preiss, of a nude maiden standing on tiptoe with her arms outstretched above her, 36cm. high. (Christie's) £8,800

An ivory figure of a girl, 'Invocation', carved from a model by D. Chiparus, 24.5cm. high. £2,500

An F Preiss ivory figure of a naked boy, seated on a tree stump, removing a splinter from his foot, 11cm. high. (Henry Spencer) £400

An ivory figure carved from a model by P. Phillipe, modelled as a nude maiden standing with her arms crossed, 22.7cm. high. (Christie's) £2,420

IVORY

'Girl with Hoop', an ivory figure carved after a model by F. Preiss, 17.5cm. high. (Christie's) £918

T.H. Paget, ivory reclining female nude, the young woman depicted lying full length, 20³/₄in. long, signed. (Bearne's) £2,100

A Preiss carved ivory figure of a little girl feeding a bird, circa 1930, 19cm. high. £2,000

An ivory bas relief attributed to Richard Garbe, of a cupid bending a vine for a goose, circa 1930, 19.5cm. high. £2,000

An ivory and fruitwood bust carved from a model by I. Sosson, of an Art Nouveau maiden, on striated marble pedestal, 27.4cm. high. (Christie's) £495

A painted ivory figure carved from a model by Ferdinand Preiss, of a young woman wearing green halter-neck bathing costume, signed on ivory base, 7¹/₂in. high. (Christie's S. Ken) £1,100

An ivory figure of a naked young woman by F. Preiss, 10¾in. high. £6,000

'Thoughts', an ivory figure carved from a model by Ferdinand Preiss, of a young woman seated with knees drawn up supporting bent elbows, signed on the base, 4½in. high. (Christie's S. Ken) £1,210

A Richard Garbe carved ivory relief of a young woman on a wooden base, inscribed 1946, 28cm. high. £6,000

JEWELLERY

Jewellery is such a versatile medium, providing scope not only for jewellers themselves, but for others like silversmiths and glass artists as well. There was of course no shortage of such talents in the Art Nouveau/ Art Deco period and most of them had a go at producing jewellery in the characteristic style, The result was that the period gave rise to some of the most charming pieces ever produced, which were further notable for their incorporation of relatively new materials, such as enamels and even plastic.

A Guild of Handicrafts Ltd. silver and enamel brooch designed by C. R. Ashbee, London hallmarks for 1907, 7.8cm. long. (Christie's)
£9,900

A plique-a-jour pendant with pearl drop and sterling silver chain, circa 1910, 15in. long. (Robt. W. Skinner Inc.) £208

An Art Nouveau pendant formed as a winged maiden, her outspread wings embellished with shaded pink and green translucent enamels, 4.5cm. wide. (Phillips London)   £500

An Art Nouveau sterling silver and plique-a-jour brooch/ pendant, French hallmark.
£380

A pendant, white metal, designed by P. Wolfers, stamped Wolfers Freres 80, P.W. 1903. (Christie's) £259

An Arts & Crafts oval white metal brooch designed by Arthur Gaskin, 4.5cm. long. (Christie's)   £660

An enamelled brooch, after a design by Henri Matisse, 6cm. wide, possibly produced in the U.S.A. (Phillips) £120

An Art Nouveau circular mirror pendant, set with small rose diamonds. (Christie's)   £756

A lapis, coral and gold brooch by Cartier in the form of a stylised scarab beetle, the head a cabochon coral. (Lawrence Fine Arts) £1,650

An Arts and Craft style moonstone set pendant, set with three cabochon polished moonstones and hung with three tear shaped moonstones. (Spencer's) £170

An unusual Art Nouveau plique-a-jour and diamanté pendant, the ivory and mother-of-pearl bust mounted in a gilt white-metal setting, 12.9cm. long. (Christie's) £3,080

A George Hunt 'Medusa' brooch, 6cm. long, maker's mark in shield, inscribed 'Medusa' on reverse. (Phillips) £1,000

An Arts and Crafts enamelled pendant, with enamelled panel depicting in naturalistic colours the profile head and shoulders of a girl, 3.5cm. (Phillips London) £260

An Art Nouveau pin/pendant, profile of a young girl on a plique-a-jour ground. (Robt. W. Skinner Inc.) £694

An Omar Ramsden pendant, the silver openwork backed with red enamel, the foliate border studded with small red garnets. (Christie's) £770

An attractive French pendant locket of triangular shape, formed as a moth in silver-coloured metal with golden linear detail, 5cm. (Phillips) £280

An attractive plique-a-jour enamelled 'peacock' pendant, the creature's body set with mother-of-pearl, its wings and neck blue enamelled, 7cm., probably Austro-Hungarian. (Phillips) £360

275

JEWELLERY

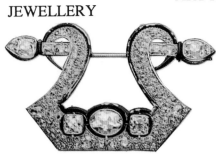

An Art Deco diamond brooch of stylised double swan design, circa 1925.
(Phillips)   £3,000

A Liberty enamelled white metal pendant on chain of trefoil design inset with mottled blue and yellow foil backed enamel.
(Christie's)   £242

An Art Nouveau ruby diamond and pearl brooch of asymmetric openwork design.
(Bonhams)   £420

Gold chip brooch in the form of a comic cat, its body a cabachon onyx and its eye a ruby.
(Finarte)   £746

Art Deco chandelier style gold earrings set with diamonds and rubies.
(Duran)   £838

An Art Deco diamond and calibre ruby watch clip by Le Coultre, with sprung cover set with square cut and brilliant cut stones.
(Phillips)   £3,000

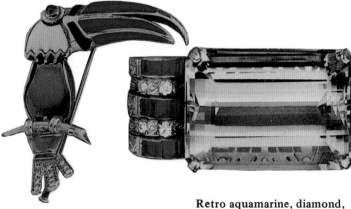

White and yellow gold brooch in the form of a toucan, the beak inset with onyx and coral and with a diamond tail.
(Finarte)   £839

Retro aquamarine, diamond, red stone, 14K. two tone gold brooch with openwork mount.
(Butterfield & Butterfield)   £4,000

A diamond cascade clip set with scrolled lines of graduated brilliants divided by pave diamond set panels.
(Phillips)   £4,839

JEWELLERY

An attractive pair of
cultured pearl and diamond
earclips with a scroll border
of diamonds.
(Bonhams)   £3,300

An Art Nouveau gold and turquoise pendant, having a plaque
of matrix held beneath a framework of interlaced entrelacs,
4cm.
(Phillips)   £380

A twin flower spray brooch,
the flowerheads with baguette
diamond centres and ruby
petals.
(Phillips)   £1,700

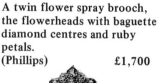

Gold pendant set with rubies
diamonds and enamel in the
style of Masriera and Carreras.
(Duran)   £1,826

A pair of delicate Art Deco pendant earrings in the design of heart
shape diamond and black enamel
tulip motifs.
(Phillips)   £2,500

An Art Deco rock crystal and
diamond brooch comprised of
a ring of rock crystal surmounted by platinum, set with round
and French cut diamonds.
(Skinner)   £1,368

An unusual and attractive moonstone opal and diamond pendant
of circular form ringed with opal
cabochans, 4.5cm. long.
(Phillips)   £780

A Liberty silver and enamel
buckle of rectangular design
pierced and cast each side
with openwork motifs, Birmingham 1901.
(Christie's)   £385

An Almeric Walter pate de verre
pendant of triangular section
moulded in relief with an insect.
(Christie's)   £352

JEWELLERY

Art Deco sapphire and diamond ring, with seven round diamonds, total weight approx. .60ct. (Skinner Inc.) £597

A Lalique gilt metal mounted glass brooch, moulded with two birds of prey flanking a cabochon, 9.5cm. long. (Phillips) £1,000

Bi-colour 14ct. gold bow brooch, circa 1940, set with six diamonds in platinum, 10 dwt., hallmarked. (Skinner Inc.) £472

A Georg Jensen white metal brooch designed by Arno Malinowski, the pierced oval decorated with a kneeling hind. (Christie's London) £66

A German horn comb, surmounted by panels of green plique-a-jour enamels amid tendrils set with marcasites, 8.5cm. wide. (Phillips) £95

A Theodor Fahrner Art Deco brooch with central faceted plaque of rose quartz flanked by two batons set with marcasites, 4.2cm. wide. (Phillips London) £780

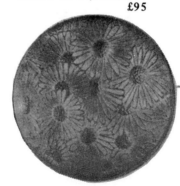

A Gaskin Arts & Crafts pendant with central amethyst, having seed pearl and fresh-water pearl drop, 4cm. wide. (Phillips) £400

A Lalique brooch, the clear and satin finished glass moulded with marguerites, on rose pink foil ground. (Christie's) £1,650

A Norwegian Arts and Crafts brooch of elliptical shape embossed with a bird flanked by three green stained chalcedony cabochons, 9.5cm. long. (Phillips London) £240

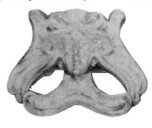

A Murrle Bennett gold wirework oval brooch, with opal matrix and four seed pearls, stamped MB monogram and 15ct. on the pin, circa 1900. (Christie's) £220

An amusing 1950s chrysoprase, ruby diamond and gold Daffy Duck brooch. (Bonhams) £280

A Kerr gilded Art Nouveau brooch, 6.5cm. across, stamped with maker's mark, Sterling and 1702. (Phillips) £300

JEWELLERY

An Edwardian diamond and enamel panel brooch, of oblong shape with canted corners, one stone deficient. (Bonhams) £2,100

A plique-a-jour pin with fresh-water pearls, probably French, circa 1910, marked 800, 1½ in. long. (Robt. W. Skinner Inc.) £119

An Arts & Crafts bangle bracelet with mounted opals and diamonds, stamped 'Peacock', 2½ in. diam., circa 1910. (Robt. W. Skinner Inc.) £1,546

A Liberty & Co. gold sapphire and moonstone pendant, probably designed by A. Gaskin, 5cm. long, 15ct. (Phillips) £380

Art Deco diamond bow pin, pave-set with 105 diamonds weighing approx. 3.00kt. and highlighted by calibre cut onyx. (Robt. W. Skinner Inc.) £2,500

Art Deco 14ct. gold, pearl and enamel pin, designed as a sailfish. (Robt. W. Skinner Inc.) £208

A Murrle, Bennett & Co. Art Nouveau brooch-pendant and chain, set with a central opal carved as a man's profile. (Christie's) £7,430

A Georg Jensen circular enamelled silver brooch, depicting a cherub in flight amid stars and holding a flaming torch, 4.70cm. diameter. (Phillips) £500

A Liberty & Co. gold and enamelled pendant, designed by Archibald Knox, suspended from a Liberty gold and enamelled brooch, 8.5cm. long. (Phillips London) £1,800

A Tiffany & Co. two-colour gold, sapphire and moonstone oval brooch, 3.3cm. across. (Phillips) £700

18ct. yellow gold and diamond pin, executed by Edward Oakes, Boston, early 20th century, approximate weight 5ct. (Skinner Inc.) £3,858

A Jean Despres Art Deco ring fashioned in carved ivory with inner silver coloured band, set with a turquoise. (Phillips) £1,550

JEWELLERY

A buckle modelled as a stylised owl with spread wings, reverse stamped Alpaca.
(Christie's)   £93

A highly unusual 'Jugendstil' plique a jour pendant in the form of a demons face holding an amethyst in its open jaws, 6.5cm. long.
(Phillips)   £1,600

An emerald and diamond fan shaped brooch, the base with a single pear shaped diamond collet.
(Phillips)   £1,613

An Argy Rousseau relief moulded pate de verre pendant, the clear glass with a square panel enclosing a white ballerina, 2in. diameter.
(Christie's)   £1,540

An Art Nouveau gold necklace set with enamels brilliants and various gems.
(Duran)   £1,836

An Arts and Crafts pendant on fancy link white metal chain, with large faceted rock crystal drop.
(Christie's)   £330

An Art Nouveau diamond brooch set with a spray of pear shaped brown diamonds, supporting a brown and white diamond drop.
(Phillips)   £2,200

A pair of Arts and Crafts circular drop earrings with engraved decoration.
(Christie's)   £200

An Arts and Crafts moonstone necklace attributed to Edward Spencer with central cruciform pendant, 7.5cm. long.
(Phillips)   £850

JEWELLERY

A double clip brooch set with diamonds and emeralds, circa 1935.
(Phillips)   £6,000

An Arts and Crafts gold and enamelled pendant necklace with a central plaque of mother of pearl having three enamelled floral plaques suspended from it, 7cm. long.
(Phillips)   £620

An attractive butterfly brooch by Mauboussin, Paris in yellow gold with sapphire and emerald body.
(Bonhams)   £1,700

A late Victorian aquamarine garnet and gold brooch with yellow gold scroll border.
(Bonhams)   £340

An Art Nouveau silver and enamel choker necklace, comprising four openwork circular panels, Birmingham 1908.
(Christie's)   £572

An Arts and Crafts pendant, with faceted rock crystal drop and white metal mount.
(Christie's)   £385

An Arts and Crafts amethyst pendant in the manner of Sibyl Dunlop, the large plaque carved with peaches and foliage.
(Phillips)   £720

A pair of Art Deco cufflinks composed of oval moonstone plaques applied with an onyx baton and rose diamond rib motifs.
(Phillips)   £1,200

Gold brooch in the form of a bird with a pearl body and ruby eye.
(Finarte)   £326

281

JEWELLERY

An Arts & Crafts pendant, in the manner of Omar Ramsden, set with three oval almondine garnet cabochons, 6cm. (Phillips) £160

A Heinrich Levinger plique a jour enamelled brooch of shaped triangular form, enamelled in shades of green between white metal threads. (Christie's) £935

Art Deco emerald and diamond ring, diamonds weighing a total of approx. 2ct. (Robt. W. Skinner Inc.) £763

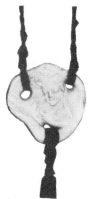

A Lalique glass pendant, the shaped circular clear glass medallion moulded with a woman and a dove. (Christie's) £286

Pair of 20th century enamelled sterling silver pins, hallmarked and stamped J.F., 1¼in. diam. (Robt. W. Skinner Inc.) £74

A Gabriel Argy-Rousseau pate-de-verre oval pendant, 6.5cm. diam. (Christie's) £990

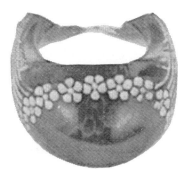

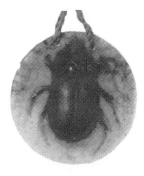

A large Arts and Crafts pendant with a large piece of turquoise matrix suspended from an openwork foliate mount, 8cm. long. (Phillips London) £200

A rare enamelled Lalique glass ring, of blue colour with domed cabochon top, 2.5cm. wide. (Phillips) £1,700

A pate de verre pendant, the mottled yellow and amber glass decorated in high relief with a red and green beetle. 4.6cm. diam. (Christie's) £605

JEWELLERY

An unusual and rare Loetz glass pendant of lobed oviform, exhibiting random splashes of violet and peacock blue iridescence, 5.3cm. long. (Phillips London) £500

A pair of very unusual Art Nouveau hair ornaments, each set with a single drop shape opaline glass, circa 1900, fitted Liberty case. (Bonhams) £3,800

An Arts and Crafts peacock brooch, designed in the manner of Ashbee for the Guild of Handicraft, 6cm. long. (Phillips London) £520

A Danish Art Nouveau hammered silver brooch set with lapis lazuli, Continental silver marks, circa 1910, 12cm. long. £150

An 18ct. gold, enamel and diamond ring and earclips, total weight approx. 2.85ct. £1,380

A Liberty & Co. diamond and aquamarine negligee necklace, 39cm. long. (Phillips) £1,450

An Arts & Crafts brooch, possibly Birmingham Guild of Handicrafts, 4cm. diam. (Phillips) £75

Demantoid, fire opal and diamond pin/pendant, circa 1900, centred by one buff top, navette shaped Mexican fire opal. (Skinner Inc.) £1,069

An Arts & Crafts ring with an oval cabochon of green turquoise. (Phillips) £70

JEWELLERY

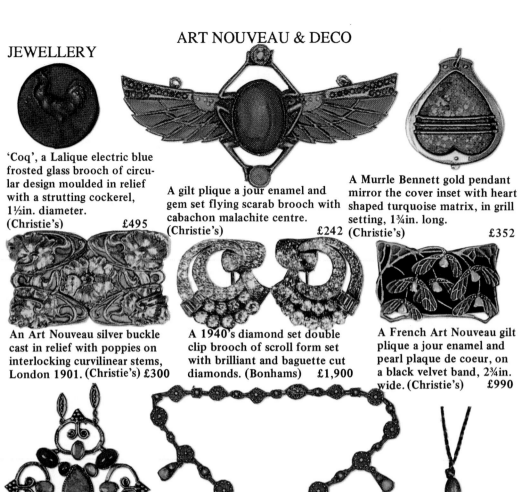

'Coq', a Lalique electric blue frosted glass brooch of circular design moulded in relief with a strutting cockerel, 1½in. diameter.
(Christie's)   £495

A gilt plique a jour enamel and gem set flying scarab brooch with cabachon malachite centre.
(Christie's)   £242

A Murrle Bennett gold pendant mirror the cover inset with heart shaped turquoise matrix, in grill setting, 1¾in. long.
(Christie's)   £352

An Art Nouveau silver buckle cast in relief with poppies on interlocking curvilinear stems, London 1901. (Christie's) £300

A 1940's diamond set double clip brooch of scroll form set with brilliant and baguette cut diamonds. (Bonhams)   £1,900

A French Art Nouveau gilt plique a jour enamel and pearl plaque de coeur, on a black velvet band, 2¾in. wide. (Christie's)   £990

An Arts and Crafts silver necklace, the openwork quatrefoil pendant set with opal doublets.
(Bonhams)   £550

An Arts and Crafts style cabachon gem pierced link and drop necklace, the centre drop with a raised motif depicting cupid.
(Christie's)   £592

An Almeric Walter pate de verre pendant moulded in relief with a dragonfly, on blue and buff silk cord.
(Christie's)   £308

Art Deco diamond synthetic sapphire, black onyx, platinum and pendant brooch.
(Butterfield & Butterfield)
                    £2,200

A gold turquoise and ruby set toucan clip brooch, the head pave set with cabochon cut turquoise.
(Bonhams)   £1,000

An Art Nouveau pierced strapwork belt buckle, the front enamelled in mottled shades of blue green, Birmingham 1909, 3.1in. wide.
(Christie's)   £220

JEWELLERY

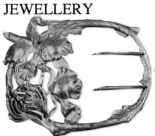

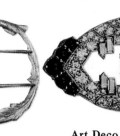

An Art Nouveau gilt metal buckle of oval design cast in relief with daffodils.
(Christie's)   £150

Art Deco sapphire and diamond double clip brooch set throughout with round and fancy cut diamonds.
(Skinner)   £5,933

An Art Deco square white metal pendant cast from a model by Marcel Renard with the bust of a man in a winged helmet, 2in. square. (Christie's)   £308

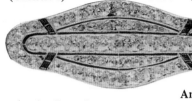

An Art Deco lozenge brooch set with lines of old mine cut stones.
(Phillips)   £800

An Art Nouveau hammered silver and enamel pendant and chain, set with oval mother of pearl, Birmingham 1908.
(Christie's)   £132

An Art Deco diamond plaque brooch with central marquise diamond, outer baguette brilliant and trapeze cut border.
(Bonhams)   £1,850

An Arts and Crafts enamelled and moonstone pendant necklace with a rectangular plaque enamelled in colours with a praying angel, 6cm. long.
(Phillips)   £920

An Art Nouveau carved horn necklace of a dragonfly resting on a flower set with purple glass cabachon, signed Gid.
(Christie's)   £286

An Art Nouveau blonde tortoise shell hair comb with applied decoration and set with rose cut diamonds.
(Christie's)   £725

A rectangular brooch mounted with a cushion shape mixed cut red spinel in a geometric frame of brilliant cut diamonds.
(Phillips)   £3,500

An Arts and Crafts white metal brooch of rectangular design with raised foliage, set with circular and oval cabachons, 2¼in. wide.
(Christie's)   £242

An attractive Art Deco diamond brooch by Cartier, Paris, hinged to open forming a rhomboid.
(Bonhams)   £9,200

Art Nouveau pin, 14ct. gold, depicting the face of a woman with flowing hair. (Skinner Inc.)
£236

An unusual H.G. Murphy gold 'tortoise' brooch, the creature having a green-stained chalcedony shell and garnet eyes, 3.5cm. long.
(Phillips) £200

Art Deco star sapphire and diamond ring, centred by one oval cabochon star sapphire, approx. 25.00ct., surrounded by 20 baguette and 22 square cut diamonds. (Skinner Inc.)
£3,459

A Georg Jensen white metal brooch, the pierced circle composed of four leaves, with central cabochon, usual marks. (Christie's London)
£418

Pink tourmaline and gold pendant, attributed to Margaret Vant, Boston, circa 1925, shield shaped open gold filigree form, 2in. wide. (Skinner Inc.) £525

A Horta gold double locket set with a sapphire and fourteen small diamonds, circa 1900, 3.5cm. diam.
£1,300

An Art Deco silver and enamel pendant, Germany.
£200

A silver brooch, stamped Georg Jensen 300 and with London import marks for 1965. (Christie's) £82

A fine and attractive Edwardian diamond brooch, central brilliant cut diamond with diamond and rose diamond set quatrefoil surround. (Bonhams) £1,350

JEWELLERY

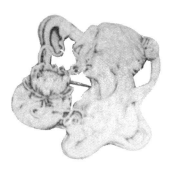

Art Nouveau pin of a peacock against a sunset background, 14ct. gold. (Skinner Inc.)
£220

An Austro-Hungarian 'peacock' brooch, its body set with mother-of-pearl, its wings set with small half pearls, 7cm. long. (Phillips)
£126

An Unger Brothers Art Nouveau brooch, 5.5cm. across, stamped 925 Sterling fine. (Phillips)
£250

Art Deco platinum and diamond brooch, set with 62 old European cut diamonds and three single cut diamonds, approx. 4.00ct. (Skinner Inc.)
£2,138

An emerald clover brooch, Tiffany & Co., set with twenty-five square-cut emeralds, weight approx. 8.50 carats.
£4,960

A Gabriel Argy-Rousseau pate de verre pendant, the translucent ground overlaid in purple and green with irises. (Christie's)
£770

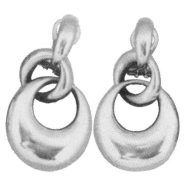

An Almeric Walter pate de verre pendant, the polychrome glass with enamel decoration moulded in the shape of a tortoise, 5.8cm. long. (Christie's) £1,045

18ct. gold double hoop ear-pendants, Italy, Cartier, 21.5dwt. (Skinner Inc.) £755

An Art Nouveau enamelled pendant, the back fitted with a mirror, the top decorated with purple and green enamelled violets. (Christie's)
£308

287

JEWELLERY

A Murrle Bennett gold and turquoise brooch of almost heart
shape with central cabachon,
2.4cm. wide.
(Phillips) £170

An Art Deco diamond emerald
and black enamel panel brooch
with pave set and baguette
diamonds, circa 1930.
(Christie's) £6,160

An Aesthetic movement silver
brooch fashioned as two interlocking squares with applied
crane and bird in flight, 2¼in.
wide.
(Christie's) £176

A fine quality Art Deco diamond
plaque brooch with central square
cut and baguette cut diamond
line.
(Bonhams) £5,600

'Serpents', a Lalique frosted
glass pendant of rectangular
design moulded in relief
with two intertwining snakes,
1¾in. long.
(Christie's) £300

An Art Deco brooch mounted
with a step cut aquamarine
flanked by diamond scroll
motifs.
(Phillips) £2,000

Gold and enamel pendant set
with diamonds featuring a
girls head in profile.
(Duran) £1,966

An asymmetrical gold bracelet
watch by Trabert and Hoeffer,
Maboussin, circa 1945.
(Phillips) £5,242

'Colombes', a Lalique opalescent glass
pendant, of arched rectangular design
moulded in relief with a woman and
two doves.
(Christie's) £440

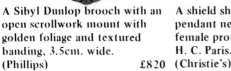

A Sibyl Dunlop brooch with an
open scrollwork mount with
golden foliage and textured
banding, 3.5cm. wide.
(Phillips) £820

A shield shaped painted enamel
pendant necklace depicting a
female profile, reverse signed
H. C. Paris.
(Christie's) £110

Gold and enamel brooch in the
form of a stylised cat with a
fish, the cats eyes of rubies, its
nose a diamond.
(Finarte) £466

JEWELLERY

An oval, gilt blue and white paste, grill design brooch, stamped on the reverse T. B.
(Christie's) £44

An emerald and diamond double clip, the centrepiece in the form of a bow with pierced chevron decoration.
(Phillips) £16,935

An Arts and Crafts circular brooch, the white metal frame chased with foliage around a central medallion of Abalone shell, 1¾in. diameter.(Christie's) £187

A Mexican tapering panel link broad bracelet with faceted onyx terminals. (Christie's) £275

A George Tarrant silver brooch designed by Geoffrey G. Bellamy, the oval frame enclosing two leaping antelopes.
(Christie's) £110

A small Art Deco cartouche shape diamond plaque brooch set with brilliants and baguettes.
(Phillips) £1,000

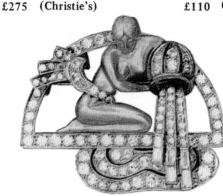

An Art Nouveau pendant set with mother of pearl and suspending a freshwater pearl by Murrle Bennett & Co., circa 1900. (Christie's) £330

An Art Nouveau gold and platinum brooch set with diamonds, in the form of a female figure pouring water from a jar.
(Duran) £2,400

A very fine and attractive Art Deco diamond brooch with geometric openwork top set with pear shaped central stone.
(Bonhams) £9,500

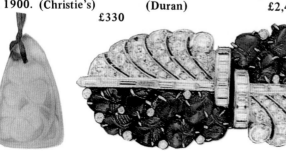

'Trefles', a Lalique opalescent glass pendant of triangular design moulded in relief with clover leaves, 2¼in. long.
(Christie's) £300

An Art Deco sapphire and diamond double clip of twin plume design, circa 1930.
(Phillips) £4,435

An Arts and Crafts pendant the white metal mount of foliage set with moonstone and amethyst.
(Christie's) £385

LAMPS

Lamps have always provided an ideal medium for artistic expression, and the Art Nouveau/Deco periods were no exception. Some great generic types emerged at this time, such as the Tiffany lamp, and most great craftsmen in such varied media as sculpture, metalwork, art glass and ceramics produced characteristic forms. These ranged from the beauty of the cameo and acid-etched offerings of Daum and Gallé, through to the outré and whimsical products of Art Deco craftsmen such as Frank Clewett.

Stylized Art Deco nickel plated table lamp with ceramic shade by Wedgwood.
(Muir Hewitt) £120

Victorian brass desk lamp, 1900. (British Antique Exporters) £65

A 1950's French floor lamp, the black painted stand in the form of a stylised praying mantis, 162.4cm. high. (Christie's) £345

A Birmingham Guild of Handicrafts hammered brass table lamp, the pagoda shade with shaped finial, mounted on a pedestal base formed by four shaped and hammered rods, circa 1893, 51cm. high. (Christie's) £4,620

An art glass table lamp, with gilt metal fittings supporting two glass shades of opal and gold, 28in. high. (Robt. W. Skinner Inc.) £295

An Art Deco spelter and pink alabaster table lamp, with a spelter model of an Egyptian slave girl perching with a torch form shade upon her knees, 20½in. high. (Christie's S. Ken) £308

Glass lamp with marbled colour decoration, 1930s.
(Muir Hewitt) £60

A French Art Nouveau ceramic lamp stand modelled as a maiden in strapless dress holding a shawl billowing behind her head, 26in. high. (Christie's S. Ken) £462

LAMPS

An Art Nouveau bronze figural lamp, cast from a model by E. Drouot, the young woman personifying music, 34 in. high. (Christie's) £1,500

A 1950s solid rosewood table lamp, 45.5cm. high. (Christie's) £1,836

'Batwomen', a large bronze and ivory table lamp by Roland Paris, the body modelled with three female figures gold patinated in bat-winged costume and ruffs, 94cm. high. (Christie's) £8,800

Scheier Pottery lamp base, circa mid 20th century, large ovoid form, sgraffito decorated with man, woman and child, 16in. high. (Skinner Inc.) £538

A pair of Moorcroft 'Iris' pattern lamp bases, with white piped slip decoration, covered in polychrome glazes on a buff and cobalt blue crackelé ground, 37.2cm. height of base. (Christie's) £660

A de Vez cameo and acid etched landscape night light, the yellow and pink glass overlaid in purple with tropical palms and islands at sunset, 17.2cm. high. (Christie's) £440

A bronze, marble and glass lamp cast after a model by M. Le Verrier, signed, circa 1925, 86.2cm. high. (Christie's) £1,404

A copper and leaded glass piano lamp, cone-shaped slag glass shade, incised mark 'KK', 13¾in. high. (Robt. W. Skinner Inc.) £216

An Art Deco figure table lamp in green patinated metal, signed Limousin, 16½in. high. £300

An important and rare Tiffany Studios leaded glass table lamp, the shallow domed shade edged with the bodies of bats, 48cm. high.
(Phillips)   £60,000

'Batwomen', a large and unusual painted bronze and ivory figural table lamp cast and carved from a model by Roland Paris the base adorned with three Batwomen each wearing a bat-cape, red cap and a mask, they stand with their hands linked beneath the original pagoda-style shade, 93cm. high.
(Phillips)   £7,200

LAMPS

Tiffany bronze and favrile blue dragonfly lamp, conical tuck-under shade of seven mesh-wing dragonflies with blue bodies and jewel eyes, 22½in. high. (Skinner Inc.) £12,425

Tiffany bronze and favrile lotus bell lamp, mottled green and white glass segments arranged in bell form geometric progression, signed "Tiffany Studios New York", 21in. high. (Skinner Inc.) £15,000

Tiffany bronze and favrile ten light lily lamp, opal glass blossom shades with green and gold pulled feather iridescent decoration, eight signed "LCT Favrile", two "L.C.T.", 22in. high. (Skinner Inc.) £15,000

Tiffany red poppy lamp, flared conical shade with brilliant and unusual striated glass segments depicting poppy blossoms above band of mottled green leaves within reticulated mesh covering, 26in. high. (Skinner Inc.) £15,000

LAMPS

A Murano panelled glass oil lamp, with caramel and green slag glass panels, 1905, 19in. high. (Robt. W. Skinner Inc.)
£473

A hammered copper and mica table lamp, circa 1910, 14¾in. high. (Robt. W. Skinner Inc.)
£833

Wrought iron lamp with mica shades, possibly England, early 20th century, cast leaf detail, unsigned, 17½in. high. (Robt. W. Skinner Inc.)
£982

A figural bronze and glass table lamp, cast from a model by Pohl, with three young women wearing diaphanous robes, dancing around the central column, total height 52cm. (Phillips)
£900

A Fulper pottery and leaded glass table lamp, New Jersey, signed Vasekraft, stamped "Patents pending in United States and Canada, England, France and Germany", 20½in. high. (Robt. W. Skinner Inc.)
£6,285

'Pipistrello', a table lamp designed by Gae Aulenti, for Martinelli Luce, the telescopic stainless steel pedestal on a black enamelled conical foot, 91cm. maximum height. (Christie's)
£935

French cameo glass lamp, cut with Roman gladiators and Art Deco borders, supported on three arm metal fixture 19in. high. (Robt. W. Skinner Inc.)
£1,056

R. Guy Cowan Pottery table lamp, Cleveland, Ohio, circa 1925, metal shade of square flaring form, simulating mica, 19½in. high. (Skinner Inc.)
£489

An Art Nouveau bronze oil lamp base with jewelled glass shade and glass funnel, cast after a model by G. Leleu, circa 1900, 57cm. without funnel. (Christie's)
£594

LAMPS

Late 19th century peach-blow fairy lamp on three-legged brass stand, possibly Mt. Washington, 8½in. high.
£400

Art Deco lamp, circa 1925, fan-shape mica covered metal shade with patinated metal standard and base, 13⅜in. high. (Skinner Inc.)
£300

Late 19th century pink enamelled satin glass lamp with matching base, 7½in. high.
£300

Leaded glass table lamp, umbrella-form shade of segmented white glass panels with swag and blossom elements, 18in. diameter. (Skinner Inc.)
£185

An important A S.A.L.I.R. 'vaso Veronese', designed by Vittorio Zecchin, the traditional Venetian shape pierced with elaborate and intricate acid-cut fretwork of a hunting scene, 51cm. high. (Christie's)
£24,200

An acid-etched and cut glass cameo table lamp, the mushroom form shade supported by three-branch chromed metal mount, 20½in. high. (Christie's S. Ken)
£1,540

Hammered copper and mica table lamp, early 20th century, with three mica panels on urn shape standard. (Skinner Inc.)
£208

Copper oil lamp, executed by Mary Steere Batchelder, 39 Hancock St., Boston, circa 1907, 13in. high. (Skinner Inc.)
£883

A 1930's Modernist chromium plated table lamp, the domed metal stepped shade with white painted reflector, 42cm. high. (Christie's)
£935

Tiffany leaded glass lamp shade on Grueby pottery base, early 20th century, with dome shaped shade in acorn pattern in colours of green variegated slag glass on shaped bronze arms and standard, acorn finial pulls, artist initialled A.L. for Annie Lingley (1899-1910). (Skinner Inc.) £11,428

Daum cameo glass table lamp with a mush-room dome shade and baluster shaft base of mottled yellow glass, 26½in. high. (Skinner Inc.) £7,600

'Hirondelles', a Lalique wall-light, with mould-ed decoration of five swallows in flight, above a hemispherical satin-finished shade, 47.5cm. diameter. (Christie's) £9,020

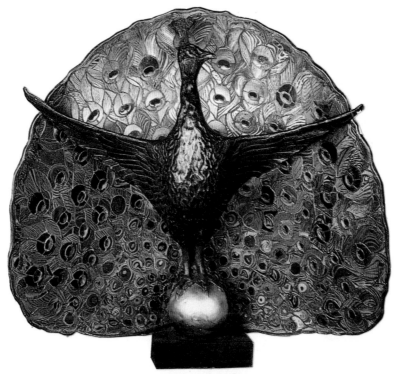

Tiffany bronzed metal and mosaic glass favrile peacock, the conventionalised full figure bird standing before an arched and curved mosaic depiction of feather plumage assembled from favrile glass segments, 31in. high.
(Skinner Inc.) £30,000

Rare Limbert copper and mica Prairie School table lamp, Michigan, circa 1913, the trapezoidal copper framed shade with cut out vine silhouette lined with mica, 24in. wide.
(Skinner Inc.) £30,864

LAMPS

One of a pair of oak and leaded glass wall lanterns, circa 1910, 23in. long. (Robt. W. Skinner Inc.) £594

'Nymph among the bullrushes', a bronze table lamp cast after a model by Louis Convers, 28.1cm. high. (Christie's) £518

A conch shell and hammered copper table lamp, designed by E. E. Burton, California, circa 1910, 24in. high. (Robt. W. Skinner Inc.) £2,023

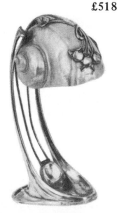

An Almeric Walter pate-de-verre and wrought-iron lamp, the amber glass plaque moulded with a blue and amber mottled peacock, 27cm. high. (Christie's) £2,200

A German Art Nouveau silvered pewter nautilus shell desk lamp, stamped M H 20, 27cm. high. (Christie's) £1,870

Early 20th century leaded cased glass lantern in vintage pattern, 13¼in. high, 9in. wide. (Robt. W. Skinner Inc.) £315

'Rudolph', a robot light fitting designed by Frank Clewett, the head formed by spherical glass shade, the adjustable arms with light bulbs forming the hands, 149cm. high. (Christie's) £935

A leaded slag glass and oak table lamp, early 20th century, the square hipped shade with coloured glass panels, 22in. high. (Robt. W. Skinner Inc.) £742

A Durand art glass lamp, with domed shade and baluster base, fitted with two socket lighting, 15in. high. (Robt. W. Skinner Inc.) £650

LAMPS

A slag glass and gilt metal table lamp, America, circa 1910, 23½in. high, shade 17¾in. diam.   £400

Art Deco gilt metal electric table lamp, showing reclining female figure, 8½in. long.   £225

A Degue Art Deco glass lamp, 35cm. high. (Phillips)
          £200

A plique a jour and metal lantern, each panel depicting a female figure in the manner of Robt. A. Bell, 34.5cm. high. (Christie's)   £1,728

A German Art Nouveau silvered pewter nautilus shell desk lamp, 29.7cm. high. (Christie's)   £2,310

A glass and metal floor lamp by Gae Aulenti, the cylindrical wirework cage with blown glass forming column and bulbous shade, 60cm. high. (Christie's)   £385

A Guerbe patinated bronze figure, in the form of a table lamp cast as an Art Deco maiden, 51cm. high, base signed. (Lawrence Fine Arts)
          £528

An art glass table lamp, open Tam o' Shanter shade of green iridescent pulled and swirled damascene design cased to opal-white glass, 19½in. high. (Robt. W. Skinner Inc.) £1,005

'The Butterfly Girl', a Goldscheider ceramic figural lamp, designed by Lorenzl, modelled as a girl wearing a combined tunic and cape, 52.50cm. high. (Phillips)   £3,450

LAMPS

Tiffany bronze and turtleback glass table lamp, with nineteen iridescent green tiles bordered above and below by mottled green square and rectangular favrile glass segments, mounted on original matching urn-form bronze base, 24in. high.
(Skinner Inc.)   £11,675

Handel signed 'Ice Crackle' finish table lamp with a continuous river scene with sail boats and trees, 34in. high.
(Du Mouchelles)   £2,850

Tiffany bronze and favrile apple blossom lamp, the domed shade of transparent green segmented background for yellow-centered pink and white blossoms on brown apple tree branches, 22½in. high.
(Skinner Inc.)   £6,214

Early Tiffany blown-out bronze and favrile Tyler lamp, the shaped dome shade of leaded glass segments arranged as twelve green swirling swags above repeating green border elements against white and mottled yellow background, 24in. high.
(Skinner Inc.) £25,000

Tiffany bronze and glass lily pad table lamp with pansy shade, the four-light standard above extraordinary blue-green striated favrile glass 'pumkin' raised upon bronze lily pad platform with two pond lily buds, signed "Tiffany Studios New York", 21in. high.
(Skinner Inc.) £23,000

A Tiffany bronze and favrile glass large linenfold lamp, twelve-sided angular gilt bronze lamp shade with amber fabrique glass panels, 24½in. high.
(Skinner Inc.) £6,850

LAMPS

A patinated bronze and ivory table lamp modelled as Pierrot seated on a bench beneath a tree, 19in. high.
(Christie's S. Ken) £770

Art Deco Daum style table lamp, on rectangular silvered base, the club shaped frosted glass shades sitting on out-stretched arms, circa 1925, 29cm. high. (Kunsthaus am Museum) £559

Leaded glass table lamp, with four repeating clusters of lavender iris blossoms and green spiked leaves, shade diam. 18in. (Robt. W. Skinner Inc.) £280

A Moe Bridges parrot lamp, with reverse handpainted scene of two exotic birds centred in a summer landscape, 23in. high. (Robt. W. Skinner Inc.) £2,721

A Fulper pottery 'Vase-Kraft' table lamp, circa 1915, 18in. high, 16½in. diam. (Robt. W. Skinner Inc.) £3,888

Copper and mica table lamp, circa 1910, flaring shade with four mica panels divided by copper straps, 26in. high. (Skinner Inc.) £988

An Art Nouveau table lamp, beaten brass inset with col-oured glass, on oval wooden base, 49cm. high. (Christie's) £432

Art pottery lamp with pierced copper and slag glass shade, circa 1905, 14½in. high. (Robt. W. Skinner Inc.) £750

An Art Deco frosted glass lamp painted in colours with banding and linear decoration, 31cm. high. (Phillips) £320

LAMPS

Glass and brass table lamp, with reverse painted border design in yellow with stylised green and red floral motif, 16in. diameter. (Skinner Inc.) £344

Rare Limbert copper and mica Prairie School table lamp, Michigan, circa 1913, branded on foot, 19in. high, 24in. wide. (Skinner Inc.) £30,864

An Art Nouveau bronze and leaded glass shade on bronze base, 22½in. high. (Christie's) £700

Boleslaw Cybis porcelain portrait bust of a lady with a bonnet, mounted on a brass plinth as a table lamp. (Schrager) £41

A hammered copper table lamp with mica shade, Old Mission Kopperkraft, San Francisco, circa 1910, 13¾in. high, 15in. diam. (Robt. W. Skinner Inc.) £1,687

A post war lacquered copper table lamp, the flaring circular base surmounted by louvred cylindrical shade with bell-shaped top, 21in. high. (Christie's S. Ken) £60

Arts & Crafts oak and slag glass table lamp, circa 1910, pyramidal shade lined with green slag glass, 26in. high. (Skinner Inc.) £401

An Art Deco alabaster lamp carved as an eagle on rockwork, supporting a sphere, 28in. high. (Christie's S. Ken) £330

An Art Nouveau iridescent glass and metal table lamp, with domed Pallme Konig shade of pink tone, 37.50cm. high. (Phillips) £1,150

LAMPS

A 1950's Italian glass and enamelled metal table lamp in the style of Gio Ponti, modelled as rocket, 39½ in. high. (Christie's S. Ken)　£220

English modernist table lamp with fluorescent bulb, 1930's, 35.75cm. high.　£1,000

Rudolph, a robot light fitting, designed by Frank Clewett, 149cm. high. (Christie's)　£2,420

An Andre Delatte cameo table lamp with metal neck mount, 52.5cm. high. (Christie's)　£1,650

A gilt bronze table lamp cast in the form of a frog with its arms outstretched, the floral motifs and frog's eyes studded with ruby glass cabochons, 14½in. high. (Christie's S. Ken)　£1,980

A Stilnova painted metal lamp, by Gaetano Scolari, Italy, circa 1959, 67cm. high. (Phillips)　£120

A W.M.F. figural pewter lamp, fashioned as an Art Nouveau maiden with children at her feet, 48cm. high. (Phillips London)　£500

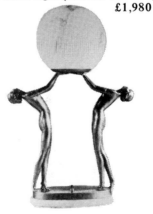

An Art Deco bronzed electric table lamp on oval base with onyx stand, 20in. high. (Anderson & Garland)　£280

An early 20th century bronzed metal three light candelabrum, in the form of a street lamp, modelled with a figure of a swaggering young man, his hands in his cummerbund, 36in. high overall. (Christie's S. Ken)　£396

LAMPS

ARGY ROUSSEAU

Gabriel Argy Rousseau (b. 1885) was a French artist in glass who worked in the Art Deco style. His favoured medium was pâte-de-cristal, a version of pâte-de-verre, having a higher lead content. It is almost transparent and gives a clear ring when sounded. In this, Argy Rousseau made a variety of objects, figurines and decorative ware such as vases, perfume burners, lamps and cigarette boxes. Many were decorated with motifs of poppies, gazelles, wolves and stylised female heads. His mark was usually *G Argy Rousseau*, impressed.

A Gabriel Argy-Rousseau pate-de-verre and wrought-iron veilleuse, 17.5cm. high. (Christie's) £3,080

A Gabriel Argy-Rousseau pate-de-verre and wrought-iron veilleuse, the grey, blue and dark blue mottled glass moulded with stylised leaves, 25.5cm. high. (Christie's) £2,200

BENEDICT STUDIOS

The Benedict Studios flourished in East Syracuse, New York State in the early years of the 20th century.

Their lamps are often unsigned, but are characterised by the frequent use of copper and mica, a mineral often used as a substitute for glass.

A mica and hammered copper table lamp, possibly Benedict Studios, New York, early 20th century, 19in. diam. (Robt. W. Skinner Inc.) £1,428

Copper and mica piano lamp, attributed to Benedict Studios, East Syracuse, New York, circa 1910, unsigned, 21½in. high. (Skinner Inc.) £1,111

BRADLEY & HUBBARD

The American glass makers Bradley & Hubbard worked out of Meriden, Connecticut, in the early 20th century. Their table lamps often feature metal pedestal bases with domed shades of iridescent or painted glass.

Their mark is usually Bradley & Hubbard Mfg Co within a triangle, set round an oil lamp.

A Bradley & Hubbard table lamp with gold iridescent shade, Mass., circa 1910, 15in. high. (Robt. W. Skinner Inc.) £416

Reverse painted and gilt metal table lamp, by Bradley & Hubbard, circa 1910, 23¼in. high. £600

LAMPS
DAUM

Auguste (1853–1909) and Antonin (1864–1930) Daum were French glass craftsmen who were much influenced by Gallé and became members of the Ecole de Nancy. They made great use of cameo glass enamelling and later also worked in pâte de verre. Acid etched pieces are also common. Their lamps are highly characteristic for their frequent use of the mushroom shade. Stems are also of glass, and these are decorated to form a uniform whole with the shade.

A Daum cameo glass table lamp with conical shade, 51cm. high, signed. (Phillips) £3,000

A Daum Art Deco table lamp, frosted glass with wrought iron, engraved with cross of Lorraine, circa 1925, 46cm. high. (Christie's) £3,240

A Daum cameo table lamp with wrought-iron, three-branch neck mount, 44.1cm. high. (Christie's) £6,050

A Daum acid etched, carved and enamelled landscape table lamp, of acid textured and cased polychrome glass, enamelled with a Dutch village in a snowy wooded landscape, 39cm. high. (Christie's) £14,300

A Daum overlaid and acid-etched table lamp with wrought-iron mount, 60cm. high. (Christie's) £7,700

A Daum enamelled and acid etched landscape table lamp with wrought-iron mounts, 48.5cm. high. (Christie's) £3,190

A Daum Art Deco glass table lamp with geometric panels enclosing stylised foliage and berries, supported on three chromed arms, 53.5cm. high. (Phillips) £6,200

A Daum carved and acid-etched double-overlay lamp, the shade of stepped conical form, with yellow ground overlaid in red and burgundy with a wooded river landscape, 32cm. high. (Christie's) £6,600

LAMPS
EMILE GALLÉ

Emile Gallé was born in 1846 and started his career as a ceramicist. In 1874 he established a small workshop in Nancy, where during 1890s he was to become the inspiration for what became known as the Ecole de Nancy, a group of French Art Nouveau artists who followed his techniques and decorating style. He made earthenware and later also experimented with stoneware and porcelain. His pieces were decorated with heraldic motifs and plant designs, and featured flowing, opaque glazes.

His forms were for the most part simple, sometimes even a little clumsy, though some of his shapes were borrowed by the Rookwood pottery in the USA, who acknowledged their debt to him.

In the early 1870s he also started experimenting with glass, and this is the medium with which he is now most associated. In fact, he revolutionised its manufacture by going completely against the traditional ideal of crystalline purity and aimed instead for an opaque, iridescent effect. He experimented with the addition of metal oxides to the glass melt, colouring glass in imitation of semi-precious stones, and also even exploited the impurities to give glass the quality of a fabric or the suggestion of mist or rain.

Gallé was much influenced by Japanese and Chinese arts and his close friendship with a Japanese botanist who was studying at the Ecole Forestière in Nancy further accentuated this. Such influence is particularly noticeable in his cameo glass pieces.

Gallé pâte de verre and

A Gallé carved and acid-etched lamp, with bronze mount, cast from a model by Pondany, the glass shade of mushroom-cap form with undulating rim, 53.5cm. high.
(Christie's)   £4,620

A Galle double overlay and wheel-carved glass table lamp, the matt-yellow ground overlaid in brown, blue and purple, circa 1900, 52.5cm. high. (Christie's)   £6,480

A Galle blowout lamp, varying shades of red on an amber ground, signed, circa 1900, 44.5cm. high. (Christie's)   £41,040

A tall Galle cameo table lamp, the domed shade and stem overlaid with claret-coloured glass, 63.5cm. high.
(Christie's)   £8,800

A Galle cameo and bronze mounted 'Veilleuse', the globular frosted glass shade with bronze dragonfly finial, resting within a mount of three further dragonflies, 18cm. high. (Phillips)£3,600

A Galle triple overlay cameo glass lamp, blue and green over a pale amber ground, circa 1900, 61cm. high. (Christie's)   £9,720

LAMPS
GALLE

clair de lune glass had a wonderful translucent glow like moonlight, and he was also notable for having developed the technique of marquêterie de verre, in which coloured pieces were pressed into semi-molten glass before it was cooled. His most complicated vases were made up of several separately coloured layers of glass, which were wheel engraved to different depths, to reveal each layer below. These would then be finished with marquetry and patination. He also used acid to bite into the glass surface, to create delicate bark or web like effects.

From the mid 1880s Gallé had further diversified into furniture design. His creations show restrained lines with the inevitable naturalistic ornamentation. Here again there was much use of plant motifs and the use of marquetry on flat surfaces.

It was around 1900 that Emile Gallé began the decorative application of glass to lighting, when he began producing lamps in the form of flowers, the bulbs being shaded by the half open petals. He used all the immense range of techniques which he had mastered in producing his lamps, and cameo, carved and acid-etched examples abound. He favoured the mushroom shades which were so to influence the Daum brothers, and the thematic and decorative integration of base and shade.

Gallé signed all his creations, and after his death in 1904 a star was added to the signature. His factory continued in operation until 1931 under his friend and assistant Victor Prouve.

A Galle carved and acid-etched double-overlay lamp, with mushroom-cap shade, the yellow glass overlaid with purple and blue marguerites, 39.2cm. high. (Christie's)   £28,600

'Peony' triple overlay glass table lamp by the firm of Emile Galle, 24½in. high; the shade 18¼in. diameter. (Christie's)   £130,811

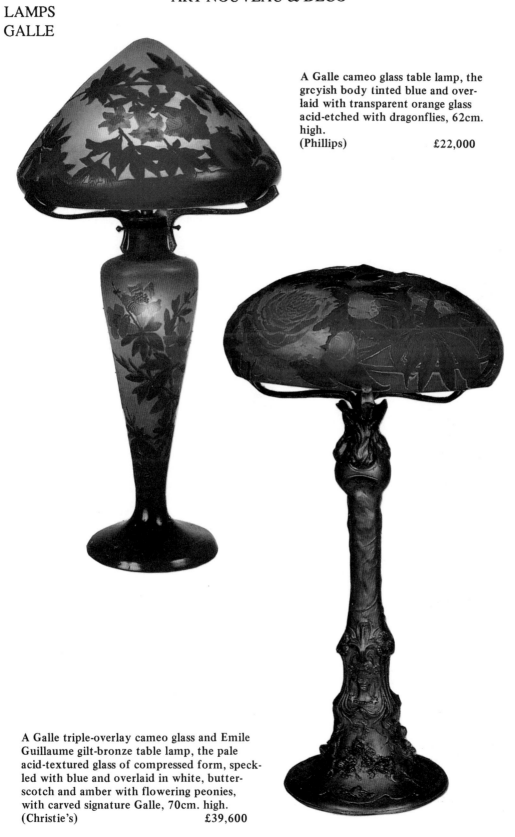

A Galle cameo glass table lamp, the greyish body tinted blue and over-laid with transparent orange glass acid-etched with dragonflies, 62cm. high.
(Phillips)   £22,000

A Galle triple-overlay cameo glass and Emile Guillaume gilt-bronze table lamp, the pale acid-textured glass of compressed form, speckled with blue and overlaid in white, butterscotch and amber with flowering peonies, with carved signature Galle, 70cm. high.
(Christie's)   £39,600

LAMPS
GALLE

A Gallé carved and acid-etched triple-overlay table lamp, the white and yellow glass overlaid in purple, blue and green, with pendent flowers and a butterfly, 58.5cm. high.
(Christie's)   £24,200

A Galle cameo glass lamp base, overlaid in deep red and etched with bell like flowers and foliage, 10in. high.
(Christie's S. Ken)   £385

A Gallé carved and acid-etched double-overlay table lamp, with mushroom-cap-shade, the yellow and red-tinted glass overlaid with red stylised flowers and fruit, 55.5cm. high.
(Christie's)   £35,200

A fine Galle carved, table lamp, overlaid with bats in the evening sky, 59cm. high. (Christie's London)
£29,700

Galle cameo glass lamp, circa 1900, 34.25cm. high.   £12,000

A Galle cameo glass table lamp with domed shade and baluster base, 60cm. high. (Christie's)   £7,560

Galle cameo glass table lamp with domed shade, signed, 42cm. high.
£8,000

An Emile Galle glass lamp, 33cm. high, circa 1900.   £12,000

Galle cameo glass table lamp signed on shade and base, 52cm. high.
£8,000

LAMPS
GALLE

Galle cameo glass lamp with green floral decoration, circa 1900, 45.5cm. high. £15,000

A Gallé carved and acid-etched double-overlay lamp, the milky-white glass overlaid with orange and yellow nasturtium, supported by a bronze naturalistic base, 38.5cm. high. (Christie's)   £9,350

A Gallé cameo glass lamp, the broad bullet-shaped shade of salmon-pink tone overlaid with reddish-orange and reddish-brown glass, 44cm. high. (Phillips)   £9,500

A Galle triple overlay cameo glass table lamp, the greyish body overlaid with lemon, pink and brownish olive glass acid etched with horse chestnut leaves and blossom, 54cm. high. (Phillips London)   £11,000

A Galle triple-overlay cameo glass and Emile Guillaume gilt-bronze table lamp, the pale acid-textured glass of compressed form, 70cm. high. (Christie's)   £39,600

A Gallé carved and acid-etched, double-overlay table lamp, the yellow glass overlaid in royal blue and purple with harebells, the base and shade with carved signatures *Gallé*, 61cm. high. (Christie's)   £41,800

A Galle cameo glass table lamp with domed shade of amber tone, 57cm. high, signed. (Phillips)   £5,800

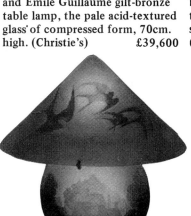

A Galle double overlay cameo glass lamp, circa 1900, 32.4cm. high. (Christie's)   £7,560

Austrian bronze lamp with Gallé Cameo glass shade, base after Friedrich Gornick, late 19th century, with stag and doe beneath trees, signed, 23$\frac{1}{2}$in. high. (Skinner Inc.)   £3,608

311

LAMPS
GRUEBY

Lamps did not feature largely in the short lived pottery venture launched by William Grueby in Boston Mass. in 1897, tiles and vases forming his principal lines. Some were produced in the early years of this century, and these feature the typical Grueby glazes, matt, opaque and mainly in shades of yellow brown, and of course dark green. Shades, and sometimes also parts of the base, were produced by other manufacturers.

A Grueby pottery lamp with Bigelow & Kennard leaded shade, circa 1905, 17¾in. diam. £2,085

Grueby pottery two-colour lamp base, Boston, circa 1905, bronze foot signed Gorham Co., 18in. high. (Robt. W. Skinner Inc.) £8,217

GUSTAV
STICKLEY

Gustav Stickley, the noted Arts & Crafts furniture designer, also ventured into lamp production. His offerings are very much what one would expect – frequent use of hammered copper, with clear signs of hand craftsmanship, simple lines, with little in the way of embellishment.

A copper and amber glass lantern, style no. 324, by Gustav Stickley, circa 1906, 15in. high, globe 5¼in. diam. (Robt. W. Skinner Inc.) £4,054

A Gustav Stickley hammered copper lamp with willow shade, circa 1905, signed, 22in. high, 20in. diam. (Robt. W. Skinner Inc.) £1,041

HAMPSHIRE

The Hampshire Pottery was founded in 1871 at Keene, New Hampshire, by J S Taft, and produced earthenware for domestic use and souvenirs for tourists. There was also some majolica production. Decoration often consisted of transfer printing in black. Lamp bases figured among their output and these can often be found teamed up with glass shades from other stables.

Hampshire pottery lamp with leaded shade, circa 1910, 19½in. high, 16in. diam. (Robt. W. Skinner Inc.) £524

Early 20th century Hampshire pottery lamp with leaded Handel shade, 21in. high, 16in. diam. (Robt. W. Skinner Inc.) £490

LAMPS
HANDEL

The Handel Company was established by Philip Handel at Meriden, Connecticut around 1885, and from 1900–1930 a branch also operated in New York City. The company produced Art Nouveau and other styles of art glass vessels, but came to be known principally for their leaded glass shades for gas and electric lighting. Many styles closely followed the designs of Tiffany, but were very much less expensive.

Handel moonlight desk lamp, with reverse painted pine forest landscape scene centring a full moon, shade 8¼in. long. (Robt. W. Skinner Inc.) £994

A Handel brass table lamp, with silvered reflective interior on brass finished three socket standard, 26in. high. (Robt. W. Skinner Inc.) £355

Leaded glass table lamp, attributed to Handel, of mottled green brickwork banded with border of bright pink apple blossoms, 23in. high. (Robt. W. Skinner Inc.) £621

Handel parrot lamp, domical Teroma glass shade signed *Handel 7128,* and by artist *Bedigie,* handpainted interior with three colourful parrots, 18in. diam. (Robt. W. Skinner Inc.) £14,286

Handel leaded glass table lamp, Meriden, Connecticut, late 19th century (some leading damage, base polished to high copper gloss), 24in. high. (Skinner Inc.) £774

An early 20th century Handel lamp on Hampshire pottery base, with Mosserine shade, 20in. high. (Robt. W. Skinner Inc.) £625

Handel type pond lily desk lamp, early 20th century, green slag and white leaded glass full blossom shade, 13¾in. high. (Skinner Inc.) £290

A Handel leaded glass lamp shade with Hampshire Pottery base, early 20th century, signed, 1851, 21in. high. (Robt. W. Skinner Inc.) £2,142

LAMPS
HANDEL

Handel leaded glass table lamp with conc shade, 23½in. high.   £1,600

Handel moonlight boudoir lamp, with reverse painted landscape scene with mountains and rolling meadows, 14in. high. (Robt. W. Skinner Inc.)   £1,118

Handel type table lamp, painted and decorated, with rust floral design, shade 16in. diameter.   £750

Handel reverse painted lamp, hand painted on the interior with wide multicoloured border band of predominantly lavender and fuchsia red scrolls, shade diam. 18in. (Robt. W. Skinner Inc.)   £2,484

A Handel adjustable desk lamp, with green glass shade, circa 1920, 12¾in. high. (Robt. W. Skinner Inc.) £446

Handel reverse painted scenic table lamp, Meriden, Connecticut, early 20th century, with brilliant sunset coloured tropical island scene, 21in. high. (Skinner Inc.)   £1,548

Handel banded poppy table lamp, reverse painted with wide border band of orange poppy blossoms, buds, pods and leaves, shade diam. 18in. (Robt. W. Skinner Inc.)   £2,950

A Handel leaded glass table lamp, the domed circular shade having rows of honey coloured marbled glass segments on the upper section, 59cm. high. (Phillips London)   £3,200

A Handel scenic table lamp, handpainted on the interior with a scenic landscape of summer birches and poplar trees, 23in. high. (Robt. W. Skinner Inc.)   £1,538

LAMPS
LALIQUE

René Lalique's work is characterised by the use of milky opalescent glass and also glass so richly coloured as to give the impression of precious stones. He used both of these in his lamp production, together with his favourite decorative motifs, dragonflies and female faces and forms. Later, he also made lamps of circular or semi-circular sheets of glass.

LE VERRE FRANÇAIS

Charles Schneider (1881–1962) opened his Cristallerie Schneider at Epiny-sur-Seine in 1913, and it is here that Le Verre Français is now recognised as having been produced. This was Art Deco glassware, cameo cut with stylized flowers, fruit and insects, chiefly in rich tones of crimson, orange, ultramarine and purple. It was produced between 1920–33, mainly for sale in large stores. Principal products were vases, bowls and lamp bases, sometimes with shade en suite. These usually consisted of a marbled glass core, with a superimposed layer of thin clear, or sometimes speckled glass.

LEGRAS

The Legras glasshouse was established in 1864 by Auguste Legras at St Denis, near Paris. It is noted for its Art Nouveau style ornamental ware, often featuring cameo snowscapes or autumn scenes. Later, Art Deco cameo glass was also produced. In 1920 the company merged with the Pantin glasshouse to become Verreries et Cristalleries de St Denis et de Pantin Réunies.

A Lalique blue stained table lamp, the shade moulded with six dancing maidens wearing classical dresses, 23.5cm. width of shade.
(Christie's London)   £7,920

A Lalique glass and metal table lamp, the frosted pyramidal shade moulded on the inside with stepped bands of beads, 51cm. high.
(Phillips)   £1,350

A Le Verre Francais acid etched table lamp with three-pronged wrought-iron mount, 42.2cm. high. (Christie's)
                    £1,760

A Le Verre Francais acid etched cameo table lamp, the milky white acid textured glass overlaid with amber fruiting vines, 46cm. high.
(Christie's London)   £4,400

A Legras etched and enamel-led glass table lamp with mushroom shaped shade, 50.6cm. high. (Christie's)
                    £1,620

A Legras glass table lamp having a domed shade, painted in coloured enamels with a pair of budgerigars and foliage, 36.5cm. high. (Phillips London)
                    £780

LAMPS
LOETZ

It was the firm of Loetz, founded at Klostermühle in Austria in 1836, which became one of the leading manufacturers of Jugendstil glass in the last years of the 19th century. Particularly striking was their iridescent glass and of all his European imitators, it was Loetz who succeeded in reproducing most closely the Favrile glass of Tiffany. Many Loetz products were in fact exported to the US.

Bronze and cameo glass lamp by Loetz, 44cm. high, circa 1900. £4,000

A Loetz glass and gilt metal table lamp. £8,000

A Loetz iridescent glass table lamp, with bronze base formed as two Art Nouveau maidens standing amid flowers, 51cm. high.
(Phillips) £900

A bronze lamp base with a Loetz shade cast from a model by M. Csadek, the base modelled as two lions seated by a tree trunk, the hemispherical shade with iridescent mother-of-pearl finish, 46cm.high. (Christie's) £1,430

A brass table lamp with a Loetz glass shade, the lightly iridescent green glass shade applied with trailed amethyst bands, 38cm. high. (Christie's) £440

MULLER FRERES

The brothers Henri and Desiré Muller, who were active during the first third of the 20th century, trained under Gallé at Nancy, before setting up their own businesses in Luneville and Croismare in 1895. Their vases and lamps, which often combine up to seven layers of glass, are usually beautifully carved. They also developed the technique of fluorogravure, using hydrofluoric acid to bite into glass painted with deep coloured or iridescent enamels. They made much use of landscape and floral motifs and sometimes applied glass cabochons.

Muller Freres cameo glass illuminated column table lamp and mushroom shaped shade, 23in. high. £2,500

A Muller Frères carved and acid-etched cameo landscape table lamp, the orange and white glass overlaid in dark amber with a wooded river landscape and deer, 48cm. high. (Christie's) £8,800

LAMPS
PAIRPOINT

The Pairpoint Manufacturing Co. started out as electroplaters in New Bedford Mass. in 1880. In 1900, they merged with the mount Washington Glass Co. to become the Pairpoint Corp., making glass only.

Their products were not much influenced by the innovations of Tiffany and Frederick Carder of the Steuben Glassworks, and they continued producing Victorian inspired floral designs.

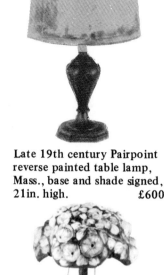

Late 19th century Pairpoint reverse painted table lamp, Mass., base and shade signed, 21in. high. £600

Early 20th century pairpoint puffy boudoir lamp, Mass., 8in. high. £1,000

Early 20th century Pairpoint reverse painted table lamp, New Bedford, base signed and numbered 3011, 22¾in. high. (Robt. W. Skinner Inc.) £1,041

Rare Pairpoint blown-out puffy apple tree lamp, with extraordinary large blown glass shade handpainted on the interior, 15½in. diameter. (Skinner Inc.) £13,514

An early 20th century pairpoint table lamp with blownout shade, New Bedford, 14in. diam. (Robt. W. Skinner Inc.) £958

A Pairpoint scenic table lamp, handpainted with four nautical scenes of tall ships separated by seashell panels, 23in. high. (Robt. W. Skinner Inc.) £1,538

Pairpoint puffy boudoir lamp, reverse painted blown-out glass shade with colourful pink and lavender pansies, roses and asters, 14½in. high. (Skinner Inc.) £1,027

Pairpoint seascape table lamp, colourfully reverse painted Directoire shade with expansive full round ocean scene, 16in. diam. (Robt. W. Skinner Inc.) £2,236

LAMPS
PAIRPOINT

Pairpoint puffy rose table
lamp with tree trunk base,
shade 8in. diameter. £1,400

Pairpoint floral and butterfly puffy table lamp, signed,
18in. high.   £3,000

Pairpoint reverse painted
open top table lamp, signed, 16in. diameter.
                    £2,000

Pairpoint blown-out puffy
lilac and trellis lamp, reverse
painted with four panels of
pink and lavender blossoms
against latticework back-
ground, 18in. diam. (Robt. W.
Skinner Inc.)   £3,416

Pairpoint butterflies and
roses puffy lamp, quatra-
form blown-out glass
dome with four butter-
fly and blossom repeats,
20½in. high.
(Skinner)   £2,639

Pairpoint floral table lamp,
large flared "Exeter" glass
shade with broad apron of
stylized blossoms of pink,
beige and amber, 22in.
high.
(Skinner)   £812

A Pairpoint boudoir lamp, with
panels of floral sprays mounted on silvered metal standard,
15in. high. (Robt. W. Skinner
Inc.)   £325

**Pairpoint bird-in-tree lamp,
handpainted in a highly stylised
frieze centring a bird with
colourful plumage, 18in. high.
(Skinner Inc.)   £757**

Pairpoint seascape boudoir
lamp, reverse painted dome
shade with whimsical Viking
ships, 14½in. high. (Robt. W.
Skinner Inc.)   £994

LAMPS
QUEZAL

Quezal glass derives its name from the brightly coloured Quezal bird of Central America. It was produced between 1901 and 1920 by Martin Bach Sr. at Brooklyn, New York with the avowed intention of imitating Tiffany's iridescent glass. A notable case is the twelve-light lily lamp, available in both Tiffany and Quezal versions.

Two Quezal gas light shades, both of opal glass in squat bulbed form, 5in. diam. (Robt. W. Skinner Inc.) £171

Quezal art glass shade on gilt lamp base, with four green and gold double hooked and pulled feather repeats, 8in. high. (Robt. W. Skinner Inc.) £404

A Quezal candle lamp, bronzed metal Art Nouveau standard with bell form gold iridescent glass shade signed on rim, 19¼in. high. (Robt. W. Skinner Inc.) £207

A Quezal desk lamp, with curved shaft adorned by a full bodied dragonfly, signed on rim, 17½in. high. (Robt. W. Skinner Inc.) £887

Rare Quezal twelve light lily lamp, gold iridescent ribbed blossom-form shades on slender stems arising from bronze leaf-pad base, 20in. high. (Skinner) £2,436

Early 20th century Tiffany bronze bridge lamp, New York, with a Quezal shade, 54½in. high. £2,500

A Quezal iridescent glass and bronze table lamp, decorated externally with green and silver-blue iridescent feathering, 64cm. high. (Phillips) £1,500

LAMPS
ROYAL DOULTON

Royal Doulton figural lamp bases set out purely as figures, and were later mounted and modified. This was done by Doulton themselves, and their catalogues from the 1930s, for example, show pages of 'Modern Decorative Electric Lamps of Royal Doulton' showing various figures beneath an assortment of shades.

A table lamp with the Royal Doulton figure Genevieve on the base, H.N. 1962, total height 44.5cm.   £230

Royal Doulton figure of 'Janet', mounted as a table lamp, issued 1936, 35cm. high.   £200

A Doulton Flambe figure by Noke, modelled as a seated Buddha, mounted as a lamp, circa 1930, 57.5cm. high. (Christie's) £864

Royal Doulton table lamp featuring 'Hinged Parasol', issued 1933, height of figure 6½in.   £375

A Royal Doulton group entitled 'The Flower Seller's Children', H.N.1206, withdrawn 1949, mounted as a table lamp. (Bearne's)   £350

ROYCROFT

The Roycroft Craft Community was established in East Aurora NY in 1895 by Elbert Hubbard, following a visit to England in 1894, when he was much influenced by the Arts & Crafts Movement. A copper workshop was opened in 1908, and here many copper lamps were produced, their simplicity of form showing a distinct Art & Crafts influence. Shades, sometimes produced elsewhere by, eg. Steuben, also reflect the stark simplicity of the Arts & Crafts ideal.

A Roycroft copper lamp with Steuben gold iridescent glass shade, circa 1910, 16in. high. £2,500

Roycroft hammered copper and mica lamp, E. Aurora, N.Y., circa 1910, no. 903, 14¾in. high. (Robt. W. Skinner Inc.)   £1,500

LAMPS

SABINO

Marius Ernest Sabino or Sabino-Marino, was a French glass artist who flourished in the 1920s and 30s. He produced Lalique inspired pieces, composed of units of pressed glass moulded on an invisible foundation and also made lampshades and vases in smoky-coloured glass.

His mark is Sabino, Paris, engraved or moulded.

One of a set of four Sabino wall lights, with moulded decoration, 38cm. high. (Christie's)
Four £1,320

A Sabino frosted glass table lamp, the shade formed as a triple cascade of water supported on three metal arms, 19.5cm. high. (Phillips London) £240

STEUBEN

The Steuben Glass Works were founded in 1903 in Corning, New York by Frederick Carder (1864–1963). Here he produced Aurene, his own version of the Peachblow glass originally produced by the New England Glass Co. in imitation of Chinese peachblow porcelain. Fine iridescent glass was also produced and lamps were made in both of these materials. In 1918 the firm merged with the Corning glass works. Steuben glass is still made today.

A Steuben Cintra sculptured lamp, of clear frosted glass with pink, blue, white and occasional yellow granules, 21in. high. (Robt. W. Skinner Inc.) £473

Steuben gold iridescent glass shade on Roycroft base, circa 1910, 10in. diameter. £1,250

Bronze table lamp with green swirl glass and calcite shade, probably Steuben, circa 1910, 14in. high. (Robt. W. Skinner Inc.) £524

A Steuben table lamp, classic form of lustrous blue Aurene mounted in Art Deco fittings, vase 11in. high. (Robt. W. Skinner Inc.) £414

A desk lamp with Steuben Aurene shade, bronzed metal standard, mirror lustre at top, 13½in. high. (Robt. W. Skinner Inc.) £325

LAMPS
TIFFANY

Art glass and lamps really come together in Louis Comfort Tiffany (1848–1933) and his favrile iridescent glass shades and designs set the standard to which all other manufacturers aspired. One of his typical designs was a cast bronze stem in the shape of a stylized plant, and a shade of multicoloured opaque favrile glass, set in irregular lozenges in a bronze mounting of overall tree or flower form.

Tiffany turtleback desk lamp, adjustable textured gold doré bronze cylinder lamp in the graduate pattern, 11¼ in. long. (Skinner Inc.) £1,405

Tiffany spider web lamp with bronze baluster base. £100,000

A Tiffany leaded glass lamp shade on Grueby pottery base, early 20th century, with dome shaped shade in acorn pattern, artist initialled A. L. for Annie Lingley, 17¾in. high. (Robt. W. Skinner Inc.) £11,428

A Louis Comfort Tiffany bronze leaded glass and favrile glass two-light table lamp, 56cm. high. (Christie's) £4,320

Tiffany bronze and favrile lotus bell lamp, mottled green and white glass segments arranged in bell form geometric progression, signed "Tiffany Studios New York", 21in. high. £15,000

A Tiffany apple blossom table lamp with pierced base. £35,000

A Tiffany bronze table lamp with lotus shade, of Oriental umbrella form with brilliant blue rectangular glass segments, 26in. high. (Robt. W. Skinner Inc.) £18,934

Tiffany Studios Nautilus' gilt bronze table lamp inset with mother-of-pearl studs, 33.5cm. high. £3,000

322

LAMPS
TIFFANY

Tiffany bronze and favrile large linenfold lamp, twelve-sided angular gilt bronze lamp shade with amber fabrique glass panels, 24½in. high.   £6,836

Spider web leaded glass, mosaic and bronze table lamp by Tiffany.   £100,000

Tiffany bronze and favrile crocus lamp, green and gold amber glass segments arranged in four repeating elements of spring blossoms, 21½in. high.   £4,660

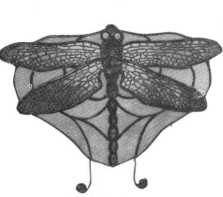

Tiffany bronze and favrile apple blossom lamp, domed shade of transparent green segmented background for yellow-centered pink and white blossoms on brown apple tree branches, 22½in. high.   £6,214

A Tiffany Studios stained glass dragonfly lamp/pendant, 25.5cm. wide, chain for suspension. (Phillips)   £500

Tiffany bronze and favrile blue dragonfly lamp, conical tuck-under shade of seven mesh-wing dragonflies with blue bodies and jewel eyes, 22½in. high. (Skinner)   £12,425

Tiffany bronze ten-light lily lamp, slender decumbent stem shade holders above lily pad stepped platform base with broad leaves, buds and vines, 16½in. high. (Robt. W. Skinner Inc.)   £8,075

Tiffany style glass and bronze dragonfly table lamp, the conical shade composed of seven radiating dragonflies with opalescent purple-pink bodies, height overall 16in. (Butterfield & Butterfield)   £1,062

One of a pair of Tiffany Studios three-light, lily-gold favrile glass and bronze table lamps, 33.2cm. high. (Christie's)   £4,400

LAMPS
TIFFANY

A Tiffany three-light table lamp, shade 40.6cm. diam., 61.5cm. high. (Christie's) £7,560

A Tiffany Studio lamp with green-blue Favrile glass moulded as a scarab, N.Y., circa 1902, 8½in. high. (Robt. W. Skinner Inc.) £1,875

A Tiffany Studios bronze and glass filigree table lamp, 42.5cm. high. (Christie's) £2,530

Tiffany bronze lamp with crocus shade, with three prong shade holder and six footed bulbous platform base, 22½in. high, shade diam. 16in. (Robt. W. Skinner Inc.) £9,938

A Tiffany Studios favrile glass and bronze ten-light lily lamp, 19½in. high. (Woolley & Wallis) £4,800

A Tiffany bronze lamp with spider and web shade, of mottled muted grey-green coloured rectangular panels divided into six segments, 19in. high. (Robt. W. Skinner Inc.) £10,650

Early 20th century Tiffany bronze table lamp with leaded shade, 22in. high. (Robt. W. Skinner Inc.) £1,748

A Tiffany Studios enamelled copper electric lamp base, circa 1900, 15in. high. (Robt. W. Skinner Inc.) £2,202

A Tiffany three-light table lamp, the bronze base bun-shaped on four ball feet, 41cm. diam. of shade, 63.5cm. high. (Christie's) £7,560

LAMPS
TIFFANY

Lead Favrile glass and bronze table lamp, by Tiffany Studios, circa 1910, 25¼in. high. £8,000

A Tiffany Studios 'lotus' leaded glass and bronze table lamp, 62.5cm. high. (Christie's)   £10,450

A Tiffany Studios 'Dragonfly' leaded glass and gilt bronze table lamp, 46.7cm. high. (Christie's)   £17,050

Early 20th century Tiffany blue iridescent candle lamp, signed, 1924, New York, 12¼in. high. (Robt. W. Skinner Inc.)   £693

A Tiffany Studios table lamp, on four-pronged spider ring attached to matching insert, 17in. high. (Robt. W. Skinner Inc.)   £1,183

A Tiffany Studios gilt bronze and glass table lamp, stamped Tiffany Studios New York 590, 48cm. high. (Christie's)   £1,728

A Tiffany Studios 'Pansy' leaded glass and bronze table lamp, 54cm. high. (Christie's)   £5,500

Tiffany favrile experimental mosque light, octagonal wooden lamp base mounted with gilt bronze conforming rim centring a light socket with octagonally panelled shade, total height 8½in. (Robt. W. Skinner Inc.)   £1,863

An important and rare Tiffany Studios leaded glass table lamp, the shallow domed shade edged with the bodies of bats, 48cm. high. (Phillips)   £60,000

LAMPS UPSTATE NEW YORK

Copper and mica table lamps, signed Upstate New York, were produced in the early years of this century. Their simple lines, hammered copper finish, and lack of fancy decoration make them very much in tune with the Arts & Crafts Movement which was flourishing at the time.

Hammered copper and mica table lamp, probably Upstate New York, with strapwork dividing four panels, 20in. high. (Skinner Inc.) £1,091

Copper and mica table lamp, Upstate New York, circa 1910, mushroom topped flaring shade with four mica panels, 29in. high. (Skinner Inc.) £1,852

WEBB

The English glasshouse of Thomas Webb & Sons was established at Stourbridge, Worcs. It is well known for its fine engraved glass and for its cameo glass, dating from the late 19th century. From 1902, Burmese glass, an American art glass shading greenish yellow to delicate pink, in matt or glossy finish was made, and was much used for lamp production. The firm continues in production today.

Late 19th century Webb decorated Burmese lamp with ruffled base, England, liner signed S. Clarke's Fairy, 5½in. high. £600

Late 19th century Webb peachblow fairy lamp in matching base, England, the base having a ruffled and fluted rim, 5½in. high. £750

Late 19th century Webb & Sons Fairy lamp, the plain shade and clear liner fitting into a decorated ruffle, 10in. high. £750

English cameo glass miniature lamp, attributed to Thomas Webb & Sons, cameo cut and carved. 9in. high. (Robt. W. Skinner Inc.) £4,348

Late 19th century Webb Burmese lamp with velvet mirrored stand, 7.3/8in. high. £350

MARBLE

Marble is surely the archetypal sculptural material, and it is perhaps inevitable that it should be somewhat neglected in a period which was so preoccupied with the discovery of new materials. There is little marble statuary from the period which shows clear Art Nouveau or Deco influence – the sculptors of the day preferred to work in other media, notably heavily subsidised chryselephantine.

Sacrifice, a blind youth holds a recumbent baby, white marble, 24in. high. £750

A 19th century French marble bust of Psyche, by Albert Carrier-Belleuse, 60cm. high. (Christie's) £2,750

Italian carved carrara marble group of two putti, circa 1900, both naked but for scanty draperies, 29in. high. (Butterfield & Butterfield) £1,719

An Italian white marble bust of Rebecca, by P. Morelli, the alluring girl wearing an oriental headdress with pendants, her long hair plaited, one plait falling over her left shoulder, late 19th century, 30in. high with socle. (Christie's) £6,380

An early 20th century Italian white marble statue of a female nude, by Alfredo Pina, 81cm. high. (Christie's) £9,350

A marble bust of Spring by Salvatore Albano, Italian, 19th century, the maiden truncated at the waist, 26³/₄in. high. (Christie's East) £2,798

Early 20th century bronze and ivory and verde antico marble group of a young woman, 7in. high. £1,500

An early 20th century English marble bas relief of a girl, by Richard Garbe, holding a knot of drapery on her left shoulder, 60cm. high. (Christie's) £550

MARBLE

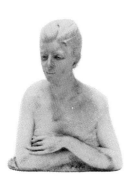

White marble portrait bust of a woman, 21in. high. £1,000

A white marble sculpture of a standing naked Venus, 26in. high. (Lots Road Chelsea Auction Galleries) £380

A white marble bust of a Bacchante in the Renaissance style, truncated as a herm, 21in. high. (Christie's East) £1,166

A 20th century English marble bust of Pharaoh's Daughter, by John Adams-Acton, 1904, 69cm. high. (Christie's) £4,400

A white marble group of four nymphs, 'The Times of the Day'. by C. Milles, 1918, 28in. high. £56,506

An allegorical white marble bust of Spring, Continental, 19th century, the young maiden with various flowers at her bosom, 21in. high.(Christie's East) £1,108

A 19th century marble bust of 'Jeune fille', probably Flora, by Albert Carrier-Belleuse, 62cm. high. (Christie's) £3,850

Pugi marble figure of a kneeling dancer on marble base, 1930's, 46.4cm. high. £750

A late 19th century Italian coloured marble bust of Beatrice, 45cm. high. (Christie's) £2,200

MIRRORS

Some very fine mirrors are to be found particularly from the Art Nouveau period, in both silver and pewter. Many of these are of the dressing table variety, and Liberty, with their Cymric and Tudric ranges, Mackintosh, and in Germany WMF, all created popular and typical designs.

Art Deco examples, often featuring a number of different materials, are also easily distinguishable for their angularity and starkness.

Shop-O'-The Crafters mahogany wall mirror, Ohio, 1910, 27½in. high, 30½in. wide. (Robt. W. Skinner Inc.)
£468

An Art Nouveau electroplated mirror and stand, the cartouche form decorated with two maidens with trumpets amid scrolling foliage, 42.8cm. long. (Christie's)
£308

A Gordon Russell oak toilet mirror, of rectangular form, with bevelled glass, pivoting on brass keys, the shaped supports of octagonal section, 60cm. high. (Christie's)
£330

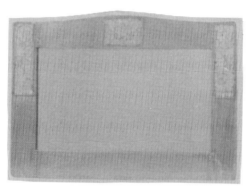

An Arts and Crafts pewter and mother-of-pearl wall mirror, decorated with rectangular panels inlaid in mother-of-pearl, 60.3 x 87cm. (Phillips)
£850

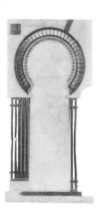

A Carlo Bugatti ebonized and vellum covered mirror, the rectangular plate with circular top, 177.5cm. high; 90cm. wide. (Christie's)
£1,210

A WMF large electroplated dressing table mirror, the semicircular base incorporating a recessed stand, 66cm. high. (Bonhams)
£1,200

A Lalique hand mirror, 'Deux Chevres', 16.20cm. diam., in original fitted case. (Phillips)
£800

A WMF Secessionist electroplated mirror, 34cm. high. (Christie's)
£825

MIRRORS

A table top mirror on shoe foot base, by Gustav Stickley, circa 1910, 21¼in. high. (Robt. W. Skinner Inc.) £432

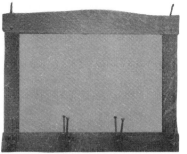

A Gustav Stickley hall mirror, style no. 66, circa 1905-06, 28in. high, 36in. wide. (Skinner Inc.) £714

Art Deco dressing table mirror in wood and plaster, 14in. high. (Muir Hewitt) £45

A Wiener Keramik oval mirror, designed by Michael Powolny, formed as a multi-coloured floral garland surmounted at the top with a yellow sparrow, 29.5cm. long. (Phillips) £280

Mirror with box base in green and amber glass, 23½in. high, 1940s. (Muir Hewitt) £35

A Liberty & Co. hammered copper mirror, the design attributed to John Pearson, decorated with two stylised cranes, 71cm. high. (Christie's London) £1,210

A painted hall mirror in the style of Robert Mallet-Stevens, 183cm. high. (Christie's) £756

A mirror attributed to Bugatti, various woods decorated with beaten copperwork and copper and pewter inlay, circa 1900, 66 x 61.8cm. (Christie's) £1,404

A German Art Nouveau bronze domed mirror, 21in. high. (Christie's) £420

ART NOUVEAU & DECO

MOTORING ITEMS

The Art Nouveau/Art Deco periods cover what is probably now regarded as the Golden Age of motoring, when the activity still retained a great deal of glamour. Art Nouveau style perhaps found its expression typically in the Lalique car mascot. In the succeeding period however, chrome was a very favoured medium, and there was plenty of chrome about motor cars. Headlights, radiator grilles therefore, as well as badges etc., all received the Art Deco treatment, and are very collectable today.

A chromium plated Healey Car Club badge, 3¼in. high. (Onslow's)   £120

B. A. R. C. Brooklands Automobile Racing Club Badge, 1930's, very rare.   £500

A Mingozzi designed lithograph 'V ͣ Corsa in salita Vittoria Cansiglio, 1 July 1928, 36 x 45cm.
(Finarte)   £125

Peugeot Revue, no's 1–52, bound in three volumes with covers and advertisements, 1923–1927.
(Onslow's)   £2,400

J. Jacquelin, Delage 1939, colour poster showing an open two seater at speed, 32 x 23in.
(Christie's)   £495

A chromium plated decanter in the form of a Bugatti radiator, by Classic Stable Ltd., 6¾in. high. (Onslows)   £260

A pair of Marchal headlamps with clear glass lenses and bulls-eye, 10in. diam. (Christie's London)   £990

A JRDC badge enamelled with stylised Brooklands racing car, 9cm. high. (Christie's S. Ken)   £605

A motorcycle racing poster by Gamy, France, 1913, 7.5/8 x 35¼in. £250

Palmares Juillet 1934 Shell, by Geo Ham, poster on linen, 79 x 60cm.
(Onslow's) £690

'Grand Prix de France Rheims 17th Juillet 1949', by Jean Des Gachons, poster on linen, 80 x 120cm.
(Onslow's) £2,000

Theodore Alexandre Steinlen: Motocycles Comiot, lithograph printed in colours, 1899, on two joined sheets of thin tan wove paper, 1,885 x 1,280mm.
(Christie's) £8,250

XXII Mille Miglia, Brescia 1 Maggio 1955, colour poster showing the Moss and Jenkinson Mercedes 300 SLR, signed and autographed by Stirling Moss, 23/300, 29 x 23½in.
(Christie's) £682

Two of twenty-one R.A.C.I. dashboard plaques, late 1920's early 1930's, approx. 3 x 2in.
(Christie's) £700

'Montaut', Baynard "En Reconnaissance", poster on linen, 155 x 115cm.
(Onslow's) £1,400

1967 Le Mans Poster, 60 x 40cm.
(Onslow's) £650

Misti [Ferdinand Mifliez] Usines D'Automobiles G Brouhot, poster on linen, 158 x 121cm.
(Onslow's) £1,400

MOTORING ITEMS

An automobile racing poster, France, circa 1906, entitled 'Circuit des Ardennes, Belges 1906-Duray, 6 Gagnant', by E. Montaut, 35¼in. wide. £250

Poster advertising the Grand Prix at the Nurburgring, 1947. £800

L D'H, Automobiles Peugeot, poster on linen, 115 x 110cm. (Onslow's) £600

Les 24 heures du Mans 1954, official programme, the front and back covers with illustrations by Geo Ham. (Christie's) £220

Peugeot, by Rene Vincent, lithograph in colours, printed by Draeger, 1170 x 1540mm. (Christie's) £800

Automobiles Peugeot La Petit Poucet Montait Une Peugeot, by Pierre Simmar, poster on linen, 200 x 140cm. (Onslow's) £2,200

XVI 1000 Miglia, Coppa Franco Mazzotti, Brescia 24 Aprile 1949, by P. Calla, lithograph in colours on card, 13 x 9½in. (Christie's New York) £629

Nick, Terrot Cycles Motorcycles, pub by Pertuy, Paris, on linen, 158cm. x 119cm. (Onslow's) £280

24 heures du Mans, 15 et 16 juin 1963, original colour poster by Guy Leygnac, unframed, 22½ x 15½in. (Christie's) £495

MOTORING ITEMS

A picnic service by Coracle for six settings, including two thermos flasks and copper spirit stove, in black vinyl covered case, 74cm. long.
(Onslow's)   £1,600

A chromium plated and enamelled B.R.D.C. badge, stamped 767 Boshier-Jones, 4¼in. high. (Onslow's)
                    £280

Philippe Chapellier, 'Eclaireurs Bleriot', published by Philippe Chapellier, Paris, on linen, 38 x 48in. (Onslow's)   £2,000

An Englebert advertising poster showing Tazio Nuvolari's Alfa Romeo B type P3, winner of the 1935 German Grand Prix, French text, 44 x 62cm.
(Finarte)   £536

A wool and felt purse with matching scarf depicting Bugatti racing car, 1920's.
(Onslow's)   £50

A Maserati poster with a Maserati valve in the foreground, designed by Adriani, 1941, 68 x 103cm.
(Finarte)   £1,161

H Behel, Georges Richard Automobiles & Cycles, pub by Camis, on linen 186cm. x 120cm.
(Onslow's)   £600

An opaque blue glass petrol pump head, lettered *Super Shell*, 17in. high.
(Christie's)   £253

Brooklands Automobile Racing Club, an aluminium and enamel Junior Car Club badge, 3½in. high. (Onslow's)
                    £110

MOTORING ITEMS

Red and white cotton Bugatti
driver's armband for the
1924 Grand Prix D'Europe.
(Onslow's)   £500

A chromium-plated and
enamelled Frazer Nash Car Club
badge, the reverse stamped 74.
(Onslow's)   £380

Aero Shell Lubricating Oil The
Aristocrat of Lubricants, by E
McKnight Kauffer, printed tin
advertisement, 1932, 48 x 74cm.
(Onslow's)   £700

Moto MV Agusta Agenzia
enamel shield, red base, 48 x
48cm., slightly worn.
(Finarte)   £201

5eme Grand Prix Automobile
Monaco 23 Avril 1933, by G.
Ham, colour lithograph, 47 x
31½in. (Onslow's)   £2,000

Geo Ham, Side-Car Cross Et
Motocross Montreuil, on linen,
123cm. x 119cm.
(Onslow's)   £180

Wakefield Castrol XXL Revels
In Revs, printed tin
advertisement, 48 x 34cm.
(Onslow's)   £460

A pair of silver trophies with
moulded foliate decoration,
inscribed Essex Motor Club
Brooklands, August 13th
1921, H. Merton 2nd Prize,
4in. high. (Onslow's)   £200

Schenkel, 'Course Automobiles
Internationale Anvers 14 Heures
22 Mai 1938', published by
Patria, Anvers, on linen,
47 x 34in. (Onslow's)   £400

335

MOTORING ITEMS

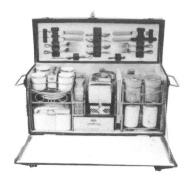

Poster, Liege, Rome, Liege Rally, 1933, 73 x 53cm. (Onslow's) £470

A fine picnic service for four settings by Coracle, with bone china cups and saucers, 61cm. long. (Onslow's) £700

Nurburgring programme 'Grosser Preis von Deutschland 26th July 1936'. (Onslow's) £793

Goodyear, double sided shaped pictorial enamel sign, 87 x 56cm. (Onslow's) £160

Olympia, Motor Show, Oct. 12 1933, colour lithograph poster, after A. E. Marty, 10 x 12½in. (Christie's) £160

Hispano-Suiza, one of two laminated showcards related to aero engines and vehicles, each 32cm. x 18cm. (Onslow's) £240

An original radiator grill for the Alfa Romeo 1750, complete with enamel badge. (Finarte) £804

Torbay and Totnes Motor Club English Riviera Trial 1935 Premier Award, a bronze figure of Victory, 10in. high. (Onslow's) £650

Join The R.A.C., printed tin-plate hanging leaflet box, 11in. high, with some member-ship leaflets. (Onslow's) £75

PEWTER

Pewter, an alloy of tin and other metals, usually copper or lead, has been used for domestic items since Roman times. During the medieval period it became the favoured metal for tableware, as a relatively cheap substitute for silver, and in 1348 the Pewterers' Company was established to set standards of workmanship and register craftsmen. By 1503 all pewterers had to register their 'touches' with the company. These marks were impressed on the handles or rims of pieces, and the system continued to operate up to 1820.

About this time pewter fell from favour. As a material associated with the Middle Ages, however, it was ripe for revival when the Arts & Crafts movement came along to extol all things medieval.

Its use in Art Nouveau settings was perhaps first taken up by the German firm of Kayser Sohn, whose pewter wares or Kayserzinnwaren designed by Hugo Leven, were sold from 1896 in the Atelier Englebert Kayser in Cologne. His tea wares with their elegant flowing decoration were the counterpart of the Liberty Tudric range in the UK.

Pewter and enamel crumb tray with Art Nouveau design, circa 1910.
(Muir Hewitt) £60

One of a pair of Art Nouveau pewter candle-sticks, 9in. high.
£380

A Loetz pewter mounted two-handled iridescent glass vase, 8¾in. high.
(Christie's) £320

A 'Victoria' radio loud-speaker with cast white metal figure of a female piper, circa 1925, 21in. high. £330

A white metal and coloured enamel dressing mirror in the Art Nouveau style, attributed to the March Bros., 50cm. high. £300

Two Argentor silvered metal candlesticks, after a design by Josef Hoffmann, circa 1910, 28cm. high. £1,000

A Jugenstil pewter mirror, with pierced frame, circa 1900, 53cm. £200

337

PEWTER

A Silberzinn pewter oil lamp, designed by Albin Muller, circa 1905, 24cm. high. £300

A Jugendstil polished pewter triptych mirror in the style of P. Huber, 32.2 x 53.4cm. (Christie's) £432

An Edelzinn pewter candelabrum, designed by J. Olbrich, 1902, 36cm. high. £3,500

A pewter mounted iridescent glass vase attributed to Loetz, circa 1900, 26.5cm. £500

A Wiener Werkstätte white-metal box, with hinged cover, decorated with a repoussé frieze of a stag and bird amid stylised trees, 8.8cm. long. (Christie's) £2,750

A Loetz white metal mounted baluster vase, the metallic orange glass with pulled loop metallic green and white decoration, 19.1cm. high. (Christie's) £638

One of a pair of pewter five-branch candelabra, probably Dutch, circa 1900, 45.5cm. high. £500

A glass jar with pewter cover and mounting, after a design by Peter Behrens, 6¼in. high. (Robt. W. Skinner Inc.) £267

An Art Nouveau electroplated pewter candlestick, formed as a freestanding scantily clad maiden holding a curvilinear branch, on pierced floral base, 32cm. high. (Christie's) £308

PEWTER

A Swedish art pewter inkwell by Svenskt Tenn, Stockholm, 12.5cm. high. (David Lay) £38

A Continental Art Nouveau pewter plaque, with the bust head of pre-Raphaelite maiden, flanked by curved uprights, 21cm. wide. (Spencer's) £60

One of a pair of Art Nouveau silvered pewter vases, each cast Flora, with copper liners, 41.5cm. high. (Christie's) £935

Pewter claret jug decorated with embossed Art Nouveau designs, circa 1870. (Spencer's) £210

A Glasgow style pewter and enamel cigar box, with an enamel plaque of a maiden holding an apron of fruit, 8¾in. wide. (Christie's) £180

One of a set of three Art Nouveau pewter wall sconces, each with two light fittings. £400

A Palme Konig und Habel vase mounted in a pewter stand, with pierced mount formed by three Art Nouveau maidens on pierced tripartite stand, 24.3cm. high. (Christie's) £528

A pair of Argentor silvered metal vases, after a design by Josef Hoffman, circa 1920, 17cm. high. £550

One of a pair of Art Nouveau pewter three light candelabra, each with flowerhead sconces with foliate drip-pans, 25.5cm. high. (Phillips) Two £580

PEWTER
KAYSERZINN

The firm of Kayser Sohn was founded in 1885 at Krefeld-Bochum, near Dusseldorf, by Jean Kayser (1840–1911). From 1896 they manufactured Jugendstil, or Art Nouveau, items such as ashtrays, beakers, vases, lamps, etc, known as Kayserzinnwaren, or Kayser pewter wares. Their principal designer was Hugo Leven (b. 1874). Pieces were characterised by their flowing floral decoration and they were sold at the Atelier Englebert Kayser.

Pair of Art Nouveau polished pewter presentation cups attributed to Kayserzinn, 9¼in. high.   £300

A Kayserzinn Art Nouveau pewter dish on four ball feet, 10½in. wide.   £200

An electroplated pewter Jugenstil mirror frame, probably Kayserzinn, 46cm., circa 1900. £700

A Kayserzinn pewter teaset, the tray 18in. wide, all with stamped marks. (Christie's) £190

One of a pair of Kayserzinn pewter candlesticks, possibly designed by Hugo Leven, circa 1900, 42cm. high.   £1,000

German pewter three-handled soup tureen with boar mount, by Kayserzinn, 15in. high. (Worsfolds)   £250

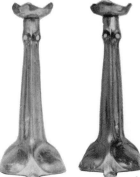

Pair of Kayserzinn pewter candlesticks on three feet, circa 1900, 30.5cm. high. (Christie's)   £378

A Kayserzinn pewter jardiniere, stamped Kayserzinn 4093. 29.8cm. high. (Christie's)   £250

PEWTER – LIBERTY

In the 1890s in England, the Art Nouveau style was championed above all by Arthur Lazenby's Liberty store, so much so that in Italy, for example, it came to be known simply as 'il Stile Liberty'. In the late 1890s Liberty appointed the Manxman Archibald Knox as their chief metalwork designer, and he set to work on a range of silverware, 'Cymric', and pewterware, 'Tudric', which epitomised everything that was Art Nouveau and which continued to be produced until 1938.

Tudric ware is characterised by the combination of Celtic motifs with the stylized natural decoration which was the essence of Art Nouveau. The range included functional items such as tankards, spoons and plates, while applied decoration was often added to vases, trays, candlesticks and clocks. Sometimes, too, pieces were decorated with applied plaques of green or blue enamel, mother of pearl or copper, and some fruit bowls were pierced and lined with coloured glass.

Liberty Tudric pewter dish, Archibald Knox design, 8in. diameter, circa 1900.
(Muir Hewitt)   £60

A Liberty & Co. pewter and enamel clock, circa 1905.   £400

'For Old Times 'Sake', a pair of Liberty & Co. 'Tudric' twin-handled vases of cylindrical shape, 20cm. high, impressed 'Tudric and 010' to base.
(Phillips)   £300

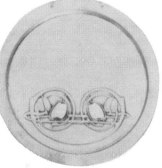

A Liberty & Co. Art Nouveau pewter circular tray designed by Archibald Knox, embellished in relief with entwined tendrils terminating with stylised honesty leaves, 25.2cm. diam.
(Phillips London)   £600

A pair of Liberty & Co. Tudric pewter twin-branched candelabra designed by Archibald Knox, with pierced decoration of leaves and berries on tendrils, on rectangular flat foot, 27.8cm. high. (Christie's) £1,870

A Liberty & Co. pewter and enamel cigarette box and cover, the rectangular form having a hinged cover inset with a rectangular enamelled panel, by Varley, 17.20cm. long.
(Phillips)   £400

A Liberty pewter and Clutha glass bowl on stand, designed by Archibald Knox, stamped Tudric 0276, circa 1900, 16.3cm. high. (Christie's)   £453

LIBERTY PEWTER

A Liberty pewter and green glass bowl, designed by A. Knox, stamped Tudric 0320 Rd, 426933, 20.3cm. diam. (Christie's) £378

Liberty's Tudric pewter beaker holder with green glass liner. (Muir Hewitt) £45

A Liberty Tudric two-handled rose bowl on raised circular foot, 24cm. diam. £400

A Liberty & Co. English pewter bowl, with Clutha glass liner, the mount pierced and embellished with plant forms, 16.5cm. high. (Phillips London) £950

Liberty's Tudric pewter three piece tea set, 1930s. (Muir Hewitt) £50

Liberty & Co. Tudric pewter two-handled motto cup, London, circa 1910, 7.7/8in. high. (Robt. W. Skinner Inc.) £121

A Liberty & Co. pewter rose bowl designed by Rex Silver, embellished in relief with heavy plant form motifs, set with glass studs, 15.6cm. high. (Phillips London) £360

One of a pair of Liberty & Co. 'Tudric' pewter and enamel candlesticks, circa 1905, 30cm. high. £700

A Liberty & Co. 'Tudric' pewter box and cover, designed by Archibald Knox, 11.9cm. high. (Christie's) £264

LIBERTY PEWTER

A Tudric planished pewter bowl raised upon four fluted cabriole supports terminating in trefoil feet, with cut card type terminals, 13in. wide over feet terminals.
(Spencer's) £150

A Liberty Tudric pewter biscuit box designed by Archibald Knox, of cuboid form stamped with a row of formalised flowers over a row of square leaves, 5in. high over handle.
(Spencer's) £320

A Liberty & Co. enamelled pewter tray, decorated with organic patterns and central turquoise enamel reserve, stamped *English Pewter,* 31cm. long. (Christie's London)
£352

A Liberty Tudric pewter and Powell green glass decanter, circa 1900, 30cm. high. £375

A Liberty and Co. pewter four piece tea service designed by Archibald Knox, the teapot with compressed globular body, stamped Made in England, English Pewter. (Christie's) £495

A Liberty pewter and enamel table clock designed by Archibald Knox, circa 1900, 14.2cm. high.
(Christie's) £1,296

A Liberty & Co. 'Tudric' pewter timepiece, showing the influence of C.F.A. Voysey, in the form of a dwelling, 34cm. high.
(Phillips) £1,850

Tudric pewter dish with stylized floral decoration, circa 1900.
(Muir Hewitt) £60

One of a pair of Liberty Tudric mugs designed by A. Knox with original green glass liners by J. Powell & Son, circa 1900, 13cm. high. £250

W.M.F. PEWTER

These letters stand for the Württembergische Metallwarenfabrik (Württemberg Metalware Factory) which was situated at Geislingen, about 30 miles from Stuttgart. Here they produced Art Nouveau and Art Deco style tableware in a stainless steel alloy of their own manufacture known as Cromagen, and also in a type of German silver which they patented as Ikora metal.

With regard to decorative pieces, mirrors, candlesticks, decanters etc, under the direction of Carl Haegele and their chief designer Beyschlag, WMF pushed the curvilinear style of Art Nouveau metalwork to its extreme. It was described variously as the Whiplash style, the Spaghetti style or, as put by Charles Rennie Mackintosh, 'resembling melted margarine'! Art Nouveau flowing-haired and flowing-robed maidens are also very prevalent on WMF pieces. A combination of pewter and green glass was a favourite medium.

A glass studio was also attached to the factory in 1921, with teaching workshops for glass and gem cutting. This was under the direction of Wilhelm von Eiff.

Ikora glass was developed in 1925 and used to make usually heavy glass objects with airbubble decoration in organised patterns and encrustations in colour. Some diatreta glass vases were also produced after 1932. This technique, which dates from Roman times, involves a double layered glass vessel with the outer layer cut away to form a delicate, intricate trellis over the lower layer, to which it remains attached by means of small decorated struts.

A WMF electroplated pewter sweetmeat dish, the trefoil scalloped form with handle formed by a freestanding Art Nouveau maiden, stamped with usual WMF marks, 31.3cm. long. (Christie's)   £308

Large WMF twin-handled electroplated metal vase with Art Nouveau handles, circa 1900, 50cm. high.   £450

A WMF electroplated pewter centrepiece, the trumpet form body with pierced panels of floral decoration and two buttress supports, 51cm. high. (Christie's London)   £286

A WMF electroplated pewter drinking set with shaped rectangular tray, circa 1900, tray 48 x 34cm. (Christie's) £648

A WMF pewter coupe, the pierced oval body formed by two Art Nouveau butterfly-maidens, with shaped green glass liner, , 17.8cm. high. (Christie's)   £308

A WMF silver plated pewter mounted green glass decanter, circa 1900, 38.5cm. high. (Christie's)   £378

W.M.F. PEWTER

A WMF electroplated metal centrepiece of boat form, circa 1900, 46cm. wide. £700

A W M.F. pewter letter tray, of curvilinear form, cast in shallow relief with a naked maiden, 10in. long. (Christie's S. Ken) £198

A WMF pewter centrepiece, decorated with flowerheads and butterflies, with cobalt-blue shaped glass liner, 42.3cm. long. (Christie's) £715

A WMF electroplated pewter vase mount, modelled with a seated male figure holding up a rose to a scantily clad maiden, on four openwork feet, (liner missing) 40.4cm. high. (Christie's) £550

A WMF silvered pewter wall plaque cast in relief with three mermaids gazing up to a maiden picking fruit from a tree, 23in. wide. (Christie's) £440

One of a pair of WMF elec-troplated candlesticks, each cast as a young woman sup-porting a flower sprouting to form the four candleholders, 48cm. high, circa 1900. £2,200

A WFM pewter mounted glass claret jug with foliate handle and hinged cover, 13¾in. high. £300

Four W.M.F. glasses on spiral stems. (Muir Hewitt) £300

A WMF silvered pewter jar-diniere cast as a conch shell with a salamander, 32cm. high. (Christie's) £486

W.M.F. PEWTER

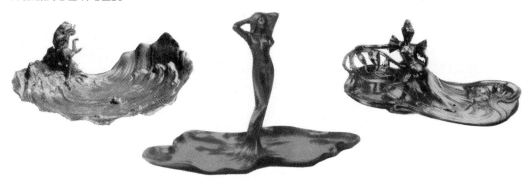

A WMF pewter dish, of shaped oval section, in the form of a river, a frog playing the flute sitting on the bank, 23cm. long. (Christie's)   £143

A WMF pewter centrepiece, cast as a young girl with flowing robe forming an irregular-shaped tray, 22.5cm. high. (Christie's)   £440

A W.M.F. pewter letter tray of curvilinear form, modelled with a maiden reading a letter, stamped marks, 12½in. long. (Christie's S. Ken)   £550

An electroplated pewter mirror frame attributed to WMF, circa 1900, 50cm. high. (Christie's)   £432

A pair of pewter W.M.F. candelabra with nymphs entwined around tendrils which form the sconces, on spreading bases, 25cm. high. (Phillips)   £900

A W. M. F. electroplated pewter lamp stand, modelled as an Art Nouveau maiden holding aloft a bulbous stand, 32.3cm. high. (Christie's)   £440

One of a pair of Art Nouveau pewter vases, attributed to WMF, with glass liners, stamped A K & Cie, 36cm. high. (Christie's)   £1,045

A WMF pewter centrepiece with rectangular clear glass tank, stamped marks, 55.5cm. wide, 31.4cm. high. (Christie's)   £825

A WMF pewter mounted green glass decanter of flaring form on four leaf molded feet, 15in. high. (Christie's)   £300

W.M.F. PEWTER

A W. M. F. pewter letter tray, with pierced and raised scrolling floral decoration and modelled with a maiden stretching her hand towards a lily, 10¼in. long. (Christie's S. Ken) £385

A W. M. F. electroplated pewter tray, with pierced and raised decoration of an Art Nouveau maiden with flowing hair and an iris, 33.1cm. diam. (Christie's) £209

A W.M.F. electroplated pewter letter tray, the oval tray cast in relief with an Art Nouveau maiden reclining beside a lily pond, 10in. wide. (Christie's S. Ken) £605

Two of a set of six WMF pewter tea-glass holders, each with scrolling handle and pierced entrelac and ivy decoration, on four feet, stamped with usual WMF marks, 7.5cm. high. (Christie's) Six £330

A pair of W.M.F. twin handled pewter vases, decorated in relief with tendril-like entrelacs, on splayed quatrefoil base, 35cm. high. (Phillips) £552

A W.M.F. polished pewter frame mirror, on easel support, cast in full relief with an Art Nouveau maiden gazing at her reflection, 14½in. high. (Christie's S. Ken) £1,045

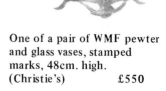

A WMF pewter mounted engraved green glass decanter of flaring form, 9½in. high, stamped marks. (Christie's) £130

A WMF electroplated pewter desk tray, the bi-partite form with scalloped edges, with central loop handle moulded as a butterfly-maiden, stamped 80, 31cm. wide. (Christie's) £308

One of a pair of WMF pewter and glass vases, stamped marks, 48cm. high. (Christie's) £550

PLASTER

Plaster is a very versatile medium, and a number of interesting sculptures appeared during the Art Nouveau/Deco periods, some disguised, for example silvered, to make them look like something completely different. Richard Garbe produced many classical/Art Nouveau figures, of naked maidens with flowing hair and drapery.

An Art Deco silvered plaster figure of a naked female with a hoop, circa 1935, 11½in. high.   £100

A late 19th century French plaster bust of 'L'Espiegle', signed on the shoulder J. B. Carpeaux, 51cm. high. (Christie's)   £1,540

A Richard Garbe green-tinted plaster figure of a naked seated maiden, 1928, 104cm. high. (Christie's)   £702

An English plaster panel, in oak frame carved 'Speed with the light-foot winds to run', 42.2 x 37.7cm. (Christie's)   £110

A Richard Garbe plaster figure of a naked maiden, 1912, 99cm. high. (Christie's)   £432

A Richard Garbe plaster figure of a naked kneeling maiden with streaming hair and flowing drapery, 102cm. high. (Christie's)   £810

'Tete de femme', a plaster head of a woman by Moshe Ziffer, 28cm. high.   £300

A James Woolford plaster figure modelled as a diving mermaid with a dolphin, circa 1930, 59cm. high. (Christie's)   £216

PLASTIC

Plastics are the great revolutionary material of the 20th century. Celluloid came first, followed by bakelite and perspex. Much early plastic tended to be brittle, however, and it was not until the late 50's and 60's that such huge technological advances were made in terms of pliability and durability that there is now a plastic suitable for just about every purpose under the sun.

One of plastic's main attractions has always been its cheapness. As such, plastic items therefore appear an unlikely choice for collectables. However, many early plastic items are now being keenly collected, perhaps as much for their nostalgia value as anything.

"Teasmade" 1950s, in ivory plastic with chromium fittings. (Muir Hewitt) £35

Perspex ice bucket, 1930s, in pale blue and ivory. (Muir Hewitt) £20

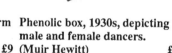

Phenolic napkin ring in the form of a stylized elephant. (Muir Hewitt) £9

Phenolic box, 1930s, depicting male and female dancers. (Muir Hewitt) £20

Perspex lamp in pale blue and pink, 1940s, 8in. high. (Muir Hewitt) £35

1950's green plastic perpetual calendar with Venetian scene. £5

Perspex and chrome lamp in black and ivory, 1940s, 8in. high. (Muir Hewitt) £20

1930s plastic powder bowl featuring a woman's head on the lid. (Muir Hewitt) £12

POSTERS

There was a great revival of interest in Art Nouveau posters in the early Seventies when no student bedroom was complete without its Toulouse Lautrec or Mucha print. Beautifully ornate and brightly coloured, they are always eye-catching, and one senses that they were designed for their aesthetic appeal, rather than for any hard-sell advertising purpose.

Lithographic poster 'La Dame Aux Camelias Sarah Bernhardt', by Alphonse Mucha, 1896, 208 x 76cm. £5,000

Henri de Toulouse-Lautrec, 'Le Photographe Sescau', lithograph printed in colours, 1894, on wove paper, Adreani's second state, 607 x 782mm. (Christie's) £13,750

Alphonse Maria Mucha: Reverie, lithograph printed in colours, 1896, on wove paper, 639 x 477mm. (Christie's) £2,420

'Chocolat Ideal', by Alphonse Mucha, circa 1900, 85 x 58cm. £500

A lithographed print, 'Carnation', signed in the block 'Mucha', 105 x 44cm., 1897. £605

Absinthe Robette by Privat Livemont, lithograph printed in colours, 1896, 104 x 75.2cm. £375

Eugene Grasset, 'Jeanne d'Arc, Sarah Bernhardt', circa 1900, lithographic poster, 116 x 71cm. £310

POSTERS

'Princenza Wilhelmina' lithographic poster by Paul Berthon, signed, circa 1900, 39 x 36cm.   £400

Henri de Toulouse-Lautrec, Au Concert, lithograph printed in colours, 1896, on cream wove paper, Wittrock and Adriani's third (final) state with the lettering, a very good impression, 320 x 255mm. (Christie's)   £19,800

'Monaco Monte Carlo', by Alphonse Mucha, 1897, 110 x 76cm.   £990

'Le Sureau (I)', lithographic print by Paul Berthon, circa 1900, 91 x 32cm.   £750

'Suzy Deguez Dans Ses Danses D'Art', by Eugene Grasset, 197 x 77.5cm., circa 1900.   £1,000

'Fap 'anis' poster by Delval, depicting colourful girl holding a glass of liqueur, 62½ x 47in., circa 1920's.   £200

Henri de Toulouse-Lautrec, Le Divan Japonais, lithograph printed in colours, 1892–3, on buff wove paper, a fine impression, the colours good and strong, 800 x 622mm. (Christie's)   £33,000

A lithographic poster, Maria del Villar, by Lion Astric, 1920's, 104 x 79cm.   £200

Jane Renouardt, by Pierre Stephen, lithograph in colours, printed by M. Picard, Paris, 1538 x 1175mm. (Christie's) £100

Alcazar Royal, by Adolphe Crespin and Edouard Duych, lithograph in colours, 1894, 1010 x 775mm. (Christie's) £280

Job, by Alphonse Mucha, lithograph in colours, 1898, on wove paper, printed by F. Champenoise, Paris, 1500 x 1010mm. (Christie's) £3,500

Cowgirl Circus Poster, 1920. £50

XXVI Ausstellung Secession, by Ferdinand Andri, lithograph in colours, circa 1904, on wove paper, 920 x 602mm. (Christie's) £8,700

Cyclistes !!! Attention, by Tichon, 1890, 51 x 37in. £100

La Revue Des Folies Bergere, by Jules Alexandre Grun, lithograph in colours, 1905, printed by Ch. Verneau, Paris, 1246 x 880mm. (Christie's) £150

G. B. Borsalino Fu Lazzaro & C, by Marcello Dudovich, lithograph in colours, 1932, printed by R. Questura, Milano, 1390 x 1000mm. (Christie's) £250

Opera, Bal Des Petits Lits Blancs, L'Intran, by Marie Laurencin, lithograph in colours, 1931, 1600 x 1196mm. (Christie's) £1,000

POSTERS

Poster for George Humphrey's bookstore, by M. Louise Stowell, 1896, 11 x 15½in. (Robt. W. Skinner Inc.)
£187

Edouard Bernerd, 'Arlette Montal', 1920's, lithographic poster, 128 x 85cm.
£120

S. V. U. Manes, 150 Vystava, Clenska, lithograph in colours, 1929, printed by Melantrich Praha, Smichov, 1250 x 950mm. (Christie's)
£120

Three, Les Maitres de l'Affiche, Volumes I-V, Imprimerie Chaix, Paris 1896-1900, sheet 403 x 315mm. (Christie's)
£13,200

G. Marconi, Le Maitre De La Radio, by Paul Colin, lithograph in colours, printed by Bedos & Cie, Paris, 1578 x 1130mm. (Christie's)
£220

A theatrical poster, chromo-lithographed on paper The Dreadnoughts, 1920, 53 x 39in.
£150

Soiree De Paris, Spectacles, Choregraphiques et Drama-tiques, by Marie Laurencin, lithograph in colours, signed in pencil and dated 1924, 796 x 578mm. (Christie's)
£170

POSTERS

Nationale Luchtvaart School, lithograph in colours, by Kees Van des Haan, backed on linen, 31 x 23in.
(Christie's) £1,320

Henri de Toulouse Lautrec: Eldorado: Aristide Bruant, lithograph printed in colours, 1892, on two sheets of thin tan wove paper, 930 x 1,354mm. (Christie's) £19,800

'Young Woman with Flowers', lithographic poster by Paul Berthon, circa 1900, 44 x 42cm. £400

"Hoyles Super Drill" original Art Nouveau poster, framed and glazed.
(Muir Hewitt) £85

1930s "Cinderella" poster.
(Muir Hewitt) £25

'8 Bells' comedy poster, by Strobridge Lithograph Co., Ohio, circa 1910, 40 x 30in. £85

Lithographic poster, 'Internationale Kunst Ausstellung', by Frans Stuck, 84 x 36cm., circa 1905. £340

'Exposition Internationale Anvers 1930', by Marfurt, lithographic poster, 104 x 74cm. £300

POSTERS

A lithographic poster, Gaby Montbreuse, by Anton Girbal, 1924, 159 x 116cm.
£400

Aero-Club de France; XVme Grand Prix des Spheriques, Reims, 19 Sept. 1926, lithograph in colours, printed by Lapina, Paris, backed on linen, 46½ x 30in.
(Christie's)
£1,540

Maurice Denis: 'La Depeche — Grand Format', a chromo-lithographic poster, 145.5 x 100cm. (Phillips)
£70

A lithographic poster, 'Lorenzaccio', 1899, 37 x 104cm.
£500

A lithographed print, 'Rose', signed in the block 'Mucha', 1897, 107.5 x 46cm. £2,000

'Bar', by E. Dantan, circa 1925.
£1,100

Semaine d'Aviation du Lyon, du 7 au 15 Mai 1910, lithograph poster in colours, by Charles Tichon, printed by Emile Pecaud, Paris, some soiling, backed on linen, 61½ x 46in.
(Christie's)
£2,860

A Walter Schnackenberg poster entitled 'Erry & Merry', litho-graph in colours, 50 x 37½in.
(Christie's)
£4,400

PRINTS

The most notable prints of the Art Deco period more often than not have distinctly erotic overtones, and the artist who most immediately springs to mind in this connection is the Frenchman Louis Icart. His sinuous female figures in their drifting skirts, often accompanied by equally sleek greyhounds, have a fantasy quality. Often his message is less subtle and on occasion borders on the pornographic, reflecting the hedonism and decadence of the times.

Claude Flight, Speed, linocut printed in colours, circa 1925, on thin Japan, signed in pencil, 220 x 205mm. (Christie's)
£2,420

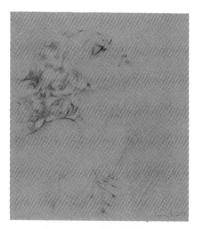

Young Woman with Flowers, lithographic print by Paul Berthon, circa 1900, 46 x 59cm. £500

'Pink Lady', by Louis Icart, etching and drypoint, printed in colours, signed lower right with artist's blindstamp, Copyright 1935, 21.6cm. x 28.7cm. (Christie's) £1,100

1920s print "Honeymoon in Venice".
(Muir Hewitt) £75

'Ecstasy', by Louis Icart, etching and drypoint, printed in colours, signed lower right with artist's blindstamp, Copyright 1935, 34cm. x 38cm. (Christie's) £2,420

'Summer Dreams', by Louis Icart, etching and drypoint, printed in colours, signed lower right, Copyright by L. Icart Sty. N.Y., 33cm. x 46cm.
(Christie's) £7,700

'Tosca', by Louis Icart, etching and drypoint, printed in colours, signed lower right with artist's blindstamp, Copyright 1928, 54.5cm x 35cm.
(Christie's) £1,320

'Fair Dancer', by Louis Icart, etching and drypoint, printed in colours, signed lower right with artist's blindstamp, Copyright 1939, 49.7cm. x 57.6cm.
(Christie's) £1,980

PRINTS

'Leda and the Swan', by Louis Icart, etching and drypoint, printed in colours, signed lower right with artist's blindstamp, *Copyright 1934 by L. Icart Cty. N.Y.*, 52cm. x 80cm.
(Christie's)   £10,450

Jennie Harbour print, 1930s, 'La Manola'.
(Muir Hewitt)   £25

'Les Boules De Neige', lithographic print by Paul Berthon, circa 1900, 48 x 59cm.   £500

'Michelle', by Erté, a serigraph, printed in colours, on wove paper, signed in pencil, numbered 198/300, printed and published by The Chicago Serigraph Workshop, Chicago, Illinois, November 1980, with margins, mounted and framed, 63.2 x 46cm. (Christie's)   £660

1920s framed print "Beauty gained is love retained".
(Muir Hewitt)   £75

Laura Knight: At The Fair, aquatint, signed in pencil, mount-stained, taped to front mount, 26 x 21cm.
(Phillips)   £300

'Papillon II', by Louis Icart, etching and drypoint, printed in colours, signed lower right, Copyright 1936, 18.5 x 24cm.
(Christie's)   £4,840

'Faust', by Louis Icart, etching and drypoint, printed in colours, signed lower right with artist's blindstamp, Edite par Les Graveurs Modernes 194 Rue de Rivoli Paris, 54cm. x 34cm.
(Christie's)   £660

'Morning Cup', by Louis Icart, etching and drypoint, printed in colours, signed lower right with artist's blindstamp, Copyright 1936, 30cm. x 64.5cm.
(Christie's)   £1,650

Toraji Ishikawa (1875-1964)
— dai oban-tate, 48.5 x 36.7cm.,
a back view of a nude dancer,
signed Ishikawa, sealed Tora.
(Christie's) £715

Paul Cesar Helleu: Madame
Wolffe, drypoint, printed in
colours, signed in pencil, 54
x 33.6cm. (Phillips) £2,400

After Sir William Russell
Flint, R.A., 'A question of
attribution', reproduction in
colours, signed in pencil,
21½ x 16in. (Christie's)
£660

Christopher Richard Wynne Nevinson: After
a German Retreat, Labour Battalion making
a Road through a captured Village, lithograph
printed in dark brown, 1918, 235 x 308mm.
(Christie's) £1,210

Rolf Nesch: Negerrevue, etching with
drypoint and aquatint printed in black,
orange-red and deep mustard yellow, 1930,
on thick fibrous Japan, 353 x 555mm.
(Christie's) £19,800

Otto Dix: Kupplerin, lithograph
printed in red, yellow and blue,
1923, numbered 5/65, 482 x
367mm. (Christie's) £22,000

Pierre-Auguste Renoir: La
Danse a la Campagne, Deuxieme
Planche, soft-ground etching,
circa 1890, on wove paper,
220 x 135mm. (Christie's)
£5,280

Henri de Toulouse-Lautrec:
Le Jockey, lithograph, 1899,
on Chine, second (final)
state, from the edition of
100, 504 x 359mm.
(Christie's) £11,550

PRINTS

Louis Icart: Mimi, drypoint with aquatint printed in colours, 1927, on wove paper published by Les Graveurs Modernes, Paris, 534 x 356mm. (Christie's)   £605

Erich Heckel: Hockende, woodcut, 1913, on soft wove paper, watermark Saskia, first state of two, 417 x 306mm. (Christie's)   £7,150

Conrad Felixmuller: Ich zeich-nend (Selbstbildnis mit Akt), woodcut, 1924, on wove paper, 545 x 335mm. (Christie's)
£1,540

Pablo Picasso: Personnages masques et Femme Oiseau, etching with aquatint, 1934, on Montval, watermark Vollard, from the edition of 250, 249 x 348mm. (Christie's)   £3,300

Jacques Villon: Les Joueurs de Cartes, after P. Cezanne, aquatint printed in colours, 1929, on Arches, signed, 487 x 601mm. (Christie's)
£1,760

Ernst Ludwig Kirchner: Halbakt, lithograph, 1909, on smooth wove paper, 256 x 149mm. (Christie's)
£24,200

Edgar Chahine, Lily Arena assise, drypoint, 1907, on Japan, signed in pencil, an artist's proof aside from the full numbered edition of 90, 548 x 440mm. (Christie's)
£462

Jacob Kramer: Vorticist Figure, lithograph, circa 1920, on laid paper, 417 x 252mm. (Christie's)   £1,430

PRINTS

Louis Icart, Méditation, drypoint with aquatint part printed in colours, finished by hand, 1930, on wove paper, signed in pencil with the artist's blindstamp, 15¹/₂ x 19¹/₂ in. (Christie's S. Ken)   £4,950

Ethelbert White (1891–1972), The Barge Breakers; Regents Canal; Sawing logs; The Weeping Ash; Plowmans' Cottage; The River Bank; and The Hamlet, wood engravings, 5¹/₂ x 7in. (Christie's S. Ken)   £418

Louis Icart, 'L'Heure de la Melodie', drypoint with aquatint printed in colours finished by hand, 1934, on wove paper, signed in pencil, published by Icart, New York, 475 x 596mm. (Christie's)   £3,080

Framed advert for Army Club cigarettes. (Muir Hewitt)   £20

'Attic Room', by Louis Icart, etching and drypoint, printed in colours, signed lower right, 36.2 x 42.1cm. (Christie's)   £4,840

Helen Adelmann watercolour fashion sketch, framed and glazed. (Muir Hewitt)   £250

'Spanish Nights', by Louis Icart, etching and drypoint printed in colours, numbered 67, Copyright 1926, 53.5cm. x 34.5cm. (Christie's)   £2,860

Felix Vallotton, La Paresse, woodcut, 1896, on wove paper, a fine impression, signed and numbered *109* in blue crayon, from the edition of about 180, with margins, 177 x 222mm. (Christie's)   £6,050

'Symphony in Blue', by Louis Icart, etching and drypoint, printed in colours, signed lower right, © Copyright 1936, 59.2 x 49.7cm. (Christie's)   £3,300

PRINTS

'Before the Raid' by Louis Icart, etching and drypoint, printed in colours, signed lower right, 46.5 x 56.5cm.
(Christie's) £2,750

'Smoke', by Louis Icart, etching and drypoint, printed in colours, signed lower right, © Copyright 1926 by Les Graveurs Modernes, 38.1 x 51.5cm.
(Christie's) £3,300

Edvard Munch, 'Das Weib', drypoint with aquatint, 1895, on firm, cream wove paper, fifth state, signed and dated '1913' in pencil, 297 x 348mm.
(Christie's) £19,800

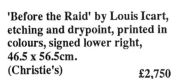

Helen Adelmann watercolour fashion sketch, framed and glazed.
(Muir Hewitt) £250

Louis Icart: Parfum des Fleurs (Le Divan), etching with dry-point and aquatint printed in colours, 1937, 447 x 643mm.
(Christie's) £1,100

Foil and paper picture, 1930s, in glazed black frame.
(Muir Hewitt) £45

Jeanne d'Arc, by Louis Icart, dry-point with aquatint printed in colors, signed in pencil (1929), 54 x 37cm. (Christie's) £572

'Martini', by Louis Icart, etching and drypoint, printed in colours, signed lower right with artist's blindstamp, numbered 52 *Copyright 1932 by L. Icart Sty. N.Y.*, 34cm. x 44cm.
(Christie's) £5,500

Woman with Irises, lithographic print by Paul Berthon, circa 1900, 87 x 61cm. £500

RADIOS

By the 1930s, radio production had become more sophisticated. The wireless was coming to be seen as an essential item for most homes, in every sense 'part of the furniture' and it began to be designed as such. Large Art Deco sets in bakelite or wood veneers are now among the most sought after examples for their fascinating designs and immense character.

Many are still in good working order, which is an added bonus, and some connoisseurs insist that they produce a mellowness of tone which has never been equalled by the modern transistor.

A French SNR Excelsior 5 radio, dark brown. (Auction Team Koeln)   £100

R F T Super Type 4 U 62 all mains receiver, with UCH11, UBF11 and UCL11, bakelite housing, by Funkwerk Dresden, circa 1950. (Auction Team Köln)   £45

An Ekco Model 313 AC mains receiver in horizontal brown bakelite case, 16³/₄in. wide, circa 1930, and a Celestion speaker in mahogany case. (Christie's S. Ken)   £198

An Ekco Type AD65 AC/DC mains receiver in circular brown bakelite case with semi-circular dial, 15¹/₂in. diameter. (Christie's S. Ken)   £209

A German radiogram, the case designed in 1928 by Prof. Bruno Paul, made by Telephonefabrik Berliner, 1930. (Auction Team Koeln)   £195

A wooden cased Berliner Wien radio with built in dual straight receiver and free swivel loud-speaker. (Auction Team Koeln)   £22

An Ekco Type A22 AC mains receiver in circular black bakelite case with circular dial, 13¹/₄in. diameter. (Christie's S. Ken)   £528

An Ekco R.S.2 3-valve mains receiver in Art Deco style brown bakelite case with triple speaker grille, 16¹/₄in. high. (Christie's S. Ken)   £121

RADIOS

A Fada yellow plastic valve radio with green marbled louvred speaker, original label, 8¼in. wide.
(Christie's S. Ken.) £605

An early Marconiphone battery powered pocket radio, circa 1955. (Auction Team Koeln) £47

An Ekco Type BS3 AC mains receiver in black Art Deco case with oxidised metal grille formed as stylised trees, 17¾in. high.
(Christie's S. Ken) £385

A Pye Model 350 four-valve receiver in horizontal walnut case with sloping control panel above fret, 17in. wide, and a Celestion Model 79 speaker in arched case.
(Christie's S. Ken) £242

Bush radio in white plastic case, 1950s.
(Ken Priestley) £60

A Pilot Model U-650 six-valve receiver in upright walnut veneered case with circular tuning dial with 'Magic Eye', 19½in. high.
(Christie's S. Ken) £286

'Ultra' AC Mains '3', wood cabinet, 1932. £75

'Phillips' Mains AC 'Super Inductance' model 830A, 1932. £150

'Ekco' AC Mains model AC74 bakelite, 1939. £75

RUGS

A surprising number of major designers of the Art Nouveau/Deco period turned their attention to rug design, Charles Rennie Mackintosh, Gustav Stickley and Archibald Knox, to name but three. By and large, the results were very much in keeping with the overall style of each – Celtic influence being clearly visible in Knox's output, while Mackintosh's showed his usual clean lines and favourite motifs. Stickley, on the other hand favoured, for him, surprisingly detailed patterns.

Oval modernist woven rug with linear design, 1930's, 375cm. wide.   £600

Pictorial hooked rug, America, early 20th century, bearing the inscription *Old Shep,* 27 x 34in. (Skinner Inc.)
£552

A wool pile carpet, signed on reverse 'Orendi', circa 1900-20, 7ft.7in. by 10ft.6in. (Robt. W. Skinner Inc.)
£2,432

A Scottish School woollen carpet, the design attributed to Charles Rennie Mackintosh, the green field with oval panel of lilac, green, puce and beige stylised flowers, 193 x 290cm. (Christie's)   £880

A Modernist rug in shades of brown and beige, 231 x 173cm.   £750

A hand-knotted woollen rug, the design possibly by A. Knox, with Celtic motif in pink and blue on a white ground, 153.5 x 86cm. (Christie's)   £345

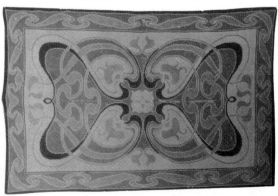

A hand-knotted rug attributed to Henry van de Velde, 146.5cm. long, 95.9cm. wide. (Christie's)
£935

One of two India Drugget scatter rugs, designed by Gustav Stickley, circa 1910, 38in. wide. (Robt. W. Skinner Inc.)   £455

RUGS

Gustav Stickley India hemp carpet, 1910, honeycomb pattern, brown on neutral ground, 11ft.8in. x 9ft.2in. (Skinner Inc.) £1,790

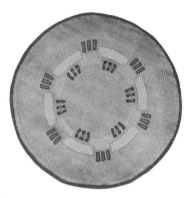

A Jules Leleu circular woollen rug, 188cm. diam. (Christie's) £864

Templeton's carpet, designed by Charles Rennie Mackintosh, circa 1910, 304cm. wide. £1,500

Gustav Stickley drugget rug, circa 1910, honeycomb pattern and Greek key border, 7ft.11in. x 5ft.1in. (Skinner Inc.) £741

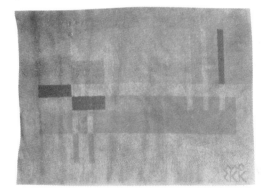

Edward McKnight Kauffer, an abstract rug woven in shades of brown, yellow and blue, 5ft.3in. x 3ft.10in. (Lawrence Fine Art) £440

Drugget flatweave area rug, 20th century, orange and black zig-zag pattern, 5ft.9in. x 3ft.2in. (Skinner Inc.) £201

Marion Dorn, an abstract small carpet woven in khaki and pale blue green, 8ft. x 4ft. 2in. (Lawrence Fine Art) £440

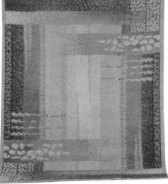

Art Deco room size rug, mid 20th century, field comprised of panels in hues of brown accented by bands of muted turquoise, 10ft. 5in. long. (Skinner Inc.) £208

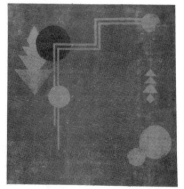

A hand-woven Art Deco carpet, the powder-pink field with circle and triangle motif, in beige, emerald green and eau de nile, 273 x 296cm. (Christie's) £1,100

RUGS

A tufted wool rug designed by Marion Dorn, 1930's, 195 x 140cm. £1,750

Early 20th century American calico cat hooked rug, 15½ x 32in. £350

1930's printed carpet, designed and fitted for Derry & Tom's, circa 1935, 200cm. wide. £500

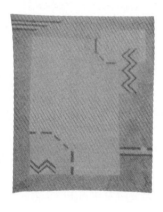

A J. J. Adnet wool pile carpet in tones of russet, black, brown and beige, circa 1930, 156.5 x 144.4cm. (Christie's) £918

A Modernist carpet, 327 x 267cm., 1930's. £1,250

A 1930s Modernist woollen carpet, woven in brown, beige, salmon pink and russet red, with linear and geometric design, 319 x 265.6cm. (Christie's London) £715

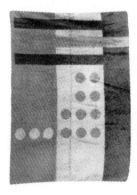

An Art Deco hand-made tufted wool carpet by Terence Prentis, 363 x 263cm. £1,750

Walt Disney, a polychrome woollen rug depicting Mickey and Minnie Mouse performing in a circus arena, 46¾ x 71in., circa 1930's. (Christie's) £385

'The River Rug' designed by C. F. A. Voysey, 400 x 335cm., circa 1903. £5,000

STOVES

Before central heating became the norm, many homes and offices boasted a wood or paraffin burning stove. These were both efficient and decorative, and are becoming very fashionable again today.

Examples from France, Germany and in particular Scandinavia, as well as North America, can readily be found, but, interestingly, the stove maker's art does not appear to have flourished much in the UK.

The Art Nouveau period by and large covers the heyday of the stove's popularity. The metalwork is often extremely fine, the overall shape elegant, and further embellishment and Art Nouveau touches were achieved by the use of coloured tiles.

Some stoves are freestanding, while others are designed to be 'plumbed in'. Some, too, are equipped with useful baking ovens or warming compartments.

Stoves were still popular well into the 1920s, although by then the style was becoming by and large more functional and austere.

Flemish enamel stove with oven with attractive coloured Art Nouveau decoration, oven with heat regulator, attachable to wall or chimney, circa 1910. (Auction Team Köln)   £268

A Flamme Bleue paraffin stove, Paris, 73cm. high, circa 1900. (Auction Team Koeln)   £29

An American Heating No. 44 decorative luminous stove, with smoke circulation system and warming compartment, 1890. (Auction Team Koeln)   £684

An Art Nouveau Amalienhuette Nr 121 room stove, circa 1910. (Auction Team Koeln)   £407

A Norwegian Eidsfor Verk 154 room stove, 1925. (Auction Team Koeln)   £296

An Art Nouveau tiled stove Le Lion 426 by Pied-Selle Fumay, Ardennes, 1910. (Auction Team Koeln)   £444

A German Art Nouveau room stove Amalienhuette Nr 182-184, 1905. (Auction Team Koeln)   £998

A Flemish enamel stove with regulating baking oven, 1925. (Auction Team Koeln) £314

A French tiled stove with expansion joint, circa 1920. (Auction Team Koeln) £592

A decorative French cast iron oven with keep warm facility and towel rails on both sides, 85cm. wide, circa 1905. (Auction Team Koeln)
£331

The American Heating No. 12 light oven with glimmer glass to all sides and urn finial, 143cm. high, circa 1900. (Auction Team Koeln) £1,053

A French cast iron and enamelled Caloria 252 cooking oven, 1915. (Auction Team Koeln)
£314

An Art Nouveau column Bjerrings stove, with warming compartment, Danish, 1900. (Auction Team Koeln)
£462

A German room stove with warming facility, 1925. (Auction Team Koeln)
£176

An American Heating No. 14 luminous stove with smoke circulation and warming compartment, 1900. (Auction Team Koeln) £1,183

A Danish Hess Vejle room stove with warming facility, 1925. (Auction Team Koeln)
£407

SILVER

The Art Nouveau/Deco periods coincided with the burgeoning talents of some remarkable practitioners of the silversmith's art. Among the best known names are Puiforcat, Jensen, Knox, Dresser, Ramsden, Ashbee & Tiffany. Some details of these craftsmen are given below, and examples of their work appear frequently in the following pages.

CHARLES ROBERT ASHBEE

(1863–1942) was a leading figure in the Arts & Crafts movement and founded the Guild & School of Handicraft between 1887–8, which later continued as the Guild of Handicraft. He aimed to revive medieval craft skills, and produced simple silver designs, often incorporating semi-precious stones and enamel decoration. Another characteristic feature was his use of silver wire. Celtic and naturalistic motifs are also common in the jewellery which he designed.

CHRISTOPHER DRESSER

Dr Christopher Dresser (1834–1904) was a Glasgow born botanist, designer and writer. He studied first at the London School of Design before training as a botanist and becoming a lecturer at the Department of Science and Art. The two strands of his training combined happily when he started to design silver in the early 1860s. His work was characterised by the simplicity of its design and the careful adaptation of form to purpose.

Dresser was also an enthusiastic collector of Japanese arts, and the influence of the Japanese style is often clear in his own pieces. He designed for leading silver manufacturers such as Hukin and Heath and for J Dixon.

GEORG JENSEN

Georg Jensen was born in Denmark in 1866. After an initial apprenticeship with a goldsmith, he studied under Mogens Ballin and at the Royal Academy in Copenhagen. He opened an unsuccessful porcelain factory with Joachim Petersen in 1900, before joining Ballin as foreman of their jewellery enterprise in 1901. In 1904 he opened his own workshop in Copenhagen and first exhibited his silver the following year.

In 1908 he opened a shop in Berlin which sold mainly silver pieces such as hand hammered coffee pots and milk jugs, and gained international recognition following his award of a gold medal at the Brussels International Exhibition in 1910.

His company expanded, becoming a Limited Company in 1916, and he employed such craftspeople as Inger Møller and Mrs Just Andersen, and designers such as H Nielsen, with whom he marketed Nielsen's Pyramid cutlery.

Following the First World War, further shops were opened in London, Paris and Stockholm, and Jost Lunning opened a Jensen shop in New York in 1920.

ARCHIBALD KNOX

(1864–1933) was born and educated on the Isle of Man. He moved to London in 1897 and became silverware designer for Liberty. In this capacity he supplied over 400 designs for the Cymric range of silverware and Tudric pewter. Often these employ the interlaced decoration of 9th and 10th century Celtic jewellery known as entrelac. Knox lectured at the Kingston School of Art in Surrey, resigning when his teaching was criticised as being 'over advanced'.

JEAN PUIFORCAT

Jean Puiforçat (1897–1945) was born into a family of French silversmiths and followed in the tradition, studying at the Central School of Arts and Crafts in London and under Louis Lejeune.

From 1922 he worked independently and exhibited at the Exposition Internationale des Arts Decoratifs in 1925 in Paris, where his products included an important lapis lazuli and silver dish and cover.

During the 1920s he became a champion of the Art Deco style and joined the Union des Artistes Modernes in 1928.

OMAR RAMSDEN

(1879–1933) studied at Sheffield School of Art. There he met Alwyn Carr, with whom he later formed a partnership which lasted until 1918, and in which Ramsden was mainly responsible for design. His early work shows Celtic influence, with hammer mark finish, while his middle period is suggestive rather of Tudor styles. He specialised in ceremonial pieces and received many commissions from the Catholic Church. Later he also produced some work in the Art Deco style.

CHARLES L TIFFANY

was an American jeweller and silversmith who established the firm of Tiffany & Co in New York in 1834. Silver was produced from 1850 and won the firm an award at the Paris Universal Exposition in 1867. Tiffany produced many commemorative pieces, and is not to be confused with his son, Louis Comfort, who took over the company in 1902, when his father died.

SILVER BASKETS

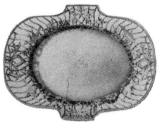

Shaped oval fruit basket by William Comyns & Sons Ltd., London, 1907, 38oz. 10dwt., 13½in. wide. £2,500

A leaf-form basket by Shiebler, New York, circa 1885, with a leaf-form handle surmounted by a cast bunch of grapes and a copper fly, 3¾in. high, 17 oz. 10 dwt. (Christie's) £3,805

An Art Deco style roll basket, 13in. long, rounded rectangular, ribbed interior and angled side handles, Birmingham, 1937, 19 ozs. (Bonhams) £330

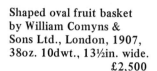

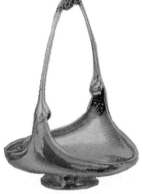

Large silver fruit basket with pierced sides and swing handle, Sheffield, 1907, 44oz., 13¼in. high. £1,250

A Georg Jensen moulded oval grape basket, on pedestal feet, the handle with ribbed scroll-work terminals, the bases of the handle applied with grapeclusters, import marks for London 1930, 37oz, 13in. high. (Christie's) £1,800

An Unger Brothers basket, 24cm. across, stamped with monogram and Sterling 925 Fine, numbered 02616. (Phillips) £320

A Wiener Werkstatte electro-plated basket, designed by Josef Hoffmann, 26cm. high. (Christie's) £990

A late Victorian quatrefoil pierced cake basket on applied shell and scrolling foliate feet, James Dixon & Son, Sheffield 1900, 12¼in., 20.25 oz. (Christie's S. Ken) £660

Sterling silver flower basket, 10in. high, 29½ troy oz. £1,000

SILVER BEAKERS

A small beaker designed by Jean Puiforcat, 4.8cm. high, silver coloured metal. (Phillips) £180

An Edwardian parcel-gilt tapering beaker and cover on ball feet, chased with rococo flowers and scrolling foliage, Child & Child, London 1903, 5¼in., 8.75oz. (Christie's S. Ken) £308

An ivory and silver cigar holder on six flattened ball feet, by Tiffany & Co., N.Y., 1881, 6½in. high. (Christie's) £3,694

An Art Nouveau beaker, the body stamped with flowers, foliage and scrollwork decoration, Mappin and Webb, Sheffield 1901, 6in., 13.5oz. (Christie's S. Ken) £352

A pair of plique-a-jour enamelled and gilt beakers, by P. Ovchinnikov with the Imperial warrant, Moscow, 1899-1908, 3¾in. high. (Christie's) £4,950

A C.R. Ashbee hammered silver beaker, the base with an openwork frieze of stylised trees set with seven cabochon garnets, London hallmarks for 1900, 11.5cm. high, 205 grams. gross. (Christie's) £1,980

BISCUIT BOXES

A Guild of Handicraft silver biscuit barrel, designed by C.R. Ashbee, with green Powell glass liner, the lid with red enamel and wirework finial, with London hallmarks for 1900, 20.5cm. high, 475 grams. gross. (Christie's) £3,960

A Liberty & Co. silver biscuit box with Birmingham hallmarks for 1902, 20oz.14dwt., 14cm. high. (Christie's) £432

A Danish white metal and ivory box and cover, stamped marks W/G and CF Heise assay mark, circa 1925, 13.5cm. high. (Christie's) £400

SILVER BOWLS

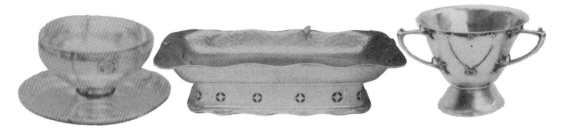

Kalo sterling silver bowl with attached underliner, Chicago, circa 1915, squat bulbous form, approximately 15 troy oz. (Skinner Inc.) £247

A shaped rectangular centre-piece bowl, by Tiffany & Co., 1878-91, 4½in. high, 18.3/8in. wide, 8½in. deep, 67oz.10dwt. (Christie's) £9,310

A Scottish Art Nouveau spot hammered rose bowl, applied with three bracket handles, J.F., Glasgow, 1904, 12½in., 49oz. (Christie's S. Ken) £715

A circular shallow bowl, on tapering shaped hexagonal foot, with openwork knop above, by Omar Ramsden, 1928, 5⅝in. high, 12oz.
(Christie's) £1,980

A silver rose bowl by Bernard Cuzner, the rounded bowl with rolled rim decorated with a repoussé rose briar frieze with five applied stylised rose heads, Birmingham hallmarks for 1911, 18.5cm. high.
(Christie's) £13,200

Georg Jensen Sterling Punchbowl, circular moulded edge resting on leaves and berries, circular base, 9½in. diam, approximately 42 troy oz.
(Skinner Inc) £2,402

A Liberty & Co. Cymric silver and copper bowl, the shallow conical silver bowl with everted rim set with band of cabochon nephrites, with Birmingham hallmarks for 1901, 20.7cm. diameter, 680 grams. gross.
(Christie's) £1,100

A James Dixon & Sons sugar bowl and cover, designed by Dr. Christopher Dresser, the spherical body flanked by two curved handles, model number 2273 and registration lozenge for 1880, 9.5cm. high.
(Christie's) £330

A Sibyl Dunlop Celtic silver stemmed bowl, applied on the exterior with Celtic entrelacs and beast masks in relief, 9.5cm. high, 1923. (Phillips London) £620

SILVER BOWLS

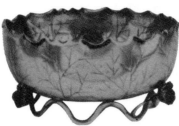

A Georg Jensen footed bowl, the lightly hammered gadrooned bowl decorated beneath with trailing vines, on a stepped foot, 25.5cm. diameter, 1050 grams. (Christie's) £1,760

A Hukin & Heath electroplate rose bowl with crimped rim, the sides stamped with stylised branches and engraved with initials, 10in. diameter. (Christie's S. Ken) £120

A punch bowl by Herbert A. Taylor for Stone Associates, Gardner, Massachusetts, 1908-1937, the sides partly fluted, marked, 39cm. diam., 106oz. (Christie's New York) £5,880

An Art Nouveau spot hammered centre bowl on a domed circular foot, Albert Edward Bonner, London, 1909, 7½in., 23.25oz. (Christie's S. Ken) £418

An important Keswick School of Industrial Arts silver presentation rose bowl and cover, made to commemorate James William Lowther being elected as Speaker to the House of Commons in 1905. (Phillips London) £3,400

A Georg Jensen circular bowl and cover of bulbous form and hammered finish, 6.5in. high, London 1921, 414gms., 13.3oz. (Bearne's) £600

A late Victorian part oxidised fluted moulded circular rose bowl, Henry Wilkinson & Co. Ltd., London, 1900, 10¼in. 37.75oz. (Christie's S. Ken) £748

Hand hammered sterling silver bowl, R. Wallace & Sons Mfg. Co., Wallingford, Connecticut, with applied rim and four plaques of Austrian style geometric motifs, 4⅝in. diameter. (Skinner Inc.) £54

A Georg Jensen footed bowl, designed by Johan Rohde, the lightly hammered bowl with everted rim, 5½in. high. (Christie's S. Ken) £550

SILVER BOWLS

An Art Nouveau Continental white metal bowl in the style of J. Hofman, 14in. across. (Christie's) £462

A centrepiece bowl marked 'Milton A. Fuller, Inc. New York/Palm Beach', circa 1900, on four lion's-paw feet, 14in diam, 68 oz. (Christie's) £2,629

A rose bowl of compressed circular ogee form, 1936, maker's mark R&Co. Ltd., possibly for Robinson and Co., 26cm., 29.5 oz. excluding grille. (Lawrence) £605

A presentation punch bowl, by Tiffany & Co., N.Y., 1890-91, 9in. high, 15¾in. diam., 101oz. (Christie's) £16,935

A Connell two-handled bowl, designed by Kate Harris, with bottle-green glass liner, London hallmarks for 1904, 39.1cm. diam., 22oz.15dwt. without liner. (Christie's) £990

A copper and silver applied bowl, by Gorham Manuf. Co., Providence, 1883, 3¼in. high. (Christie's) £1,000

Edwardian Art Nouveau rose bowl, by Hamilton & Inches, Edinburgh, 1902, 9in. diam., 38oz. £800

A Liberty and Co. Cymric christening bowl, of circular form repoussé with two Celtic symbols and engraved *Diana From Her Godmother Edith 1904*, Birmingham 1900, 221 grammes, 5in. diameter. (Spencer's) £200

An inlaid silver Indian-style bowl, by Tiffany & Co., for the Columbian Exposition, circa 1893, 6¼in. high, 56oz. 10dwt. (Christie's) £80,000

A trophy bowl for the New York Yacht Club, by Tiffany & Co., circa 1884, 15½in. diam., 97oz. 10dwt. £15,000

An Edwardian Arts & Crafts circular hammered bowl, by A. E. Jones, Birmingham, 1908, 10in. across handles, 9oz. (Woolley & Wallis) £190

A sugar bowl, the cover with a green stone finial, by Tiffany & Co., N.Y., 1877-91, 3¼in. high, gross weight 13oz. (Christie's) £6,894

SILVER BOWLS

A sterling silver bowl, by Arthur Stone, 1910-37, 5.3/8in. diam., 7 troy oz. (Robt. W. Skinner Inc.) £702

An Omar Ramsden silver gilt bowl, London hallmarks for 1935, 46.2cm. wide. (Christie's) £9,350

Frederick Smith repoussé sterling fruit bowl, Denver, circa 1889, round with scalloped rim, 15 troy ozs. (Skinner Inc.) £212

A Ganetti silver modernist powder bowl and cover, the lift off cover with copper loop handle and mirrored interior, 7in. diameter. (Henry Spencer) £100

A Georg Jensen footed bowl, hemispherical form with inverted rim, supported by eight foliate brackets on concave circular base, London import marks for 1930, 11.5cm. high, 505 grams. (Christie's) £638

A footed fruit bowl by Whiting Manufacturing Company, North Attleboro or Newark, circa 1885, on a spreading cylindrical foot with a serpentine border, 4³/₄in. high, 21 oz. 10 dwt. (Christie's) £4,497

A punch bowl, the hemispherical body divided into arched panels, maker's mark probably that of Chas. S. Harris & Sons, 1929, 28.2cm. diam., 37.5oz. (Lawrence Fine Art) £506

An Edwardian gilt-lined two-handled rose bowl on four stylised bracket feet, the bowl embossed with a Celtic band, London 1908, 10in. diameter, 64oz. (Christie's S. Ken) £1,430

An Edwardian hammered sugar bowl, in Art Nouveau style, by A. E. Jones, Birmingham, 1908, 4¼in. diam., 4.5oz. (Hobbs & Chambers) £100

A footed bowl designed by J. Rohde, stamped Dessin J.R. 925 S Georg Jensen 242, circa 1920, 12.6cm. high, 16oz. (Christie's) £1,188

A plain hexagonal sugar bowl, on six curved feet and with foliate pierced rim, by Omar Ramsden, 1935, 4¹/₂in. wide, 7oz. (Christie's) £605

A Georg Jensen footed bowl, stamped marks GJ 925.S 4, 7.6cm. high, 129.2gr. (Christie's) £374

SILVER BOWLS

A circular silver bowl by
Herbert Taylor, Massa.,
circa 1925, 9.7/8in. diam.,
24oz. 10dwt.   £600

Silver and silver gilt bowl
by Jean E. Puiforcat, 18oz.
£4,000

A large punch bowl, by
Walker & Hall, Chester 1906,
21.7cm. high, 69oz. £1,800

A Hukin and Heath electroplated two handled bowl with
hinged cover decorated with
four engraved roundels of
stylised floral motifs, designed
by Dr C. Dresser and date code
for 26th March 1879, 19.1cm.
high. (Christie's)   £9,900

A footed bowl, stamped
Georg Jensen 925 S 197B,
11.1cm. high, 8oz.19dwt.
(Christie's)   £594

A Continental moulded oval
fruit bowl on openwork rococo
floral, foliate and trellis-work
feet, bearing import marks for
London 1899, 13$^{1}/_{4}$in., 55oz.
(Christie's S. Ken)   £3,080

A Repouse Compote by Tiffany
& Company, New York,
1883–1891, the sides formed of a
finely repoussé and chased band
of mythological figures, 33 oz. 10
dwt.
(Christie's)   £3,459

A Georg Jensen bowl and
cover, stamped with C. F.
Heise assay mark 100B and
with London import marks
for 1925, 11.9cm. high, 242gr.
(Christie's)   £715

A German late 19th/early 20th
century circular fruit bowl,
fitted with a clear glass liner,
Eugen Marcus, 8in. diameter.
(Christie's S. Ken)   £330

SILVER BOWLS

Silver rosebowl with
embossed decoration,
7in. diam.   £250

A heavy Celtic Revival bowl,
the almost hemispherical
body with a lightly hammered
finish, 1937 by the Gold-
smiths and Silversmiths Company Ltd., 17.5cm. across
handles, 13.3oz. (Lawrence
Fine Arts)   £132

Unusual Art Deco silver
and silver gilt bowl by
Jean E. Puiforcat, 24oz.
£4,000

An Omar Ramsden silver punch
bowl with everted rim, London
hallmarks for 1931, 23.6cm.
wide, 65oz.14dwt. (Christie's)
£4,400

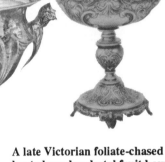

A late Victorian foliate-chased
boat-shaped pedestal fruit bowl
on a shell and foliate-chased
domed circular base, Goldsmiths
& Silversmiths Co. Ltd., London
1900, 12¾in., 34.75oz.
(Christie's S. Ken)   £1,210

A Victorian novelty rose bowl
modelled as a waterlily,
supported by leaves at either
side, the junction applied with a
frog, by Hukin & Heath, 1885,
25.6cm. diameter, weighable
40.5 ozs.
(Phillips)   £1,500

A large Sybil Dunlop
silver punch bowl,
16.5cm., 1938. £2,500

An Unger Brothers silver
bowl of flower form, 15.4cm.
diam., stamped maker's
monogram, Sterling 925
Fine, 0850 (3oz.). (Phillips)
£100

A silver two-handled punch
bowl, London 1905, 10½in.
diam.   £750

SILVER BOXES

Silver cigarette box and cover, in the Art Nouveau style, by Ramsden & Carr, circa 1903, 7½in. wide. (Bermondsey) £750

A Georg Jensen white metal cigarette box, stamped GJ 925S and inscription 6 Oktober 1933, 10¾in. wide. (Christie's) £1,210

A shaped oblong silver casket by Omar Ramsden, 1921, 8¾in. long, gross 53oz. (Christie's) £3,024

A C.R. Ashbee hammered silver spice box and cover, set with seven cabochon garnets, stamped *C R A* with London hallmarks for 1899, 9.5cm. high, 145 grams. gross.
(Christie's) £1,485

An Arts & Crafts hammered silver box, by Chas. Horner, Birmingham hallmarks for 1902, 15.3cm. long, 5oz. 12dwt. (Christie's) £440

A shaped square silver casket, by Omar Ramsden, 1929, 4½in. high, 18oz.4dwt. (Christie's) £1,080

A Guild of Handicraft silver and enamel box and cover, London hallmarks for 1901, 10cm. diam., 6oz.5dwt. gross weight. (Christie's) £462

A William Hutton & Sons silver casket, the hinged cover inset with high relief panel in mother-of-pearl, pewter, enamel and copper of a lakeside scene, 1902, 31.5cm. long. (Christie's London) £4,620

An A. E. Jones Arts and Crafts silver and copper jewellery casket, with a turquoise enamelled disc and pierced heart-shaped hinge, Birmingham hallmarks for 1929, 13.6cm. long. (Christie's) £660

SILVER BOXES

An attractive Edwardian silver box and cover by Nathan and Hayes, of plain rectangular form, Chester 1901, 37 grammes. 6cm. wide. (Spencer's) £75

A rectangular cigarette box, designed by Jorgen Jensen, Dessin JJ, Georg Jensen 857 A, 16cm. wide, 13oz.15dwt. (Christie's) £660

A silver gilt box, the lid inset with an enamel plaque, Birmingham hallmarks for 1922 and maker's monogram SB, 9cm. long, 2oz.17dwt. gross wt. (Christie's) £165

A Liberty & Co. silver box and cover, the tapering swollen cylindrical body and domed cover set with small turquoise stones, together with two silver match box covers. £286

A green stained box, by George Anton Scheidt, with pierced and chased white metal mount of scrolling tendrils, 6.3cm. long. (Christie's) £242

A sterling silver box with pierced enamel hinged cover, Worcester, Mass., 1925, 3¾in. wide. (Robt. W. Skinner Inc.) £256

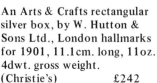

An Arts & Crafts rectangular silver box, by W. Hutton & Sons Ltd., London hallmarks for 1901, 11.1cm. long, 11oz. 4dwt. gross weight. (Christie's) £242

A Continental oblong wood lined cigarette box decorated in the Art Deco style, 6¼in. long, engraved dated 1938. (Christie's) £450

A cigarette box, by Ramsden and Carr, the bowed hand-hammered sides with applied entrelac band, London, 1908, 3¾ x 3¼in. (Bonhams) £650

SILVER BUCKLES

A Liberty hammered silver and enamelled belt buckle, the pierced floral decoration enamelled in blue and green, Birmingham hall marks for 1910. 7.5cm. long. (Christie's) £550

A Guild of Handicrafts Ltd., cloak clasp, the design attributed to Charles Robert Ashbee, its body picked out with opal cabochons, 13cm. wide. (Phillips London) £900

A William Comyns silver buckle in two pieces, of sinuous outline, formed by interwoven foliage, 11.5cm. wide, 1902. (Phillips London) £160

Sterling silver Arts & Crafts belt buckle, England, circa 1900-1904, two turquoise stones in symmetrical openwork organic design, 3¼in. wide. (Skinner Inc.) £108

A rare early Mokume cloak clasp by Tiffany & Co., New York, 1876, in the Japanese taste, 6½in. wide, extended, 3 oz. 10 dwt. (Christie's) £1,571

A leaf-form belt buckle by Frank M. Whiting, North Attleboro, circa 1885, applied with a spider, a fly, a bee, and a butterfly, 3⅛in. long, 1 oz. (Christie's) £291

A Liberty & Co. 'Cymric' silver belt buckle, set with an oval cabochon lapis lazuli, stamped 'Cymric', L & Co and Birmingham hallmarks for 1900, 11cm. long. (Christie's) £330

A Guild of Handicrafts Ltd. silver enamel and amethyst buckle/cloak clasp, designed by C. R. Ashbee, circa 1902, 13.75cm. wide. £7,150

A Lalique gold, diamond, opal and enamel choker buckle, circa 1900, 7.5cm. wide. £17,600

SILVER CANDELABRA

One of a pair of French six-light candelabra, by J. Chaumet, Paris, 1918, 24½in. high, 471oz. (Christie's) £15,496

Pair of French four-light candelabra, by Puiforcat, Paris, circa 1900, 17¼in. high, 210oz. (Christie's) £5,811

Sterling silver and copper candelabra, possibly Metcalf & Co., Upstate New York, circa 1905, 13in. high. (Skinner Inc.) £185

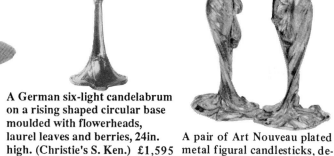

A pair of W.M.F. figural twin-branch candlesticks, each in the form of an Art Nouveau maiden, 27.5cm. high. (Phillips) £1,450

A German six-light candelabrum on a rising shaped circular base moulded with flowerheads, laurel leaves and berries, 24in. high. (Christie's S. Ken.) £1,595

A pair of Art Nouveau plated metal figural candlesticks, designed by C. Bonnefond, each modelled as a girl with long hair, 36.5cm. high. (Phillips) £1,300

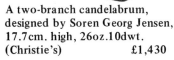

One of a pair of Georg Jensen five-branch candelabra, designed by Harald Nielsen, 40cm. high. (Christie's) £15,400

One of a pair of Georg Jensen candelabra with five cup-shaped candle nozzles and circular drip pans supported on U-shaped branches, 27cm. high. (Christie's) £21,600

A two-branch candelabrum, designed by Soren Georg Jensen, 17.7cm. high, 26oz.10dwt. (Christie's) £1,430

SILVER CANDLESTICKS

Small Jensen silver candle-stick, hammered, London, 1930, 7.25cm. high.   £200

One of a set of six candle-sticks designed by H. Nielsen, stamped Dessin H.N. Georg Jensen 747B, 2cm. high, 7oz. 3dwt. (Christie's)   £648

One of a pair of Liberty & Co. 'Cymric' silver and enamel candlesticks, Bir-mingham, 1901, 15.25cm. high.   £1,000

A pair of James Dixon & Sons silver candlesticks, Sheffield hallmarks for 1904, 22cm. high. (Christie's)   £825

Two of four silver candle-sticks, by Omar Ramsden, two 1919, two 1922, loaded, 22.5cm. high. (Phillips)
£3,000

Pair of candlesticks designed by S. Bernadotte, stamped Georg Jensen 355B Sigvard and London import marks, 25.9cm. high, 25oz.11dwt. (Christie's)   £918

One of two Cooper Bros. & Sons Ltd. silver candlesticks, 19cm. high, 1903.
£500

A pair of Georg Jensen white metal candlesticks, designed by Harald Nielsen, the cylindrical candle holder with everted rim, 14cm. high, 1.425 grams. (Christie's London)   £2,420

One of a pair of Edwardian candlesticks with trumpet-shaped foot, by Gilbert Marks, 1902, 13in. high, 41oz. (Christie's)   £3,672

SILVER CANDLESTICKS

One of a pair of Georg Jensen candlesticks, designed by S. Bernadotte, 6cm. high, 8oz.16dwt. (Christie's) £605

One of a pair of Liberty & Co. three-branch silver wall sconces, with Birmingham hallmarks for 1901, 29oz., 20cm. high. (Christie's) £1,188

One of a pair of Art Deco silver candlesticks by Walker & Hall, Sheffield, 1934. £2,000

Pair of WMF Art Nouveau silver coloured metal candlesticks, 11in. high. (Reeds Rains) £300

A pair of stylised silver and green onyx candlesticks, probably made by Dixon & Sons for Hyams, 22cm. high, London marks for 1907. (Phillips) £620

A pair of Leuchare silver and shagreen candlesticks with silver drip pans, 8in. high, London 1887. £550

A Faberge two-colour gold, silver-gilt and enamel taperstick, St. Petersburg, 1908-17, 5.6cm. high. £8,000

A pair of George VI candlesticks, the plain oval sockets raised upon swept oval columns, Birmingham 1945, by A & J Zimmerman Ltd., 6in. high. (Spencer's) £360

One of a pair of candlesticks designed by J. Rohde, stamped Dessin JR Georg Jensen GI925S 453, circa 1920, 15cm. high. (Christie's) £918

SILVER CASTERS

A William Hutton & Sons silver sugar caster, the cover with openwork decoration set with a cabochon amethyst, London hallmarks for 1902, 19.3cm. high, 320gr. (Christie's London) £1,760

Liberty & Co. silver sugar caster, Birmingham, 1930, 11cm. high, with detachable domed top. £400

A plain cylindrical sugar caster with domed cover, by Goldsmiths & Silversmiths Co., London, 1911, 7¼in. high, 11.50oz. (Christie's) £150

An Omar Ramsden hammered silver sugar caster, the elaborately pierced cover with beaded rim and Galleon plaque, London hallmarks for 1936, 15.3cm. high, 250 grams. (Christie's) £1,430

A matched pair of late Victorian gadrooned and spiral-fluted sugar casters on foliate-chased gadrooned circular bases, Edward Hutton, London 1892 and William Hutton & Sons Ltd., London 1896, 8in. and 7³/₄in., 15.75oz.(Christie's S. Ken) £550

An amber, coral and malachite sugar caster, designed by Anton Rosen, stamped marks GJ 826 GJ, 19.9cm. high. (Christie's) £2,200

An Elkington silver sugar caster, maker's marks and Birmingham hallmarks for 1938, 5oz.2dwt., 8.5cm. high. (Christie's) £237

A sugar caster designed by Harald Nielsen, stamped Dessin H.N. 925S Georg Jensen S Wendel A/S 645, circa 1949, 11.4cm. high, 7oz.14dwt. (Christie's) £432

An Edwardian hammered baluster sugar caster by Ramsden & Carr with buntop, 1907, 17.5cm. high, 8ozs. (Phillips) £575

SILVER CENTREPIECES

An Art Nouveau centrepiece of open boat shape, 57.5cm. long, silver coloured metal, possibly Austrian or German. (Phillips)   £1,600

An Art Nouveau Edward VII dessert stand centrepiece of hammered design, 13in. high, Hamilton and Inches, Edinburgh 1904, 2228 gms, 71.6 oz. (Bearne's)   £1,250

One of a pair of late 19th century repousse sterling silver compotes, by Tiffany & Co., 9.3/8in. diam., 40 troy oz. (Robt. W. Skinner Inc.)   £850

A WMF plated centrepiece of twin-handled boat-shape with clear glass liner, 46cm. long. (Phillips)   £420

A large French parcel-gilt centrepiece, the central hardstone plinth supporting a detachable loosely draped female figure, the ground signed *H. Wadere*, circa 1897, 34½in. high, gross 25,860grs. (Christie's)   £16,500

A centrepiece bowl, by Gorham Manuf. Co., 1880, 3.1/8in. high, 7½in. diam., 11oz.10dwt. (Christie's)   £365

An early George V centrepiece, the central trumpet vase flanked by three smaller trumpet vases, the whole with cast reel and bobbin borders, Sheffield 1913, 906 grammes. (Spencer's)   £520

A German white metal Art Nouveau centrepiece, decorated with pierced floral and scrolling decoration, on four pierced cabriole legs, 26.7cm. long, 250 grams without liner. (Christie's)   £286

A table centrepiece with a large central vase, applied with rococo scrolling foliate rims, William Hutton & Sons Ltd., Sheffield, 1919, 12½in.. 27½oz. (Christie's S. Ken)   £352

SILVER CHAMBERSTICKS

An Art Nouveau oil chamberstick with leaf-capped loop
handle, 14.25cm. diam.
(Phillips)   £300

A Perry Son & Co. pain-
ted metal candlestick,
designed by Christopher
Dresser, circa 1880,
14cm.   £100

Liberty & Co. silver
candlestick with squat
trumpet body and
dished base, Birmingham,
1900, 9.25cm. high.
                             £500

A Tiffany & Co unusual late
19th century American
Aesthetic Movement parcel
gilt chamberstick, with in-
curved sides, circa 1880,
11ozs. (Phillips)   £6,000

An Art Nouveau silver 'counter-
balanced' candlestick, 16.5cm.
high, marked KK, London,
1905. (Phillips)   £200

C.R. Ashbee, a Guild of
Handicrafts bedroom
candlestick, raised hammered
border chased with branches of
stylised leaves and berries,
London 1900, 7oz.
(Woolley & Wallis)   £780

A Hukin & Heath electro-
plated chamberstick with
snuffer designed by Dr.
C. Dresser, stamped H & H
9658 Rd No. 228142,
12.5cm. high. (Christie's)
                          £918

A Victorian fluted and foliate-
stamped taperstick on a rising
shaped circular base, Henry
Wilkinson and Co., Sheffield,
5³/₄in. (Christie's S. Ken.) £660

A Perry Son & Co. maroon
painted metal chamber
candlestick, designed by Dr.
C. Dresser, registration
lozenge for 1883, 14.5cm.
high. (Christie's)   £302

SILVER CHOCOLATE POTS

A silver baluster shaped chocolate pot, by Samuel Kirk & Son Co., Baltimore, 1903-07, 10¼in. high, gross wt. 25oz. (Christie's) £1,000

A silver chocolate pot by Tiffany & Company, New York, tapering cylindrical and partly reeded, on a moulded circular foot, marked, 9¼in. high, gross weight 31oz. (Christie's) £1,949

A sterling silver Martele chocolate pot, by Gorham Mfg. Co., circa 1900, 11½in. high, 23 troy oz. (Robt. W. Skinner Inc.) £2,083

SILVER CLARET JUGS

A Hukin & Heath claret jug designed by Dr Christopher Dresser, the tapering cylindrical clear glass body surmounted with white metal section, 9½in. high. (Christie's) £880

A James Dixon & Sons electroplated claret jug designed by Dr. Christopher Dresser, with angled handle, the conical body with tapering cylindrical neck and triangular spout, 21.7cm. high. (Christie's) £11,000

A cut glass and silver-gilt claret jug by William B. Durgin Company, Concord, New Hampshire, circa 1900, 12½in. high. (Christie's) £4,497

A Continental Art Nouveau silver-mounted plain tapering clear glass claret jug with star-cut base, bearing import marks for London 1903, 9in. (Christie's S. Ken) £605

Edwardian Art Nouveau claret jug with silver hinged domed lid, Birmingham 1905, 10½in. high. £800

A rare, mounted glass, ovoid shaped claret jug on circular foot with coronet pierced gallery collar, 34.5cm. high, 1922. (Phillips) £6,000

SILVER COASTERS

A Liberty & Co. silver and enamel wine coaster, Birmingham hallmarks for 1905, 9.5cm. diam., 2oz.14dwt. gross wt. (Christie's) £462

A set of six Wiener Werkstatte circular wine glass coasters, designed by J. Hoffman and K. Moser, 5.5cm. diam., silver coloured metal. (Phillips) £900

A good coaster with slightly bevelled sides, the surface hammered and applied with a frieze of stylised leaf motifs, 1926, 5.2cm. high, 11.5cm. diam. (Phillips) £750

A Hutton & Sons silver wine bottle coaster, 16.80cm. high, total weight 19oz., maker's marks for Sheffield, 1905. (Phillips) £260

A silver tea glass holder, with applied troika horse heads, by V. Akimov, Moscow, circa 1900, overall 4¾in. high, with glass liner, 206.9gr. (Christie's) £495

A George V two handled bottle holder of cylindrical form pierced and cast with stylised flower heads, London 1910, 535 grammes, 16.5cm. high. (Henry Spencer) £340

A wine coaster, stamped marks 925.S Georg Jensen & Wendel A/S 289A, 9.5cm. high, 14oz.10dwt. (Christie's) £990

A cup holder, the openwork frame of a trellis of roses having a leaf decorated handle, inscribed *Omar Ramsden me fecit*, London 1927, 6.5oz. (Woolley & Wallis) £300

One of a pair of Omar Ramsden silver wine coasters, London, 1934, 14cm. diam. £3,520

SILVER COCKTAIL SHAKERS

Electro-plated cocktail shaker in the form of a champagne bottle, 13½ in. high. **£400**

A chromium plated cocktail shaker in the form of an airship with spirit measures contained in the base, German, 1920s, 30.5cm. high. (Christie's S. Ken) **£682**

A plated cocktail shaker in the form of a dumbbell. (Phillips) **£140**

A Sabattini electroplate picnic cocktail set comprising a cylindrical stacking system of six cups and decanter, 15¾in. high. (Christie's S. Ken) **£143**

A Georg Jensen cocktail shaker, with two handles each shaped as fruiting vines, cylindrical lid with pine finial, stamped maker's mark, 24.5cm. high, 500 grams. (Christie's) **£2,200**

A Michelsen silver cocktail shaker designed by Kay Fischer, Danish silver marks, circa 1935, 18oz.5dwt., 24.5cm. high. (Christie's) **£561**

A Danish white metal cocktail shaker, the cylindrical form on a flared circular foot, Copenhagen marks for 1941, 23cm. high, 440 grams. (Christie's London) **£330**

An Art Deco glass cocktail shaker with silver mounts, Birmingham, 1936, 8in. high. (Dreweatt Neate) **£400**

A recipe cocktail shaker, the outer sleeve of which revolves to reveal the correct ingredients. **£165**

SILVER COFFEE POTS

Early 20th century repousse decorated sterling silver coffee pot, Gorham Mfg. Co., 12.7/8in. high, approx. 26 troy oz. (Robt. W. Skinner Inc.) £718

A parcel-gilt coffee pot and sugar bowl by Tiffany & Company, New York, 1892–1902, coffee pot 8³/₄in. high; bowl 4in. diam. (Christie's) £2,214

A Liberty silver coffee pot, designed by Archibald Knox, with Birmingham hallmarks for 1906, 21.5cm. high. (Christie's) £2,000

A black coffee pot by Gorham, Providence, 1888, with a narrow curving spout and handle with insulators, 9¹/₂in. high, 14 oz. 10 dwt. (Christie's) £425

A 1960's silver coffee pot and hot water jug, by H. Brown, Birmingham hallmarks for 1963, 29cm. high, 40oz.12dwt. gross weight. (Christie's) £550

A coffee pot by Dominick & Haff, New York, 1881, with a domed cover, a pointed finial scrolling handle and a narrow spout, 10³/₄in. high, 23 oz. 10 dwt. (Christie's) £1,440

A silver Martele coffee pot by Gorham Manufacturing Company, Providence, 1899, of baluster form, 10¼in. high, 32oz. (Christie's) £2,274

A Liberty & Co. silver jug, the lightly hammered tapering cylindrical body with domed hinged cover, with Birmingham hallmarks for 1915, 22cm. high, 536 gr. gross. (Christie's London) £440

A coffee pot by Samuel Kirk & Son Co., Baltimore, 1903–1907, with a domed cover, cuirving spout and handle with insulators, 9¹/₄in. high, 23 oz. (Christie's) £982

SILVER CONDIMENTS

A Hukin & Heath silver condiment set designed by Dr. C. Dresser, London hallmarks for 1881, 14.2cm. high. (Christie's) £1,045

A Liberty and Co. Cymric hammered silver condiment set, comprising two bombe sided salts, similarly decorated mustard pot stamped with maker's marks and London hallmarks for 1897, height of mustard pot 7.8cm. (Christie's) £770

A Hukin & Heath electroplated metal and cut-glass condiment holder, designed by Dr. Christopher Dresser, complete with two original spoons, registration lozenge for 1878, 9cm. high. (Christie's) £2,420

A James Dixon & Sons electroplated condiment holder, designed by Dr. Christopher Dresser, the wide circular base on three ball feet, 20.8cm. high. (Christie's) £880

A three-piece condiment set in the Art Nouveau style, by Wm. Hutton & Sons Ltd., Birmingham, 1905. (Lawrence Fine Art) £154

A pair of Edwardian novelty peppers, the articulated bodies with porcelain heads, 13.5cm. long, 1905. (Phillips) £1,300

A Charles Boyton hammered silver four-piece condiments set, the mustard pots with spoons and glass liners, 1947, 10oz. (Christie's) £648

A Liberty & Co. three-piece silver condiment set, Birmingham hallmarks for 1899, pepper-pot 5.5cm. high. (Christie's) £385

A Charles Boyton hammered silver four-piece condiments set, London hallmarks for 1947, 11oz. (Christie's) £626

SILVER CRUETS

A boat-shaped cruet stand by Omar Ramsden, 1925, 10in. long, gross 42oz. (Christie's) £3,888

An Elkington & Co. electroplate cruet stand, 1880's, 12.5cm., together with a dish. £200

A Hukin & Heath electroplated cruet, designed by C. Dresser, mark April 1878. £1,000

A Hukin and Heath four-piece electroplated cruet, designed by Dr. Christopher Dresser, with patent registration marks for 1879, 13cm. high. (Christie's) £660

A Hukin & Heath electroplated six piece cruet and stand designed by Dr Christopher Dresser, fitted with three faceted cut glass bottles and stoppers, two similar shakers and mustard pot with hinged cover, 1878, 23.1cm. high. (Christie's London) £4,400

An Elkington three piece cruet and holder, the design attributed to Dr Christopher Dresser, with slender column and T-shaped handle, 12.7cm. high. (Christie's) £198

A Hukin & Heath electroplated cruet set, attributed to Dr. C. Dresser, 4¾in. high. (Christie's) £200

A William Hutton electroplated cruet, design by Christopher Dresser, circa 1900. £300

A Hukin & Heath electroplated six-sided cruet frame, designed by Dr. C. Dresser, with lozenge for 11th April 1878, 9cm. high.(Christie's) £594

SILVER CUPS

A Georg Jensen hammered silver and amethyst cup and cover, Copenhagen mark and London import marks for 1926, 19.9cm. high. (Christie's) £4,400

Gorham Martelé sterling presentation loving cup, Rhode Island, circa 1902, 11in. high, approximately 92 troy oz. (Skinner Inc.) £3,510

A loving cup, by Gorham, Providence, circa 1905, with an applied grapevine border and three sinuous handles, 19¼in. high, 107oz. (Christie's New York) £4,842

A trophy loving cup by Tiffany & Co., New York, circa 1889, with a serpentine brim and three curving handles formed as anchors, 9in. high, 57 oz. 10 dwt. (Christie's) £1,505

An Art Nouveau three-handled coupe, the twisted whiplash handles curving up from the base and joining the body with foliate terminals, Charles Edwards, London 1904, 8¼in. high, 12oz. (Christie's S. Ken) £220

A presentation loving cup, by Dominick & Haff, Newark, for J. E. Caldwell & Co., 1895, in original mahogany box, 11½in. high, 82oz. (Christie's) £5,985

A Guild of Handicraft silver chalice, supported on wire work brackets and pentagonal stem, the flanged foot with repoussé decoration, with London hallmarks for 1902, 21.5cm. high, 275 grams. (Christie's) £418

A James Powell & Son silver and green glass two-handled cup, London hallmarks for 1909, 19oz.12dwt., 22.8cm. high. (Christie's) £594

A Wakeley & Wheeler silver cup and cover designed by R. Y. Gleadowe, Birmingham silver marks for 1938, 30oz.10dwt., 37cm. high. (Christie's) £8,100

SILVER DISHES

An oval meat dish and cover, designed by H. Nielsen, stamped marks Dessin HN Georg Jensen 600S, 46.7cm. wide, 129oz. (Christie's)
£7,700

A Hukin & Heath electroplated metal spoon-warmer, supported on four spike feet, oval body, angular bar handle, the bar of ebonised wood, 14.5cm. high. (Christie's)
£935

A C.R. Ashbee silver muffin dish, set with three chrysoprase, the domed cover with a wirework finial set with another chrysoprase, with London hallmarks for 1900, 13cm. high, 650 grams. gross.
(Christie's)
£2,860

A silver gilt basketweave dish, by Tiffany & Co., New York, circa 1890, in the form of an Indian basket, 5¾in. diam., 5oz. (Christie's New York)
£830

An attractive Arts and Crafts Movement butter dish and cover of compressed circular shape, the hammered surfaces chased with stylised chrysanthemum motifs, 6cm. high, 12.5cm. diameter, by H. Haseler, Birmingham, 1911, 14 ozs. (Phillips) £900

One of a set of twelve plates, by Redlich & Co., New York, circa 1900, 9¾in. diam., 160oz. (Christie's)
£3,192

An Arts & Crafts fluted circular cake stand on a rising foot, J.S.B., London, 1915, 12¼in. high, 26.75oz. (Christie's)
£352

A medallion butter dish by Gorham, Providence, circa 1865, repoussé and chased with a band of cartouches, scrolls, and foliage, 5in. high, 16 oz. (Christie's)
£623

One of a set of four French silver gilt cake plates, by J. Chaumet, Paris, circa 1918, 10½in. square, 104oz. (Christie's)
£5,036

SILVER DISHES

A Joel F. Hewes sterling silver hand-raised, footed candy dish, circa 1908, 6in. diam., approx. 10 troy oz. (Robt. W. Skinner Inc.) £238

A Guild of Handicraft twin-handled silver porringer and cover with spoon, the cover with turquoise and wirework finial set with mother of pearl, with London hallmarks for 1903, 340 grams. gross. (Christie's) £3,300

An electroplated muffin dish, designed by C.R. Ashbee, the domed cover with a wirework finial set with abalone, 14cm. high. (Christie's) £528

A Guild of Handicraft silver dish, designed by C.R. Ashbee, the border decorated with a pierced frieze of stylised galleons, London hallmarks for 1906, 20.5cm. diameter, 250 grams. (Christie's) £528

A Hukin and Heath silver sugar basin designed by Dr Christopher Dresser, with hinged loop handle, the hemispherical bowl with raised double-rib decoration, with stamped maker's marks and London hallmarks for 1879, 12.5cm. diam. 182 grams. (Christie's) £3,960

A small ten-sided dish with a moulded border, decorated in the centre with an applied boss, modelled as a Tudor rose, 15cm. diameter, 1932, 6.5 ozs. (Phillips) £280

One of a pair of French second-course dishes, by J. Chaumet, Paris, circa 1918, 14in. diam., 136oz. (Christie's) £6,198

An unusual Georg Jensen silver sweetmeat dish of shell shape, supported on an open-work foliate and beaded stem, 10.5cm. high. (Phillips London) £820

One of a set of twelve plates, by Gorham Manuf. Co., 1907, 10¼in. diam., 204oz. (Christie's) £2,903

SILVER DRESSING TABLES SETS

Liberty & Co. four piece dressing table set, comprising pin tray, hair brush, clothes brush and hand mirror, Birmingham 1924 and 1925, 25.2cm. (Lawrence) £462

A Liberty & Co. silver and enamelled hair brush designed by Jessie King, of repoussé foliate and swagged decoration with mottled blue and green enamelled details. (Christie's) £198

Three pieces from a dressing table set, die stamped with foliage in the Art Nouveau style, Chester 1903/04/05, by W. Neale. (Lawrence Fine Art) £77

FLASKS

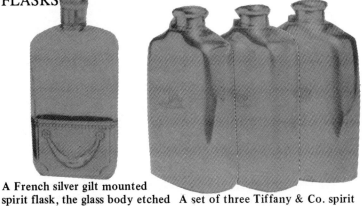

A French silver gilt mounted spirit flask, the glass body etched with scroll foliage, late 19th/ early 20th century, 13.6cm. (Lawrence Fine Arts) £154

A set of three Tiffany & Co. spirit flasks, the flattened rectangular bodies with screwed hinged covers, 20.6cm. high. (Christie's) £1,430

A silver presentation flask by Gorham Mfg. Co., 1888, 7¾in. high, 19oz. 10dwt. £1,500

A curved shaped oblong silver spirit flask with detachable gilt lined cup and cover, by Omar Ramsden, 1924, 6½in. high, 18oz. (Christie's) £1,188

Mauser Co. Sterling Bottle Carrier, New York, c. 1900, in the form of a wine bottle with repousse vine decoration, 11¹/₂in. high, approximately 27.5 troy oz. (Skinner Inc) £909

An amusing flask, by Tiffany & Co., New York, 1891-1902 decorated with etched scenes of brownies frolicking and quarrelling and avoiding mosquitoes, marked, 7¾in. high, 15oz. (Christie's) £5,188

SILVER FLATWARE

A Georg Jensen 180-piece 'acorn' pattern table service, first designed in 1915 by Johan Rohde, 181oz. weight not including knives. (Christie's)   £20,520

A knife and fork designed by Henry van de Velde, the handles with curvilinear art nouveau design, circa 1900. (Christie's)
£864

A Liberty & Co., Cymric silver spoon, designed by Archibald Knox on the occasion of Edward VII's Coronation in 1902, 16cm. long. (Phillips London)   £320

A Guild of Handicraft Ltd. silver preserve spoon, stamped G. of H. Ltd. and London hallmarks for 1902. (Christie's)   £280

A Georg Jensen 64-piece 'chess pattern' table service stamped Georg Jensen, Sterling, Denmark, 50oz.12dwt. weight not including knives. (Christie's)   £1,836

A Guild of Handicraft silver jam spoon, designed by C.R. Ashbee, set with abalone, with London hallmarks for 1906, 45 grams. gross.   (Christie's)   £198

A caddy spoon with hammered fig-shaped bowl and stylised flower handle set at centre with a cornelian boss, 1921. (Phillips) £380

A Guild of Handicraft silver butter knife, designed by C.R. Ashbee, with twisted wirework 'cage' handle set with a faceted amethyst, with London hallmarks for 1905, 35 grams. gross.
(Christie's)   £896

A pair of grape shears, by Tiffany & Co., circa 1880-85, of shaped scissor-form, 8in. long, 5oz. (Christie's)   £2,660

One of a pair of jam spoons designed by Georg Jensen, the hammered and cut bowls in the form of a leaf with curving handles. (Christie's)   £216

A Liberty & Co. silver and enamel ceremonial spoon, designed by Archibald Knox, the shaped handle with elaborate entrelac design and blue-green and red enamel, Birmingham hallmark for 1900, 20.5cm. long, 95 grams. gross.
(Christie's)   £3,300

SILVER FLATWARE

A. D. W. Hislop set of four silver spoons and forks designed by Charles Rennie Mackintosh, stamped with maker's marks and Glasgow hallmarks for 1902. (Christie's London)   £22,000

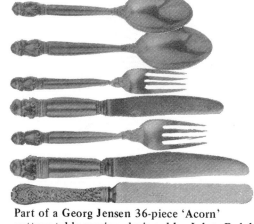

Part of a Georg Jensen 36-piece 'Acorn' pattern table service, designed by Johan Rohde. (Christie's)   £1,870

An 89-piece 'Cactus' pattern table service, designed by Gundorph Albertus, stamped marks, 102oz., weight not including items that are part steel. (Christie's)   £2,700

An E. Bingham & Co. 42-piece electroplated table service, designed by Charles Rennie Mackintosh, with flat trefoil finials, the knives with black bakelite handles and steel blades. (Christie's)   (Forty-two)   £7,700

A 134-piece 'Pyramid' pattern table service designed by Harald Nielson, stamped marks, 181oz.5dwt., weight not including items that are part steel. (Christie's)   £6,480

A Guild of Handicraft sixteen piece silver fruit service, comprising eight forks and eight knives, chrysoprase chamfered handles, with London hallmarks for 1905, in fitted case. (Christie's)   £1,540

SILVER FLATWARE

Part of a 146-piece flatware service, by Tiffany & Co., New York, 1878-1900, in the original fitted oak box, 230oz. excluding knives. (Christie's) £4,655

A Georg Jensen 48 piece table service, stamped maker's marks, after 1945, 2,700grs. gross weight. (Christie's London) £2,750

Part of a 24-piece set of parcel gilt dessert knives and forks, by Tiffany & Co., circa 1880-85, knives 8¼in. long, 48oz.10dwt. (Christie's) £2,992

Three of seven parcel gilt condiment servers, by Tiffany & Co., circa 1880-85, serving spoon 9½in. long, sauce ladles each approx. 7in. long, 13oz. (Christie's) £3,657

Part of a 140-piece mixed metal flatware service, by Tiffany & Co., 1880-85, dinner fork, 8.1/8in. long, ladel 13in. long, 201oz. 10dwt. excluding knives. (Christie's) £59,855

Part of a Georg Jensen 75-piece 'Pyramid' pattern table service, designed by Harald Nielsen, 1926, stamped marks, 132oz.6dwt. gross weight. (Christie's) £6,060

SILVER FRAMES

A William Hutton & Sons Art
Nouveau silver and enamel
photograph frame, decorated
with stylised honesty and green
and blue enamelling, 1904,
22.3cm. high. (Christie's
London)   £2,420

A Victorian silver mounted
dressing glass, on a ebonised
base with easel supports, 1885 by
William Comyns, 32.3cm.
(Lawrence)   £660

A Ramsden & Carr silver
picture frame, with London
hallmarks for 1900, 15.5cm.
high. (Christie's)   £950

A Liberty silver and enamel
picture frame, designed by
Archibald Knox, with
Birmingham hallmarks for
1904, 21.2cm. high.
(Christie's)   £3,888

An Art Nouveau silver
photograph frame, the shaped
square frame with floral
repoussé decoration, one corner
with drape motif, Birmingham
hallmarks for 1904, 15.8cm.
high. (Christie's)   £1,100

An Edwardian Art Nouveau
silver and enamel photograph
frame, Wm. Hutton & Sons
Ltd., London, 1904, 10.25in.
high, also an Elkington & Co.
vase, Birmingham, 1906.
(Reeds Rains)   £750

A William Hutton & Sons
silver and enamelled picture
frame, the top having interwoven tendrils picked out in
green and violet enamels,
20.5cm. high. (Phillips London)
£2,700

A silver repoussé picture frame
of shaped rectangular form,
decorated in relief with a stylised
foliate pattern, Chester
hallmarks, 32.7cm. high.
(Christie's)   £990

A silver repousse picture
frame, shaped rectangular
form, decorated in relief with
flowers and insects, Birmingham hallmarks for 1907,
29.5cm. high. (Christie's
London)   £715

SILVER FRAMES

A Victorian heart-shaped photograph frame, decorated with cherubs faces amongst scrolling flowers and foliage, 7¹/₂in. high, William Comyns, London 1897.
(Bearne's) £300

A Liberty & Co. 'cymric' silver and enamel frame, Birmingham, 1903, 23cm. high. £5,000

A Victorian heart-shaped dressing table mirror, within a frame of scrolling foliage, masks, drapes and trelliswork, 11in. high, William Comyns, London 1897. (Bearne's) £450

An Art Nouveau silver shaped oval photograph frame with easel support, John and William Deakin, Birmingham 1904, 12in. high. (Christie's S. Ken) £264

A William Hutton and Sons silver and enamel picture frame, with repoussé entrelac decoration, the top corners decorated with blue-green enamel, London hallmarks for 1903, 19.3cm. high.
(Christie's) £1,650

A William Hutton & Sons silver and enamel picture frame, with repousse decoration and entre-lac motif, London hallmarks for 1903, 20.4cm. high. (Christie's) £990

A silver and enamel repoussé photograph frame, decorated in relief with stylised and green enamel flowers, Birmingham hallmarks for 1904, 21.5cm. high.
(Christie's) £935

A decorative Edwardian photograph frame, in the Art Nouveau style with ivy on a wood back, 1901, 24.8cm. high x 21.5cm. wide.
(Phillips) £3,000

A Liberty and Co. silver photograph frame, the top and base decorated with band of mistletoe, stamped maker's mark L & Co. and Birmingham hallmarks for 1892, 21.3cm. high. (Christie's) £880

SILVER GOBLETS

One of three Desny electro-plated goblets, conical bowl and small conical foot connected by angled flange, 1920's, 12cm. high. £572

A large goblet designed by H. Nielsen, stamped Dessin H.N. G.J. 535, circa 1928, 19.9cm. high, 25oz.15dwt. (Christie's) £1,725

A 20th century enamelled and jewelled sterling silver chalice, approx. 4 troy oz. (Robt. W. Skinner Inc.) £376

An Arts & Crafts Movement chalice in medieval style, by Omar Ramsden & Alwyn Carr, London, 1912, 5.2in. high, 10oz. all in. (Christie's) £760

An Arts and Crafts silver two handled goblet by Skinner & Co., the flared bowl with knopped base, with London hallmarks for 1907, 14.5cm. high, 309 grams. (Christie's) £242

One of two Edwardian silver gilt goblets, by Edward Barnard & Sons Ltd., 1902 and 1903, 10¼in. high, 46oz. (Christie's) £990

An Omar Ramsden beaten silver goblet, the foot with inscription MCMXXI, 5in. high, London hallmarks for 1920. (Christie's) £180

One of a pair of presentation Art Nouveau goblets, by Omar Ramsden and Alwyn Carr, London 1913, 5in. high. (Woolley & Wallis) £820

A C.R. Ashbee hammered silver goblet, the foot with a radiating repoussé pattern of stylised buds, London hallmarks for 1899, 12cm. high, 300 grams. (Christie's) £550

SILVER INKSTANDS

An Edwardian novelty ink-
stand in the form of an ear of
maize, maker I.S.B., London,
1907, 9in. long, 9oz.
(Woolley & Wallis)   £800

A martele inkstand, by Gorham,
Providence, circa 1905, the
stand repousse and chased
with serpentine ribs and
flowers, marked *Martele. 9584,*
10¼in. wide, 9oz. (Christie's
New York)   £1,383

Late Victorian, cyclist's
novelty inkwell, Birming-
ham, 1896, 5¼in. wide.
          £500

A Victorian Scottish inkwell,
by Aitchison of Edinburgh,
1885, inkwell 15cm. high.
(Phillips)   £900

A silver oblong inkstand with
flat hinged lid, the interior with
two glass inkwells and silver dip
pen, 9in. wide, Birmingham
1918, 32oz. (Capes, Dunn & Co.)
          £275

Faberge rock crystal and
silver inkwell, St. Petersburg, circa 1900, 5¾in.
high.   £1,500

An Edwardian silver and
tortoiseshell tapering square
inkstand on bracket feet, by
Goldsmiths & Silversmiths
Company Ltd., London 1902,
4¾in. (Christie's)   £638

A Liberty & Co. silver
and enamel portable ink-
well, Birmingham, circa
1900, 13.5cm. wide.
          £500

A Guild of Handicraft white
metal and enamel inkwell,
attributed to C. R. Ashbee,
seven sided on ball feet,
10.5cm. high. (Christie's)
          £1,728

SILVER JUGS

A silver oval covered cream jug, by Omar Ramsden, 1925, 11cm. high, 8.5oz. (Phillips) £800

A James Dixon & Sons electroplated cream jug, designed by C. Dresser, 1880's, 9.5cm. £300

Lebolt sterling silver hand-hammered water pitcher, Chicago, circa 1920, 9½in. high, 26 troy oz. £450

A Christofle electroplated jug, mounted with an unpierced wooden handle, the base stamped with marks and Gallia, prod. Christofle, Italy, 22.5cm. high. (Christie's) £242

A Georg Jensen silver cream jug, supported on three foliate feet and having a leaf and magnolia bloom handle, 7.5cm. high. (Phillips) £220

A small pitcher, designed by J. Rohde, stamped marks JR Georg Jensen GJ 295 432A, circa 1928, 22.7cm. high, 17oz. (Christie's) £1,045

A pitcher, by Tiffany & Co., New York, 1869-1891, the cast handle in the form of stylised leafage above classical mask handle join, marked, 22cm. high, 36oz. (Christie's New York) £2,213

Georg Jensen sterling pitcher, Denmark, with openwork grapevine decoration, 9in. high, approx. 30 troy oz. (Skinner Inc.) £1,840

A 19th century American 'ivy chased' jug, by Tiffany & Co., circa 1870, 23cm. high, 27.5oz. (Phillips) £2,100

SILVER JUGS

Tiffany sterling silver water pitcher of circular bulbous form, circa 1880, 8¾in. high, approx. 30 troy oz. (Stalker) £666

A plated pitcher, by Meriden Britannia Co., circa 1885, the entire surface spot hammered, the sides repousse and chased with a dragonfly, waterlilies and flowers, marked, 26cm. high. (Christie's New York) £691

A jug with ebony handle, stamped Georg Jensen 407A, 23.2cm. high, 35oz. 5dwt. gross weight. (Christie's) £1,836

A silver water pitcher, attributed to Dominick & Haff, New York, circa 1880, with an everted brim and a scroll handle, marked Sterling on base, 6¾in. high. (Christie's) £974

A silver hot water jug, of oval section, by Omar Ramsden, 1930, 27cm. high, 36.5oz. (Phillips) £2,700

A Hukin & Heath electroplated jug, decorated with three vertical copper bands, 20.3cm. high. (Christie's London) £99

A pitcher of baluster form with an open handle, by Gorham Manuf. Co., 1897, 8¾in. high, gross weight 31oz. (Christie's) £1,306

A vase-shaped pitcher, in the Japanese taste, by Gorham Manuf. Co., Providence, 1885, 9in. high, 40oz.10dwt. (Christie's) £4,618

An Elkington & Co. electroplated jug designed by Dr. C. Dresser, 19.3cm. high. (Christie's) £1,296

405

A late Victorian chamber pot, with a scroll handle. (Woolley & Wallis)   £480

Liberty & Co. silver stopper by Archibald Knox, Birmingham, 1906, 6.5cm. high.   £250

French silver gilt powder jar, Paris, circa 1900, compressed cylindrical body with chased spiral fluting and leaf motif, signed *A. Bucher*, approximately 10 troy oz. (Skinner Inc.)   £540

A silver, onyx and coral paper knife and book mark, signed Cartier, London, 1934, 14cm (Lawrence Fine Arts)   £198

An Art Nouveau circular plaque stamped in high relief with a classical maiden seated in a garden, stamped with Sheffield hallmarks, 11$\frac{1}{2}$in. diameter, 11oz. (Christie's S. Ken)   £374

A Victorian electroplated letter rack in the style of Christopher Dresser, by Hukin & Heath, 12.9cm. high.   £125

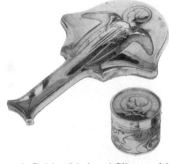

A Hukin & Heath plated spoon-warmer with ebony handle, the design attributed to Dr. C. Dresser, stamped H & H 2857, 14.4cm. high. (Christie's)   £259

A Lacloche Freres patterned silver and red gold minaudiere set with five sapphires, stamped with import marks for 1935, 13oz.14dwt., 13 x 8.6cm. (Christie's)   £1,080

A Goldsmiths' and Silversmiths' Co. silver handmirror, designed by Kate Harris, and a Goldsmiths' and Silversmiths' Co. silver box and cover, London hallmarks for 1890. (Christie's)   £1,100

SILVER MISCELLANEOUS

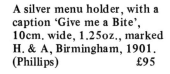

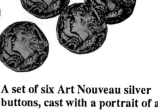

A Hukin & Heath electroplated articulated metal letter-rack, designed by Dr. Christopher Dresser, with three movable supports on either side, stamped *H&H 2555*, 12.5cm. high.
(Christie's) £550

A silver menu holder, with a caption 'Give me a Bite', 10cm. wide, 1.25oz., marked H. & A, Birmingham, 1901.
(Phillips) £95

A set of six Art Nouveau silver buttons, cast with a portrait of a girl, Chester 1902.
(Spencer's) £120

A rare elephant tusk humidor by Tiffany & Company, New York, the body formed by an oval shaped section of an elephant's tusk, repousse and chased in stylized floral motifs in the Indian taste, 10½in. high.
(Christie's) £6,172

An amusing German minaudiere, embossed on the front with two cats and a kitten in a wicker basket, 9.50 x 6.50cm., bearing marks for Louis Kuppenheim of Pforzheim, and '900'.
(Phillips) £600

An Edwardian oblong card case die-stamped with an Art Nouveau profile bust portrait of a maiden with flowing hair and elaborate headdress, Chrisford & Norris, Birmingham 1905, 3¾in..
(Christie's S. Ken) £330

An imperial silver and enamel Art Nouveau desk folder, Moscow, 1908-17, 43.5cm. high. £2,000

A Russian table lighter of urn or tureen shape by Karl Faberge, decorated with swags and bead borders, circa 1910, 9.8cm. high. (Phillips) £700

An unusual pair of sugar nips formed as a Dutch doll, the head enamelled with a face and hair, London 1911, 3½in.
(Christie's S. Ken) £495

SILVER MUSTARDS

A mixed metal mustard pot by Dominick & Haff, New York, 1880, the surface engraved in an all over blossom pattern, 6.04cm. high, gross weight 3oz. (Christie's)   £584

A William Hutton & Sons silver mustard pot, of drum shape with vertical ribs and set with garnet cabochons, 7cm. high, maker's marks for Birmingham 1905. (Phillips)   £400

A mixed-metal mustard pot and spoon by Dominick & Haff, New York, 1880, with a circular low-domed hinged cover with a ball finial, 2½in. high, gross weight 4oz. 10 dwt. (Christie's)   £1,383

A C. R. Ashbee silver mustard pot, set with six turquoise cabochons, London hallmarks for 1900, 8cm. high. (Christie's)   £864

A pair of Ramsden and Carr silver mustard-pots, supported on four pad feet, cylindrical blue glass liners, stamped maker's mark RN & CR and London hallmarks for 1903, 7cm. high. (Christie's)   £330

A rare example of a Bates improved mustard pot, the plain cylindrical body with spread base, by Arnold Neale Baily and Thomas House Bates, 1914, gross weight 2.5oz. (Phillips)   £575

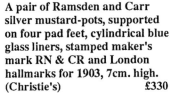

A C.R. Ashbee hammered silver mustard pot, set with three amber cabochons, original clear glass liner, stamped *C R A* with London hallmarks for 1900, 6.5cm. high, 100 grams. gross. (Christie's)   £880

Crichton Brothers, a pair of mustard pots, 4in. diam., with moulded borders, scroll handles and detachable blue glass liners, London, 1913, 10.5oz. (Bonhams)   £360

A Guild of Handicrafts silver mustard pot, designed by C. R. Ashbee, with London hallmarks for 1902, 8.5cm. high, 4oz.11dwt. gross weight. (Christie's)   £918

SILVER SALTS

A Faberge silver salt in the form of an elephant, circa 1900, 3.2cm.
£2,500

A pair of electroplated salt cellars, each cast as a dog, one standing, the other sitting, marked Orfevrerie Gallia. (Christie's)   £880

A Guild of Handicraft lidded hammered silver salt dish, set with a cabochon amethyst, with green Powell glass liner, with London hallmarks for 1904, 5.5cm. high, 50 grams. gross. (Christie's)   £308

A salt cellar by Gorham, Providence, 1872, with a bail handle attached to angular handles, on four flaring cylindrical raking legs, 3in. high, 2 oz. (Christie's)   £415

A pair of knife rests and open salts, by Tiffany & Co., 1878-91.   £1,000

A C.R. Ashbee hammered silver salt stand, the vertical supports with openwork design of stylised trees set with heart-shaped amber cabochons, London hallmarks for 1900, 5cm. high, 50 grams. gross. (Christie's)   £462

A pair of Guild of Handicraft Ltd. silver salts, designed by C. R. Ashbee, 5.70cm. high, London hallmarks for 1900, with green glass liners. (Phillips)   £1,500

One of a pair of Guild of Handicraft Ltd. silver salts, the design attributed to C. R. Ashbee, the bowls embossed and pierced with fish, 4cm. high, marks for G of H Ltd. 1907. (Phillips)   £2,000

Two of a set of four Hukin & Heath silver salts with salt spoons, Birmingham hallmarks for 1879, 6oz. 4dwt, each 3.4cm. high. (Christie's)   £864

SILVER TANKARDS & MUGS

Late 19th century Dutch silver-coloured metal tankard, 5¾in., 8oz. £500

An unusual late Victorian shaving mug, the hinged cover engraved with a monogram, London 1899, by Alex Clark, 251 grammes gross. (Henry Spencer) £290

A Liberty & Co. 'Cymric' silver tankard designed by Archibald Knox, 1901, 19.25cm. high. £3,960

A trophy tankard by Tiffany & Co., New York, circa 1890, with a low circular cover and scrolled handle, 10¼in. high, 47 oz. (Christie's) £2,618

A repousse tankard, by Tiffany & Co., N.Y. finished March 10, 1893, for the World's Columbian Exposition, Chicago, 1893, 10in. high, 52oz. 10dwt. (Christie's) £17,291

A late Victorian baluster tankard with moulded girdle, by J. Round, Sheffield 1900, 21.5cm. high, 25oz. £1,000

A silver applied enamelled copper mug, by Gorham Manuf. Co., Providence, 1881, 6½in. high. (Christie's) £1,154

A George V christening mug of waisted octagonal form, with foliate cast handle and foot rim, London 1910, 148 grammes. (Henry Spencer) £85

An Omar Ramsden hammered silver tankard, London hallmarks for 1914, 16oz., 12.5cm. high. £1,000

SILVER TAZZAS

A tazza with two scrolling strapwork handles, by Tiffany & Co., 1870-75, 6½in. high, 12.5/8in. wide, overall, 23oz.10dwt. (Christie's) £923

A Georg Jensen miniature tazza, designed by J. Rohde, 4.8cm. high, together with a similar tazza. (Christie's) £308

A circular tazza, by The Moore Co. for Tiffany & Co., circa 1865-69, marked on base with the 550 Broadway mark, 6.5/8in. high, 17½in. wide, overall, 41oz. (Christie's) £2,694

A large tazza, designed by Georg Jensen, assay mark with London import mark for 1924. 26.5cm. high, 36oz. 6dwt. (Christie's) £4,000

A covered tazza designed by J. Rohde, stamped Dessin J.R. Georg Jensen 43, circa 1920, 15.5cm. high, 14oz. 9dwt. (Christie's) £1,080

Georg Jensen sterling tazza, Denmark, 1925-30, with pendant bunches of grapes on a spiral chased stem with spreading foot, 7¼in. high, approx. 18 troy oz. (Skinner Inc.) £982

Silver and ivory tazza by Adie Bros. Ltd., 12.75cm. diameter, 1930. £1,000

A small tazza designed by G. Albertus, stamped GI 925 S 468, circa 1928, 8.9cm. high, 9oz.5dwt. (Christie's) £756

Attractive Guild of Handicraft Ltd. silver and enamel tazza, London, 1905, 15.25cm. high. £2,500

SILVER TEA CADDIES

An Edwardian tea caddy, Sheffield 1903 by Richard Martin and Ebenezer Hall of Martin, Hall and Co., 9.3cm. (Lawrence) £264

A late Victorian tea caddy, Birmingham 1900 by T. Hayes, the cap Birmingham 1896, 10.6cm. (Lawrence) £220

Guild of Handicrafts Ltd. silver tea caddy, London, 1906, 7cm. high, on four ball feet. £300

A Liberty & Co. silver and enamel tea caddy of oval section, Birmingham hallmarks for 1907, 9.3cm. high, 5oz.2dwt. gross weight. (Christie's) £220

A Ramsden & Carr silver tea-caddy and spoon, London hallmarks for 1931, 10.9cm. high, 13oz.7dwt. gross wt. (Christie's) £1,650

A Victorian silver mounted glass tea caddy, Chester, 1900. (Reeds Rains) £220

A late Victorian tea caddy in the Art Nouveau style, Chester 1900, 213gr. (H. Spencer & Sons) £190

Late 19th century Faberge silver tea caddy in the form of a large tea packet, Moscow, 13cm. wide. £8,000

A silver and copper tea caddy and cover by Albert Edward Jones, Birmingham, 1913, 5in. high. £150

SILVER TEA KETTLES

A tea kettle on stand, retailed by Starr and Marcus, N.Y., circa 1910, 14½in. high, 53oz. 10dwt. (Christie's) £798

A conical shaped tea kettle, by Mappin & Webb, possibly designed by C. Dresser, complete with stand and spirit burner. (Reeds Rains) £50

A Victorian style part-fluted compressed tea kettle with a burner, probably George Fox, London 1912, 11½in., 45oz. (Christie's) £550

A fine tea kettle and stand by Tiffany & Co., New York, 1881–1891, in the Japanese taste, 12³/₄in. high, 467 oz. (Christie's) £7,198

A William Hutton & Sons silver kettle and stand, the design probably by Kate Harris, of broad cylindrical shape embellished with abstract ivy and swirls, 30.50cm. London 1901. (Phillips) £1,200

A kettle on stand and a teapot, by Tiffany & Co., New York, 1876-1891, each globular, kettle 13in. high, gross weight 85oz. (Christie's New York) £1,176

A Hukin & Heath electroplated picnic kettle with folding tripod stand and spirit burner, designed by Dr. C. Dresser, 14.5cm. high. (Christie's) £172

An F. Minsfiberg kettle-on-stand with ivory handle and ivory finial, 29.2cm. high. (Christie's) £1,650

A tea kettle and stand by The Goldsmiths & Silversmiths Co. Ltd., 1930, 31cm. high, 66oz. all in. (Lawrence Fine Art) £726

SILVER TEAPOTS

A Charles Boyton hammered silver teapot, London hallmarks for 1933, 21oz. 19dwt., 12.5cm. high. **£1,000**

An electroplated teapot, the design attributed to Dr. Christopher Dresser, 15cm. high. **£250**

A silver teapot and cover modelled as a pomegranate, the chased details realistically rendered, its leafy branches forming a handle rendered in ivory, late 19th century, 12.8cm. long. (Christie's London) **£2,420**

An Elkington & Co. electroplated barrel-shaped metal teapot, designed by Dr. Christopher Dresser, with ebonized curving wooden handle, stamped with a variety of Elkington & Co., 17cm. high. (Christie's) **£3,300**

A. W. M. Hutton & Sons electroplated teapot and hot-water jug, designed by H. Stabler, 15.7cm. high. **£350**

An unusual part fluted tapering teapot with rising curved spout, the base engraved: "Patent Trade S.Y.P. Mark Teapot", James Dixon & Son, Sheffield 1912, 9¼in., 42oz. gross. (Christie's) **£528**

A Hutton & Sons silver teapot, of broad cylindrical shape with angular spout, wickered loop handle and flat cover, Sheffield 1909, 16.5cm. high. (Phillips) **£340**

A Napper & Davenport silver 'cube' teapot, Birmingham, 1922, 13.25cm. **£2,000**

A square teapot, the hinged cover with a green stone finial, by Tiffany & Co., N.Y., 1877-91, 5in. high, gross weight 15oz. (Christie's) **£10,886**

SILVER TOAST RACKS

A Hukin & Heath plated toastrack, attributed to Christopher Dresser with open rectangular base supported on block feet, 11.5cm. high. (Phillips) £560

A late Victorian small five bar toast rack, the arched upright on a wrythen fluted 'shell' base, Sheffield 1900, 103 grammes, 5in. long. (Spencer's) £70

A Hukin & Heath electroplated toastrack designed by Dr. Christopher Dresser, with registration mark for 9th May 1881. (Phillips) £300

An unusual silver-gilt toastrack, the five divisions formed from crossed apostle spoons, and surmounted by a coronet handle, London, 1910. (Bonhams) £140

A rare James Dixon & Sons electroplated toastrack designed by Dr Christopher Dresser, the rectangular frame with seven triangular supports, each with angular wire decoration, on four spike feet and with a raised vertical handle, stamped with maker's marks and facsimile signature Chr. Dresser, 16.4cm. high. (Christie's) £14,300

A toastrack, the base in the form of 'The Man in the Moon', the handle as a cast owl, 17cm. wide, 5cm. high, circa 1900. (Phillips) £260

A Hukin and Heath electro-plated toast rack, the wirework frame with seven supports, on a convex base, stamped *H & H,* 12cm. high. (Christie's London) £220

A Charles Boynton silver toast-rack of oval, almost boat shape, 9.5cm. high, 5.5oz., marked CB for London 1936. £500

A four-division toast-rack, on four bun feet and with central bracket handle, by Omar Ramsden, 1932, 3in. long, 6oz. (Christie's) £500

SILVER TOAST RACKS

London & North Eastern Railway ornate toast rack with coat of arms. (Onslow's) £110

A Hukin & Heath electroplated toastrack designed by Dr. Christopher Dresser, with registration mark for 9th October 1878, 12cm. high. (Phillips) £2,700

A novelty five bar toast rack in the form of a swan, 7in. long. £100

A rare James Dixon & Sons electroplated toast rack, designed by Dr. Christopher Dresser, divisions with lunette shaped designs, central loop handle, 8.5cm. high. (Christie's) £4,400

Late 19th century silver plated on brass toast rack with pierced base. £20

An Elkington & Co. electroplated toast rack, designed by Dr. Christopher Dresser, with a tall central 'T' base and three low triangular shaped supports on either side of it, 13.5cm. high. (Christie's) £7,150

A six-division toast-rack, on four bun feet and with central bracket handle, by Omar Ramsden, 1928, 4in. long, 7oz. (Christie's) £600

A Hukin & Heath plated toastrack, designed by Christopher Dresser, the arched base on four bun feet supporting six pronged divisions, 12.50cm. high. (Phillips) £220

A Guild of Handicraft toast rack, designed by C.R. Ashbee, the end panels with repoussé decoration of stylised trees, London hallmarks for 1906, 13cm. high, 220 grams. (Christie's) £1,430

SILVER TRAYS

A rectangular tea tray, the raised gadroon rim with shell motifs at the angles, Sheffield, 1936 by Emile Viner of Viner and Co., 62cm., 89.4oz. (Lawrence Fine Arts) £1,155

Tiffany sterling and mixed metal salver, circa 1880, decorated in the Japanese taste with a dragonfly and maple branch on a hammered ground, 11¾in. wide, approximately 19 troy oz. (Skinner Inc.) £7,817

Tiffany sterling silver butler's tray, rectangular, stylised foliate border, 21in. wide. (Skinner Inc.) £8,280

An Edwardian dressing table tray of rectangular form, Chester 1901, by John and William Deakin of James Deakin and Sons., 30.5cm., 12.4oz. (Lawrence) £374

A Hukin & Heath electroplated tray, designed by Dr Christopher Dresser, with plain gallery rim and ebonised bar handles, 48.6cm. wide. (Christie's London) £880

An Edwardian shaped oblong trinket tray die-stamped with rococo shells, flowers and scrolling foliage, William Hutton and Sons Limited, Birmingham 1905, 11½in., 9.75oz. (Christie's S. Ken) £341

A sterling silver strapwork tray, signed Shreve & Co. San Francisco Sterling, circa 1918, 12½in. diam., 26 troy oz. (Robt. W. Skinner Inc.) £378

A Tiffany sterling silver sealing wax set, N.Y., circa 1891-1902, 8½in. sq., wt. approx. 20 troy oz. (Robt. W. Skinner Inc.) £432

A silver tray, by Howard & Co., N.Y., circa 1900, 18¼in. diam., 78oz.10dwt. (Christie's) £1,000

SILVER TRAYS

Tiffany & Co. Sterling Tray, New York, early 20th century, 20in. long., approximately 74 troy oz. (Skinner Inc) £1,233

A Russian Art Nouveau rectangular pen tray, by O. Kurlyukov, 26cm. wide. £1,000

A Georg Jensen circular tray, designed by Johan Rohde, the handles cast with interlocking scrolls, 13in. diam. (Christie's S. Ken) £660

A Wiener Werkstatte plated oval tray, designed by Josef Hoffmann, embellished with vertical lobes and fluting, 34cm. wide. (Phillips) £800

W.M.F.silver plated dish with handles, 8in. diameter. (Muir Hewitt) £50

An inlaid waiter with an everted brim, on four cast feet, by Tiffany & Co., 1878-91, 9½in. diam., gross weight 10oz. (Christie's) £11,971

One of a pair of silver bread trays with open foliate handles, by S. Kirk & Son Co., Baltimore, 1903-07, 14¼in. long, 44oz. (Christie's) £1,000

A silver smoking tray, by Tiffany & Company, New York, circa 1900, the hammer faceted tray with three rectangular wells for cigars and cigarettes, 10¼in. wide, 30oz. (Christie's) £779

An oval tray on eight claw and ball feet, by Omar Ramsden, 1923, 22¾in. long, 85oz. (Christie's) £1,620

SILVER TUREENS

A Hertz large oval white metal tureen, flanked either side by applied sprays of stylised foliage, stamped marks, 14in. wide.
(Christie's) £250

A tureen designed by Henning Koppel, the cover stamped HK H 10 Georg Jensen 925 S 1034, 72cm. long, 105oz.
(Christie's) £22,000

A fine silver tureen and cover by Tiffany & Co flanked either side with scroll handles, 12½in. high, 68oz.10dwt. £3000

A Hukin & Heath electroplated metal tureen, designed by Dr. Christopher Dresser, with bone finial and cylindrical bar handle, on three spike feet, with registration lozenge for 1880, 25.5cm. high.
(Christie's) £6,600

A Sybil Dunlop hammered silver tureen and cover, on circular foot the spherical body chased in relief with two band of scrolling foliage, flanked either side with scrolled handles, London 1922, 4½in. high.
(Christie's) £600

A fine tureen and cover, designed by Georg Jensen, the bombé bowl with curved leaf and bud handles on four scroll feet with stem and flower head decoration, 31.5cm. long, 1980 grams.
(Christie's) £13,200

A Georg Jensen silver two-handled tureen and cover, Danish silver marks, circa 1930, 62oz., 25cm. high.
(Christie's) £3,456

A covered tureen, by Samuel Kirk & Son, Baltimore, 1880-1890, the low domed cover with a pineapple finial, marked, 10in. high, 57oz. (Christie's New York) £1,383

Late Victorian American sterling silver turtle soup tureen, 12¼in. long, 46 troy oz. £2,000

SILVER URNS

Silver gilt urn, by Howard & Co., New York, circa 1900, 14in. high, 45 troy oz. £1,250

Tiffany sterling coffee urn on stand, 1938–47, tapering fluted body cast with basketweave and Renaissance motifs, 15in. high, approximately 90¹/₂ oz. (Skinner Inc.) £4,509

A silver plated Art Nouveau covered urn, circa 1900, 16¼in. high. (Robt. W. Skinner Inc.) £134

A two-compartment caviar container of urn-shaped form, by Omar Ramsden and Alwyn Carr, 1903, 25.5cm. high, 27.75oz. (Phillips) £1,500

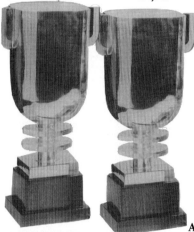

A pair of silver plated metal and perspex Urns, each of hexagonal bucket form on tubular stem and square base, 20¼in. high. (Bonhams) £800

A Puiforcat silver urn, of shouldered ovoid form, tapering to an everted scalloped rim, with domed cover and carved ivory finial, 34.5cm. high. (Christie's London) £880

A tea urn, by Gorham, Providence, 1890-1910, the conical cover with an ivory urn finial, marked, 17½in. high, gross weight 94oz. (Christie's New York) £1,383

An Art Deco chromium plated tea urn of tapering form, 42cm. high, stamped 'REG 849217'. (Phillips) £520

A plated tea urn, by Gorham, Providence, 2nd half 19th century, on four angular supports each surmounted by a figure of a seated Chinese man, marked, 14¾in. high. (Christie's New York) £1,037

SILVER VASES

A William Hutton & Son silver and glass vase, stamped maker's marks, and London hallmarks for 1902, 11.2cm. high. (Phillips)   £100

An ovoid vase, by Tiffany & Co., N.Y., 1878-90, 6.5/8in. high, 14oz. (Christie's)
£4,322

Black, Starr and Frost sterling vase, New York, early 20th century, with an overall chased flowering clematis vine, 14³/₄in. high, approximately 44 troy oz. (Skinner Inc.)   £1,512

A Liberty silver vase, the design attributed to A. Knox, stamped Cymric. L & Co within three lozenges and with Birmingham hallmarks for 1907, 17cm. high. (Christie's)   £270

A pair of Georg Jensen vases, stamped marks Dessin G J 925.S Georg Jensen 107A, 13.2cm. high, 332.5gr. (Christie's)   £385

A bud vase, the body inlaid in copper and niello with butterflies and cherry blossoms, by Tiffany & Co., 1872-91, 5in. high, 3oz.10dwt. (Christie's)   £1,862

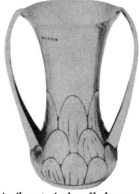

A silver twin-handled vase, 16.6cm. high, 12.5oz., stamped E.J.B. maker's marks, Birmingham, 1909. (Phillips)   £280

A WMF Ikora patinated metal vase, shouldered ovoid shape with short cylindrical neck, 23.6cm. high. (Christie's)   £302

A vase by Towle, Newburyport, circa 1910, with a moulded circular rim and footrim, 9⁵/₈in. high, 30 oz. (Christie's)   £654

SILVER VASES

An Art Nouveau baluster vase chased with lilies of the valley, the base impressed with a date 1896, 7¼in., 14.75oz. (Christie's) £275

A pierced vase by Tiffany & Co., New York, 1902–1907, with fluted sides, scalloped rim, scrolling handles and a repoussé foliate base, 11½in. high, 51 oz. 10 dwt. (Christie's) £2,618

A silver enamelled bud base, by Tiffany & Co., N.Y., circa 1893, 5.3/8in. high, 5oz.10dwt. (Christie's) £834

A cut glass and silver vase by Gorham, Providence; glass by Hawkes, circa 1912, 15in. high. (Christie's) £1,107

A pair of Liberty & Co. 'Cymric' silver and enamelled vases designed by Archibald Knox, Birmingham marks for 1903, 12.5cm. high. (Phillips) £3,600

A trophy vase by Whiting Manufacturing Co., New York, 1887, with a flaring scalloped rim, the sides etched with mermaids riding seahorses, 15½in. high, 37 oz. 10 dwt. (Christie's) £2,945

A Liberty and Co. 'Cymric' three-handled waisted vase, the handles enamelled with entwined strap-work in shades of blue, green and purple, Birmingham 1901, 6¾in. high. (Christie's S. Ken) £1,540

An enamelled vase by Gorham, Providence, 1897, with a flaring square rim and foot, the front and back cast with a pond and lilypads, 7¾in. high, 16 oz. (Christie's) £1,440

A Liberty & Co. 'Cymric' silver and enamel vase, the body decorated with a band of blue and orange enamelled stylised fruit branches, Birmingham hallmarks for 1905, 19.2cm. high. (Christie's) £990

SILVER VASES

A silver cylindrical vase
by Gorham Mfg. Co.,
circa 1895, 13¼in. high,
42oz. 10dwt.   £2,000

A tapering cylindrical vase
with four angular handles,
London 1914, 7½in. high.
£450

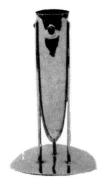

Liberty & Co. 'Cymric'
silver vase by Archibald
Knox, Birmingham,
1903, 15cm. high. £750

A Cartier two-handled silver
vase, London import marks
for 1930, on ebonised stand,
29.2cm. high, 60oz.15dwt.
(Christie's)   £1,100

Pair of silver vases by
Gorham Manufacturing
Co., marked 'Martele',
14½in. high, 69oz.
10dwt.   £5,000

An Edwardian Irish spot-
hammered flaring vase applied with foliate decorated
scroll handles, Goldsmiths &
Silversmiths Co. Ltd., Dublin
1903, 8¼in., 28.75 oz.
(Christie's)   £572

A Liberty & Co. 'Cymric'
silver and enamel vase,
the design attributed to
A. Knox, 1902, 19.25cm.
£5,000

A WMF Ikora patinated metal
vase, ovoid shape, inlaid with a
figure on horseback in silver,
gilt and dark grey, 20.2cm.
high. (Christie's)   £388

A Vase by Tiffany & Company,
New York, 1892, with two cast
handles, each in the form of two
swan's heads with elongated
necks, 13¹/₄in. high, 30 oz.
(Christie's)   £2,421

SILVER VESTA CASES

An Edwardian rectangular vesta case, one side enamelled with a wasp, Birmingham 1905. (Christie's S. Ken) £264

A silver and coral guilloché enamel match box, workmaster's stamp of Michael Perchin and Fabergé in Russian script, Petersburg 1905, 3½in. x 2¼in. (Woolley & Wallis) £950

A Continental gilt-lined vesta case, enamelled with a standing lady dressed in black stockings and a camisole holding a cat in the gathered folds, 2in. (Christie's S. Ken) £396

A Victorian combined vesta case and cachou box, engraved all over with leafage, 'Cachous', Birmingham, 1887. (Phillips) £130

A stylish French gold vesta case, with rounded top and base set with bands of calibre set rubies, flanking a row of five small diamonds. (Phillips London) £320

A gold match safe, 19th century, with floral and scroll motifs and a gem set clover in central cartouche. (Robt. W. Skinner Inc.) £255

An enamelled oblong silver vesta case, probably German, importer's mark Simon & Alder, London 1903, 1¾in. high. £1,000

A novel late Victorian vesta case designed as an advertisement, of rounded oblong form, decorated in polychrome enamel with an oval cartouche, maker's mark *WJD*, Birmingham, 1894. (Phillips) £280

An Edwardian rectangular vesta case, the front enamelled with an oval vignette of a dog, R.B.S Chester, 1906, 2in.(Christie's S. Ken) £110

SPELTER

Spelter is another name for zinc, especially for impure zinc. It was smelted in England from around 1730, and was much in demand during the 19th century for cheap decorative items such as candlesticks, clock cases and statuettes. The terms lead spelter, aluminium spelter etc indicate alloys of zinc with these metals.

Stylized silvered spelter figure on marble base, holding blue glass clock, 20in. high, 1930s.
(Muir Hewitt)   £450

1920s cold painted spelter figure of a dancer.
(Muir Hewitt)   £275

Art Deco lamp with spelter figure.
(Muir Hewitt)   £395

American spelter figure holding dish, 1930s, marked *Frankart*, 8in. high.
(Muir Hewitt)   £175

1920s figure of lady fencer in cold painted spelter.
(Muir Hewitt)   £420

Stylized 1920s spelter figure of a dancer, 9in. high.
(Muir Hewitt)   £195

Stylized spelter figure on alabaster base, with mirror, 11½in. high, 1930s.
(Muir Hewitt)   £200

Art Deco spelter figure lamp with stylized 1930s lady supporting crackle glass shade, 22in. high.
(Muir Hewitt)   £500

TERRACOTTA

Terracotta is a fired clay, principally associated with sculpture, and terracotta figures feature among the antiquities of China, Greece & Rome. The art was revived during the Renaissance, and in the 18th century France became a leading centre of production. The popularity of the medium lasted well into the Art Nouveau period, and busts of typical flowing haired maidens were produced.

A late 19th century French terracotta bust of 'L'Esperance', signed J. B. Carpeaux 1874, 54cm. high. £990

A Belgian terracotta face mask by L. Nosbusch modelled as Rudolf Valentino, 14in. high. £200

A 19th century French terracotta bust of Mademoiselle Marguerite Bellanger, by Albert Carrier-Belleuse, 69cm. high, on a glazed terracotta socle. (Christie's) £8,800

A pair of 19th century French terracotta busts of 'L'Espiegle' and 'Le Printemps', signed J.-Bte-Carpeaux, 48cm. and 55cm. high. (Christie's) £3,080

A 19th century French terracotta bust of Louise Brogniart, after Houdon, 50cm. high. (Christie's) £550

A terracotta bust of an Art Nouveau maiden, with long flowing hair, embellished with large trailing poppies in a green patination, 42cm. high. (Phillips) £400

Model for 'Gateway of Youth', plaster with terracotta coloured painted finish, 22 x 18in. £200

French terracotta bust of a young woman, Charles Eugene Breton, dated 1916, smiling with long tresses bound at the back, 22in. high. (Skinner Inc.) £396

TRAVEL POSTERS

The last years of the 19th century and the early part of the 20th saw a complete revolution in the speed and scope for travel, and it was this period, before travelling became commonplace, and still had more than a whiff of the exotic about it, that saw the golden age of the travel poster. Many famous artists gave their talents to design these, and succeeded in making even humble Skegness seem a highly desirable destination. Decorative in their own right, travel posters hark back to a more peaceful, leisured age.

'Take Me by The Flying Scotsman', designed by A. R. Thomson. (Onslow's) £1,300

'Empress of Britain, Canada's Challenger', published by Canadian Pacific. (Onslow's) £400

'Belgium, Harwich, Antwerp', by Higgins. (Onslow's) £195

Robert Bartlett, Scotland By 'The Night Scotsman', pub. by L.N.E.R., quad royal, 40 x 50in. (Onslow's) £1,500

'The Continent, Via Harwich', by Higgins. (Onslows) £500

Skegness Is So Bracing, poster by John Hassall. (Onslow's) £350

For Real Comfort, New Statendam, Holland-America Line, by Adolphe Mouron Cassandre, lithograph in colours, 1928, 1050 x 806mm. (Christie's) £1,000

Penaga, Great Southern & Western Railway Paris In London, on linen, double royal. (Onslow's) £460

TRAVEL POSTERS

Ellis Silas, 'Orient Line To Australia', double royal. (Onslow's) £490

'Edgware by Tram', double crown, 1929. (Onslow's) £75

L. C. Mitchell, 'Mount Cook New Zealand', double royal. (Onslow's) £230

L.N.E.R. Camping Coaches In England and Scotland, poster, published by L.N.E.R., 1939. (Onslow's) £80

'The Golfing Girl Well Out On The True Line', by The Caledonian Railway, 102 x 76cm. (Onslow's) £3,400

In Winter to Vienna, published by Waldheim-Eberle, double royal. (Onslow's) £60

Aberdeen & Commonwealth Line to Australia, by P.H. Yorke, double royal. (Onslow's) £80

Harold McCready, 'Imperial Airways City of Wellington', double crown, April 1929. (Onslow's) £600

Rio de Janeiro by Royal Mail to South America, by K. Shoesmith. (Onslow's) £240

TRAVEL POSTERS

Guy Lipscombe, 'LBSCR Southsea', double royal. (Onslow's) £520

Jack Roussau, 'Chemins de Fer de L'Etat de Brighton Paris A Londres' (Thames punting), double royal on linen. (Onslow's) £150

Roger Soubie, 'Vichy', 106 x 76cm. (Onslow's) £840

H. Cassiers, 'Red Star Line' (Belgenland), double royal. (Onslow's) £130

The Broads, poster by Gerald Spencer Pryse. (Onslow's) £170

'East Coast Types No. 5 The Deck-Chair Man'. (Onslow's) £130

'Express Ease, The Harrogate Pullman', published by L.N.E.R., designed by George Harrison. (Onslow's) £500

'Imperial Airways The British Airline Weekly Service Between Africa India Egypt and England', double royal. (Onslow's) £500

Montague B. Black, 'White Star Line Europe To America' (Olympic), double royal. (Onslow's) £700

TRAVEL POSTERS

Cunard Line 'Quickest Route New York to London and the Continent via Fishguard', by Odin Rosenvinge. (Onslow's) £1,000

Leslie Carr, 'The World's Greatest Liners Use Southampton Docks RMS Queen Mary and SS Normandie', published by SR, quad royal, 1936. (Onslow's) £550

Air France poster, Amerique du Sud, lithograph in colours, printed by Perceval, Paris, backed on linen 39 x 24in. (Christie's) £275

Frank H. Mason, 'SS Arnhem New Luxury Ship Harwich-Hook of Holland Service', published by LNER, quad royal. (Onslow's) £95

'The Continent Via Harwich', designed by Higgins. (Onslow's) £400

H. G. Gawthorn, 'Lowestoft', published by LNER, quad royal. (Onslow's) £700

John Vickery, 'Tasmania Australia', double royal. (Onslow's) £300

Etoile Du Nord, by Adolphe Mouron Cassandre, lithograph in colours, on wove paper, 1048 x 752mm. (Christie's) £850

'Dunbar, First Class Golf', designed by Alfred Lambart. (Onslow's) £370

TRAVEL POSTERS

Poster, 'P & O Cruises'.
(Onslows)   £95

P. Irwin Brown, 'Your
Continental Holiday', published by the big four railway
companies, quad royal, 1932.
(Onslow's)   £720

Odin Rosenvinge, 'Royal Line
from Bristol Fastest To Canada'
(Royal Edward), double royal.
(Onslow's)   £250

Austin Cooper, Cruden Bay By East
Coast Route, quad royal, 40 x 50in.
(Onslow's)   £660

'The Flying Scotsman's
Cocktail Bar', published by
L.N.E.R., designed by
Maurice Beck. (Onslow's)
                          £1,300

'The Wye Valley', published by
GWR. (Onslow's)   £110

L'Oiseau Bleu, by Adolphe
Mouron Cassandre, lithograph
in colours, 1929, on wove
paper, 996 x 616mm.
(Christie's)   £780

Nord Express, by Adolphe
Mouron Cassandre, lithograph
in colours, 1927, on wove
paper, 1048 x 752mm.
(Christie's)   £1,300

Brien, 'Silloth on the Solway
Finest Seaside Golf', published
by LNER, double royal.
(Onslow's)   £740

TRAVEL POSTERS

'Holland American Line
Southampton to New York'
(Statendam), by G. H. Davis.
(Onslow's)   £580

'Cunard Europe America'
(Aquitania), by Odin Rosen-
vinge, with loss to right margin.
(Onslow's)   £420

'United States Lines to
America Safety Courtesy
Comfort and Speed'. (Onslow's)
                        £100

'Cunard Europe America'
(Berengaria), by Odin Rosenvinge. (Onslow's)   £850

S. R. Badmin, 'Come and
Explore Britain', published by
The Travel Association, double
crown on linen. (Onslow's)
                        £300

'Cunard Line to All Parts of
the World' (Lusitania).
(Onslow's)   £720

'Cunard Line to All Parts of
the World' (Mauretania).
(Onslow's)   £1,250

'Cunard USA and Canada', by
Frank H. Mason. (Onslow's)
                      £2,500

E. McKnight Kauffer, 'Spring',
published by LT, double royal,
1938. (Onslow's)   £170

TRAVEL POSTERS

'Cunard Line to New York', by
Charles Pears, loss to right
margin. (Onslow's)   £540

Air Atlas, Casablanca,
lithograph poster in colours,
1950, printed by Hubert Baille &
Cie, Paris, backed on linen,
39 x 24½ in.
(Christie's)   £154

'Cunard The Connecting Link
Europe America'. (Onslow's)
                          £770

'Cunard USA—Canada', extensive loss to right side.
(Onslow's)
             £120

'Cunard Line A Cunarder In
Fishguard Harbour Quickest
Route New York to London',
by Odin Rosenvinge. (Onslow's)
                          £440

'Grand Trunk Railway System
to Canada'. (Onslow's)   £200

'Cunard Line Europe—America',
by Kenneth D. Shoesmith.
(Onslow's)   £2,800

'White Star Line Canada's Call
to Women'. (Onslow's)
                          £250

'Cunard Europe—America', by
W. S. Bylitipolis. (Onslow's)
                          £700

TRAVEL REQUISITES

A tan leather Harrods gentleman's fitted dressing case, the interior finished in polished hide lined leather, 40 x 66cm.
(Onslow's) £160

A fine large leather Gladstone bag, with key and straps, initialled M.W.H., little used with foul weather cover.
(Onslow's) £200

A Louis Vuitton brown grained leather suitcase, interior finished in canvas with two straps, labelled *Louis Vuitton Paris, Nice, Lille, London,* 55 x 34 x 18cm.
(Onslow's) £550

A Louis Vuitton Johnny Walker whisky traveling drinks case, fitted for one bottle of whisky, two bottles of mineral water, one packet of cheese biscuits, two glasses and ice container.
(Onslow's) £2,000

A Louis Vuitton gentleman's cabin trunk, bound in brass and leather with leather carrying handle, on castors, 91 x 53 x 56cm.
(Onslow's) £830

A Louis Vuitton special order tan pigskin gentleman's fitted dressing case, accessories include silver tooth brush, soap and talc containers, 54 x 32cm., circa 1930.
(Onslow's) £2,500

A Louis Vuitton shaped motor car trunk, covered in black material, interior with three matching fitted suitcases, 85 x 65 x 50cm.
(Onslow's) £3,500

A Louis Vuitton shoe secretaire, bound in leather and brass, fitted with twenty-nine shoe boxes with lids, one drawer and tray, 112 x 64 x 40cm.
(Onslow's) £4,300

A fine tan leather hat box by The Our Boys Clothing Company Oxford Street, with red velvet lining.
(Onslow's) £110

TRAVEL REQUISITES

A Louis Vuitton yellow fabric covered motor car suitcase, brass bound, with nickel-plated padlock shaped lock, 59 x 39 x 17cm.
(Onslow's) £360

A Louis Vuitton cabin trunk, vermin proof for use in the tropics, covered in zinc and brass bound, interior finished in white cotton, 85 x 49 x 47cm.
(Onslow's) £2,200

A Malles Goyard cabin trunk, covered in Malles Goyard patterned material, bound in leather and brass, 85 x 49 x 47cm.
(Onslow's) £400

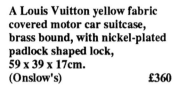

A Louis Vuitton suitcase, No 761119, with key and leather LV luggage label, 62 x 40 x 17cm.
(Onslow's) £1,700

A Louis Vuitton shoe secretaire, fitted with thirty shoe boxes with lids, two large drawers top and bottom and tray, 112 x 64 x 40cm.
(Onslow's) £11,470

A Louis Vuitton gentleman's cabin trunk on castors, covered in LV material, fitted with three trays, one with compartments, 90 x 51 x 48cm.
(Onslow's) £1,100

A Garrison black fabric covered picnic service for six persons, complete with yellow and gold crockery, 56 x 40 x 30cm.
(Onslow's) £400

A Louis Vuitton "Sac Chauffeur", the two circular halves covered in black material, the lower section watertight, 89cm diameter, circa 1905, designed to fit inside spare tyres.
(Onslow's) £3,000

A matching white hide suitcase and hat box by John Pound, with chromium-plated locks and foul weather covers, the suitcase 56 x 36cm.
(Onslow's) £280

WAR POSTERS

It was during the First World War that advertising took its first steps towards the sophisticated, hard-sell image that it has today. Volunteers were needed as cannon-fodder, and the laid-back genteel invitations of prewar advertisements were not going to do the trick. The result was a rash of war posters which appealed unashamedly to the emotions – emotional blackmail, some might say – and which most people are still familiar with today.

'Care of Arms is Care of Life Mud Snow Ice in your rifle muzzle cause burst barrel', 38 x 25cm. (Onslow's) £30

'The Pilot's Home Because Nobody Talked!', 39 x 26cm. (Onslow's) £120

John Gilroy, 'We Want Your Kitchen Waste', double crown. (Onslow's) £170

J. C. Leyendecker, 'USA Bonds Third Liberty Loan Campaign Boy Scouts of America', double crown. (Onslow's) £160

A U.S. Army Recruiting poster, American Lithograph Co. N.Y. 1909, image 35½ x 24¾in. £70

'An Appeal To You', 98 x 63cm. (Onslow's) £45

'Don't Forget That Walls Have Ears!' by Fougasse. (Onslow's) £350

'Zec, Women of Britain Come Into the Factories', double crown. (Onslow's) £300

WAR POSTERS

H. M. Bateman, 'Coughs and Sneezes Spread Diseases', canteen, double crown. (Onslow's) £480

E. Kealey, 'Women of Britain Say Go!' double crown. (Onslow's) £240

Saville Lumley, 'Daddy What Did You Do In The Great War?' double crown. (Onslow's) £310

Marc Stone, 'The Downfall of the Dictators is Assured', double crown. (Onslow's) £70

Abram Games: 'Join the ATS', signed by the artist and model and dated *1941*, double crown, together with a scrap book of photocopies and cuttings concerning the famous poster. (Onslow's) £3,000

'El Hombre del Momento', double crown. (Onslow's) £120

'When? – It's Up To Us!' double crown. (Onslow's) £130

'Talk Less You Never Know', original artwork by Noke, signed, gouache, 57 x 44cm. (Onslow's) **£170**

Henry Raleigh, 'Halt The Hun! Buy US Government Bonds Third Liberty Loan', double crown. (Onslow's) £16

WAR POSTERS

'Save Serbia our Ally',
published by the Serbian
Relief Committee of America,
by Theophile Steinlen,
36 x 24in. (Onslow's)   £75

'Polish Army in France', by
W. T. Benda, on linen,
36 x 27in. (Onslow's)   £110

'Your King and Country Need
You', by Lawson Wood, No.17.
(Onslow's)   £70

'The Veteran's Farewell,
Enlist Now', by Frank Dadd,
sepia. (Onslow's)   £110

'Follow Me, Your Country
Needs You', by E. V. Kealey,
No.11. (Onslow's)   £85

'Blue Cross Fund, Help the
Wounded Horses at the War',
by A.J.M., on linen.
(Onslow's)   £55

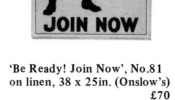

'Are You In This', by Lord
Baden Powell, No. 112.
(Onslow's)   £130

'Be Ready! Join Now', No.81
on linen, 38 x 25in. (Onslow's)
£70

'National Service, Women's
Land Army', by H.G. Gawthorn.
(Onslow's)   £100

WAR POSTERS

'Careless Talk May Cost His Life Don't Talk About Aerodromes or Aircraft Factories', 50 x 34cm. (Onslow's) £210

'Keep Mum She's Not So Dumb! Careless Talk Cost Lives', 39 x 26cm. (Onslow's) £85

'Subscribe to the 5½% Loan', depicting a worker turning shells on a lathe, Russian. (Onslow's) £110

'War, To Arms Citizens of the Empire', published by the Underground, on linen, colour lithograph. (Onslow's) £250

'Britishers You're Needed, Come Across Now', by Lloyd Myers, on linen, 41 x 28in. (Onslow's) £150

'National Service, Women Clerks Wanted At Once', by Savile Lumley. (Onslow's) £170

'See the World and Get Paid For Doing It', by Alfred Leete. (Onslow's) £110

'Who's Absent, Is It You?' by V. Soutril, No.125, on linen. (Onslow's) £58

'Everyone Should Do His Bit, Enlist Now', by Baron Low, No.121. (Onslow's) £100

WOOD

Wood carving is one of the oldest artistic activities known to man, yet apart from some fine Art Nouveau carvings in the medieval style, the Art Nouveau/Deco period produced little of note in this field. Perhaps the kaleidoscope of new materials which were being discovered at the time, and their apparently amazing potential, had something to do with this. Whatever the reason, most wooden carvings of the time are fairly lightweight both in content and quality, and often take the form of humorous caricatures.

A wooden bust of a negress by Forrest, 18½in. high. (Christie's) £140

Wooden match and cigarette holder, 7in. high, 1930s. (Muir Hewitt) £25

The Offering, signed and dated *William Fuller Curtis MCMII,* in carved wood relief with gilt highlights, 29 x 5ft.8in. (Skinner Inc.) £6,173

A painted wood caricature figure of Douglas Fairbanks, Snr., by Betterway, Vienna, 51cm. high, circa 1930. (Phillips) £200

A lacquered rosewood and gilt panel by N. Brunet, deeply carved in intaglio with two pumas by a lakeside, mounted on gilt-wood frame, 50.7cm. x 99.5cm. (Christie's) £2,750

A painted wooden caricature figure of Charlie Chaplin, by Betterway, Vienna, 52cm. high, circa 1930. (Phillips) £170

WOOD

Carved polychrome wooden cigar store figure, America, circa 1900, of a seated man carved in the full round, 52in. high. (Skinner Inc.) £452

A pair of carved oak bookends, by Robert Thompson of Kilburn, known as the Mouseman, each carved with a large bird, 25.6cm. high. (Phillips London) £480

A stylish carved rosewood model of an antelope, designed by Jacques Adnet, modelled as the spirited creature caught leaping through stylised zig-zag foliage, 25cm. high. (Phillips London) £780

A monumental parcel-gilt, carved wooden panel, from H.M.S. Britannic, by Professor A.H. Gerrard, deeply carved and incised with a frieze of eight wild horses amid stylized foliage, 75cm. high x 270cm. wide. (Christie's) £8,250

A wood sculpture of a seated man with hat, probably by Gaitis. £5,000

A carved and gilded wood panel from the S. S. Mauritania, 92.5 x 177cm. overall, 1930's. £2,000

Wooden parrot on stand, 12in. high, 1930s. (Muir Hewitt) £20

WOOD

A beechwood sculpture, carved as reclining woman, in the style of Hagenauer, 43.4cm. long. (Phillips) £200

Carved and painted eagle, America, early 20th century, the stylised figure painted in naturalistic colour, 13¾in. high. (Skinner Inc.) £800

A carved mahogany wood figure, American, 20th century, in the form of a mermaid with fish-scale details, 42in. long. (Christie's) £1,200

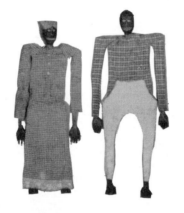

1930's carved hardwood figure 'Contemplation' of a young lady resting her head on her palms, 2ft. 6in. high. (Phillips) £225

Two large carved and painted articulated dancing dolls, American, early 20th century, 43½in., 41in. high respectively. (Christie's) £1,000

Motherhood, a carved oak figure by James Woodford, carved *JW* monogram and inscribed paper label *No.3, Motherhood, English Oak, James Woodford, 19 St Peter's Sq., W6,* 90cm. high. (Christie's London) £1,760

An Art Nouveau wood photograph frame, carved in relief with a young maiden dressed in flowing robes stretching up to a flower, 14in. high.(Christie's S. Ken) £100

A Galle marquetry oval tray, inlaid in various woods with stylised chrysanthemums, 60cm. long, signed. (Phillips London) £180

Hand painted Art Nouveau picture frame, circa 1910, 7in. high. (Muir Hewitt) £45

INDEX

447